Introduction to Infrared and Electro-Optical Systems

Introduction to Infrared and Electro-Optical Systems

Ronald G. Driggers
Paul Cox
Timothy Edwards

Artech House
Boston • London

Library of Congress Cataloging-in-Publication Data
Driggers, Ronald G.
  Introduction to infrared and electro-optical systems / Ronald G. Driggers, Paul
Cox, Timothy Edwards.
    p.   cm.
  Includes bibliographical references and index.
  ISBN 0-89006-470-9 (alk. paper)
  1. Infrared technology.   2. Electrooptical devices.   I. Cox, Paul.   II. Edwards,
Timothy.   III. Title.
TA1570.D75   1998
621.36'72—dc21   98-53327
                                                                           CIP

British Library Cataloguing in Publication Data
Driggers, Ronald G.
  Introduction to infrared and electro-optical systems. – (Artech House
  optoelectronics library)
  1. Electrooptics   2. Imaging systems   3. Infrared equipment   4. Optoelectronics
  5. Electrooptics – Mathematics
  I. Title   II. Cox, Paul   III. Edwards, Timothy
  623.7'314

  ISBN 0-89006-470-9

Cover design by Lynda Fishbourne

© 1999 ARTECH HOUSE, INC.
685 Canton Street
Norwood, MA 02062

International Standard Book Number: 0-89006-470-9
Library of Congress Catalog Card Number: 98-53327

This book is dedicated to Rita, Nancy, Sarah, and the Driglets (Driggers Triplets)

Contents

Preface

This book is intended to provide the reader with a complete introduction to infrared and electro-optical imaging systems. In particular, this introduction includes a strong emphasis on the analysis and design of these systems. Imaging systems can be analyzed with the same tools and techniques as electrical circuits and modern communications systems. The requisite courses for an undergraduate electrical engineering degree provide the majority of skills necessary to perform detailed system-level performance evaluations. Linear-shift-invariant (LSI) system principles and analytical function manipulations combined with calculus and domain transformations provide the mathematical foundations of imaging system analysis. Here, the system begins with the various sources of light, continues with its propagation through the atmosphere, the formation of an image, conversion to an electrical signal at the detectors, subsequent signal processing, and display to a human observer. This book presents a systems analysis approach, which allows an understanding of this complex process and results in quantitative characterizations of performance metrics such as modulation transfer functions, minimum resolvable temperature difference, and probability of object discrimination. We then use these metrics to analyze a number of infrared and electro-optical systems.

Goodman [1] and Gaskill [2] both provide excellent treatments of optical systems using LSI principles. However, the optical elements are only a part of an infrared or electro-optical imaging system. The performance analyses of these systems include source characteristics, atmospherics, detectors, electronics, displays, and human vision (or automatic processing). LSI principles can be applied to all these components, but like Goodman's and Gaskill's treatments of optics, the subject matter for each component can consume an entire text. We present LSI system principles here, but limit our discussions to the basic descriptions of the components necessary to indoctrinate the student and to calculate overall system performance. References have been included at the end of each component section, which can provide additional component-level detail.

Lloyd [3] and Holst [4] provide excellent treatments of overall imaging system performance. These texts are used by many practicing analysts as references in the performance estimation of proposed and actual imaging systems. They are not intended as an introduction to imaging systems and assume that the reader has some background in optics, detectors, or other components within the system.

Therefore, we provide an introductory text that emphasizes the LSI system approach. The analysis is direct, yet elegant, and provides an effective means for evaluating the performance of infrared and electro-optical imaging systems. In particular, the LSI approach allows impact assessment on performance for changes in components such as entrance-pupil shapes, detector shapes, and display characteristics. The reader is led through a number of analysis-and-design examples where the effects of these component changes are realized.

While there are many excellent books in the field, they can be roughly divided into two categories: those that focus on a particular component and system-level books where the reader is assumed to have some background in the subject area. This book is written to complement these texts by bridging the two categories. This complementary nature of the text allows the reader to understand the entire analysis-and-design process.

We begin with an introduction to two-dimensional functions and mathematics used to describe image transfer characteristics and imaging system component models. Next, LSI principles are presented to show image transfer characteristics for application to imaging systems. The final background chapter is that of diffraction, showing the fundamental limits of imaging system performance. In this chapter, the diffraction concepts of coherent imaging systems are presented to show the development of the incoherent diffraction principles.

Following the review of basic background material, the components of an imaging system are presented. An imaging system "map" is used to chart the flow of information through the system. The map begins with the source of radiation and traverses through the atmosphere and into the imaging system. The path continues with the image forming optics and then onto the detector. The detector converts the light into an electrical signal that is amplified and processed by system electronics. This electrical signal continues to a display or, in some cases, an automated processor (e.g., target tracker). A display converts the electrical signal into an optical signal for human visual consumption. The human eye is typically included as part of system performance, so it, too, is considered a component in the imaging system. Each of the components in the map is addressed in Chapters 5 through 10. These chapters include component descriptions, component analysis techniques, and LSI modeling descriptions. There you have it: analysis begins with the sources of light and ends with the response of the eye and brain.

The emphasis then turns to infrared and electro-optical system performance descriptions, design rules, and examples. Chapters 11 and 12 provide infrared and electro-optical system performance analysis techniques, respectively. These are the chapters where the components are brought together to provide an overall system description. The sources of radiation and the atmosphere are typically not included in imaging system performance estimates intended for generic application to a variety of target, background, and atmospheric conditions. The analysis process then continues here as system-scenario performance, which includes the source, atmosphere, and imaging system performance characteristics to give discrimination performance of an imaging system within a given scenario. Both these chapters provide a number of analysis-and-design exercises that solidify the LSI concepts. The reader is carefully led through these exercises so that he or she is comfortable with the underlying principles. Finally, design guidance in the areas of waveband selection, search, and sensor tradeoffs is provided in Chapter 13.

There are two target audiences for this book. The first is the senior or first-year graduate student with an interest in electronic imaging systems. This book is intended to provide these students with the necessary tools to enter an engineering position in the field of infrared or electro-optical systems. It provides them with the nomenclature, component descriptions, and performance parameters to understand sensor-related issues. The second audience is the practicing engineer who requires a reference of sensor and basic scenario performance calculations. Numerous analyses and designs are given throughout the text.

The authors would like to thank a number of people who made this book possible. The introduction was reviewed and edited by Keith Krapels, Rich Vollmerhausen, and Nancy Davis. Larry Andrews and Pierre Schonbaum reviewed the mathematics chapter. Kenneth Barnard and Michael Currin reviewed the chapter on diffraction, and Roy Williams reviewed the LSI chapter. Also, Carl Halford contributed a number of sections to the LSI systems chapter. Stacey Taylor reviewed the sources of radiation chapter. Raymond Deep and Glenn Vinson provided broadband images. The atmospherics chapter was reviewed by John Schroeder and Norm Kopeika. John Schroeder provided the MODTRAN graphs given in the chapter. Barry Johnson and John Gunderson reviewed and edited the optics chapter. Glenn Boreman reviewed the detector chapter, and Charles Bray reviewed the electronics chapter. Rich Vollmerhausen and Gary O'Brien reviewed the display, human vision, and automatic target recognition chapter. Mike Lloyd reviewed the infrared systems chapter, and Shapour Ahmadi reviewed the electro-optical systems chapter. Bill Blecha provided a discussion of the common-module FLIR. John Leachtenaur provided material and reviews of the General Image Quality Equation and National Imagery Interpretation Rating Scale section. The design and considerations chapter was reviewed by Mike Lloyd and Lew Boyleston. Gerald Holst provided a technical editorial review of the entire manuscript and Ryan Driggers provided drawing support. Sarah Edwards copyedited the entire manuscript and provided formatting and guidance. Our sincere thanks are extended to these people who took a good deal of time from their busy schedules to provide their input to this text.

REFERENCES

[1] Goodman, J. W.,   *Introduction to Fourier Optics*, San Francisco: McGraw-Hill, 1968.

[2] Gaskill, J. D., *Linear Systems, Fourier Transforms, and Optics,* New York: Wiley, 1978.

[3] Lloyd, J., *Thermal Imaging Systems,* New York: Plenum Press, 1975.

[4] Holst, G. C., *Electro-Optical Imaging System Performance,* Orlando, FL: JCD Publishing, 1995.

Chapter 1

Introduction

In grade school, we learned that humans have five senses: sight, sound, touch, taste, and smell. The data rates associated with each of these senses vary considerably. Most scientists agree that touch, taste, and smell have extremely low information rates compared with those of sight and sound. Using generous estimates of a 12-bit sound amplitude resolution and a hearing bandwidth of 20 kHz, the human sound data rate is in the ballpark of 240 Kbps. A conservative estimate of the sight bandwidth with 8 bits of amplitude resolution, 125 million picture elements (or retinal detectors [1]), and a 10-Hz imaging rate results in 10 Gbps. This line of thinking confirms our commonsense appreciation of vision and verifies that the visual data volume to our brain is orders of magnitude larger than all the other senses combined.

In likeness of the human eye, we have created a large number of vision, or imaging, devices, with high-data-rate information collection. Imaging devices range from endoscopes used in surgery to night-vision devices used on the battlefield. The analysis and design techniques presented in this book are applicable to these imagers.

The majority of examples and scenarios used in this text concentrate on long-range (i.e., large object distance) imagers. A major design and analysis issue with these systems is whether a particular object can be discriminated at a given distance under defined conditions. The subject matter in this book provides both the designer and the analyst with the necessary tools to address this issue.

The title of this book, *Introduction to Infrared and Electro-Optical Systems*, may seem redundant because electro-optics has been previously defined as "the field of systems that convert photons to electrons [2]," regardless of wavelength. Systems that include the spectral region of 0.4- to 0.7-µm wavelengths, the visible light band, are described as *visible* sensors. Those responding to the spectral region from 0.7- to 14-µm wavelength light are referred to as *infrared* sensors. The infrared spectrum is further divided into three subregions.

The near- or shortwave infrared (SWIR) region is from 0.7 to 2 μm, the midwave infrared (MWIR) region is from 3 to 5 μm, and the longwave infrared (LWIR) region is from 8 to 14 μm.

In this book, electro-optical (EO) systems are those that respond to wavelengths within the 0.4- to 2-μm region (note that this includes the visible and SWIR bands). Most of the light collected by an EO sensor corresponds to light that was reflected by objects in the scene. The 3- to 5-μm (mid-wave or MWIR) and the 8- to 14-μm (longwave or LWIR) band imagers are collectively infrared sensors and are called *forward-looking infrared (FLIR)* systems or *imaging infrared (I^2R) sensors*. These sensors respond primarily to light that is emitted by objects in the scene. While the analytical techniques for the I^2R and EO sensors are similar, the performance descriptors are different. For example, many of the I^2R performance parameters are described with the concept of differential temperature quantities, where EO systems are described in terms of radiant contrast.

1.1 I^2R and EO SYSTEMS

Figure 1.1 is presented throughout this book as an example of a standard model (and road map) in the study of I^2R and EO systems. The diagram depicts a cascaded system where the input signal is the optical flux and the output is an image presented by a display for human consumption. The object flux is either reflected external light or self-emitted light. This flux then passes through the atmosphere, which degrades both the amplitude and the phase of the light. These effects manifest themselves as a reduction in information content of the signal. In addition, particles in the atmosphere reflect unwanted stray light into the sensor. The EO or I^2R sensor's first components are the optics that collect the photons from the target, background, and any stray atmospheric flux. The optics then image the scene onto a detector plane. The detector transforms the light into electrical signals that represent the spatial distribution of the flux amplitude leaving the scene. The detector system may be a *staring array,* a *linear array,* or a *single detector*. A staring array is a two-dimensional arrangement of detectors, and a linear array is a column (or a few columns) of detectors. In a linear array system, a scanner moves the image across the detectors. For a single-detector system, a two-dimensional scanner moves the image across the detectors in both the horizontal and vertical dimensions. Electronics consist of preamplifiers, postamplifiers, filters, processors, and digitizers. These components can be considered as signal conditioners because the primary purpose of the electronics is to prepare the detector signal for either display or automated image processing. The electronic output signal can then be converted to an optical signal that can be displayed for human vision. In some systems, the signal undergoes additional analysis in a target tracker, automatic target recognizor (ATR), or an aided target recognizer (AiTR), whose output is used for operator cueing.

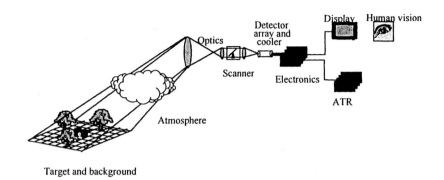

Figure 1.1 I²R and EO systems.

1.2 WAVELENGTH ISSUES

The design or analysis of an imaging system for a given purpose yields performance indicators that are strong functions of wavelength. This spectral dependence results from many different factors, including the scene's characteristics, atmospheric degradation, and the individual response of the sensor's components.

First, the object of interest, or target, has two surface characteristics defined as *reflectivity* and *emissivity*. Typically with EO sensors, the important target parameter is reflectivity, whereas emissivity may be dominant in an I²R sensor analysis. That is, targets with reflectivities near that of their backgrounds are difficult for EO and near-infrared sensors to exploit. Targets with emissivity (and temperature) characteristics near that of their backgrounds are difficult for I²R sensors to exploit. Both reflectivity and emissivity are functions of wavelength. A detailed discussion of these characteristics is presented in Chapter 5.

Once a photon leaves the target in the direction of the sensor, the atmosphere changes the photon path by refraction or scattering actions. The process whereby the atmosphere transmits or absorbs photons is highly dependent on the characteristic frequency of the incident light. Figure 1.2 shows the atmospheric transmission [3] of a 1-km horizontal path length at sea-level through what is defined as a standard U.S. atmosphere. Note that transmission is high for the visible, near-infrared, midwave, and longwave bands. Sensors are not effective in the 5- to 8-μm band because of the poor transmission of the atmosphere at these wavelengths.

The transmission of light through an imaging sensor can also be characterized as a function of wavelength. The optical sensor components, comprising lenses, filters, and mirrors, have reflectivity and transmission characteristics that are highly wavelength dependent. Finally, detectors convert photons to electrons with an efficiency that is a strong function of wavelength.

The diffractive nature of light is also affected by frequency. Diffraction can be thought of as the curving and spreading of light as it propagates through space. Light behaves this way even in a vacuum. Short wavelengths tend to propagate in straighter lines, whereas long wavelengths tend to curve more, especially when passing by small obstructions. This phenomenon results in a limit of image quality for a particular sensor. Diffraction can be seen by imaging a point source of light located very far from the sensor. Finer point images result from shorter wavelengths.

Each of the characteristics introduced above is discussed in more detail in later chapters. All these characteristics must be considered in order to design or analyze sensors effectively. For example, the averaging of transmission or some other wavelength-dependent characteristic over a spectral band and using these averages in a cascade of performance may cause significant error. While the error may be acceptable for some limited applications, an exact solution requires that each wavelength response be treated separately. The collective system response is then determined by summing the individual wavelength responses of the entire system (object, atmosphere, sensor, display, and observer).

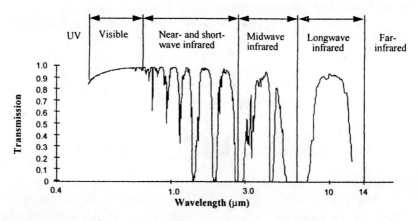

Figure 1.2 Atmospheric transmission for a 1-km horizontal path.

1.3 TYPICAL EO SCENARIO

EO systems are those that utilize the 0.4- to 2.0-μm waveband. The human eye is responsive to part of this waveband (i.e., 0.4 to 0.7 μm); therefore, EO systems provide images that look very similar to normal human vision. Some EO systems extend into the near or short-infrared spectral region, but they usually include the human visual band. Targets, backgrounds, and clutter (objects that could be easily

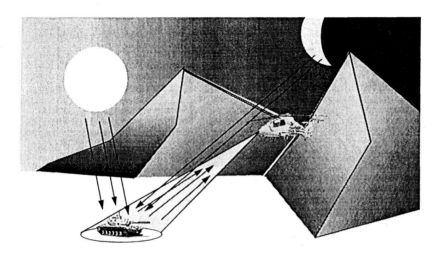

Figure 1.3 Typical EO scenario.

mistaken for targets) characteristics are usually reflectivity driven in the EO wavelengths. Illumination, sometimes called "external radiation," is provided by sunlight, moonlight, starlight, or artificial means. Targets and backgrounds reflect the illuminating light as shown in Figure 1.3, where the reflectivities of these surfaces are strong functions of wavelength. The light is not only reflected by the targets and background, it is also reflected, or scattered, by atmospheric, aerosol, smog, or smoke particles. The light reflected by targets and backgrounds must also be transmitted through the atmosphere to be collected by the EO sensor. Transmission lessons from the atmosphere have prompted the development of human-made obscurants. Smoke is a widely used battlefield cloaking obscurant where the EO transmission of light is intentionally inhibited.

The light that enters the sensor is a mixture of target and background reflections that have been transmitted through the atmosphere along with atmospheric scattered light. The light enters the aperture of the sensor and some percentage (again, as a function of wavelength) is transmitted to the sensing elements. The sensing elements can be detectors, tubes, or image intensifiers. Image intensifiers are used when moonlight, starlight, or a small active illumination is present. The output of the sensing elements is amplified, processed by electronics, and routed to some monitor or display device. Humans then view the display device for information-gathering purposes.

A human uses the information shown on the display to detect, recognize, or identify targets. The detection task is the process of determining if a potential target is present. The recognition task is the gross classification of targets into major groups such as tanks, trucks, ships, cars, and the like. The identification task is a higher level of discrimination within a major group (e.g., a T-62 tank from a T-72 tank).

The output of the sensor electronics is not always displayed and viewed by a human for interpretation. In some systems, the output of the EO system is input to an ATR or AiTR. In these cases, a signal or image processor performs part or all of the detection, recognition, or identification. In the AiTR case, the human bears the burden of the final classification level (i.e., an AiTR processor may detect objects, whereas the human performs the recognition or identification).

1.4 TYPICAL I²R SCENARIO

The typical I²R sensor provides a visual representation of an object at night or under poor lighting conditions. The I²R sensor is used for battlefield night vision, surveillance of unlit areas, and fire detection within smoke-filled spaces onboard ships. There are two primary I²R transmission windows through the atmosphere: the MWIR 3- to 5-μm band and the LWIR to 8- to 14-μm band. In the remainder of the infrared band, the atmospheric absorption is too high for long-distance imaging (see Figure 1.2). MWIR and LWIR bands may mean slightly different spectral regions; however, the majority of I²R sensor engineers use the convention above.

A typical scenario for an I²R sensor is shown in Figure 1.4. Although solar reflections can influence the perceived image dramatically, the usual mode of I²R operation is at night. All bodies above the temperature of absolute zero emit electromagnetic radiation according to Planck's law. A hotter object corresponds to higher electromagnetic or, in this case, optical power emissions leaving the object. The emissive surface characteristics of a radiating object determine the spectral emission weighting of the light. The emitted light propagates through the atmosphere, where a percentage reaches the entrance aperture of the sensor. The amplitude and phase of the light entering the sensor aperture is altered by transmission properties of the lenses and filters and by the reflectivity of the mirrors. When the light is collected onto the detectors, a portion of the photons are converted into electronic signals. Like EO systems, these signals are presented to observers through displays or are input to computer target-recognition equipment.

For common terminology today, a large number of engineers and scientists are using the I²R description of infrared sensors, yet many still use FLIR to describe military systems. This historical term is also used to categorize the progression of infrared imaging through the designation of first-, second-, and third-generation FLIRs. The differences in the generations of FLIR technology are discussed in Chapter 11.

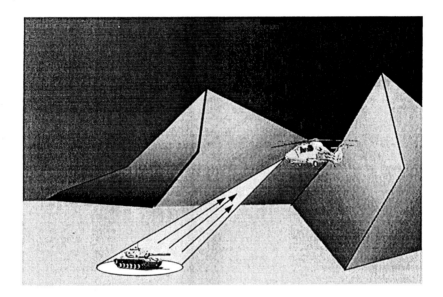

Figure 1.4 Typical I²R scenario.

1.5 ANALYTICAL PARAMETERS

The descriptions of the typical I²R and EO scenarios were given in generalities, when really the specifics involve a large number of analytical parameters [4]. They can be grouped into illumination, target, atmospheric, optics, detectors, electronics, display or processing, and human visual parameters. Some of these parameters are listed in Table 1.1. Sensor analysis begins with a mathematical description of the appropriate characteristics showing all independent variables. Certain approximations or simplifying assumptions are usually made at some point along the way. Many of the errors in sensor design are committed at this early stage. There is no substitute for a clear understanding of the required function of a system, characterization of the objects of interest, and the parameters of the operating environment.

The above is not an exhaustive list of parameters. Many of them are functions of both wavelength and space. Some of the parameters change with time and some are relatively constant. Other important system requirements or attributes include mechanical specifications (jitter and drift), size, weight, power, cost, reliability, and maintainability.

One begins to see the complexity of I²R and EO sensor design. There are easily over 100 parameters to address before the construction of an I²R or EO sensor. In some cases, certain parameters may be less important. Without complete knowledge of the system's limitations, it is possible to neglect a particular parameter that may lead to the failure of a system to meet desired expectations.

Table 1.1
Analytical parameters

Analytical parameters	
Illumination	**Sensor detector**
Spectral irradiance	Responsivity
	Detectivity
Target	Noise characteristics
Reflectivity	Detector angular subtense
Emissivity	
Size and spatial characteristics	**Sensor electronics**
Temperature	Temporal characteristics
	Digital or analog
Atmosphere	filter characteristics
Weather conditions	
Obscurants	**Display**
Transmission	Resolution
Optical transfer function	Brightness and contrast
Scattering	
	Human psychophysics
Sensor optics	Temporal response
Lens transmissions	Image transfer function
Mirror reflectivity	Brightness dependence
Filter transmission	
Aberrations	**ATR or AiTR response**
Diffraction	Discrimination probability
Aperture size and shape	False-alarm rate

1.6 SENSITIVITY AND RESOLUTION

The performance of I^2R and EO sensors can be discussed in terms of two general parameters: *sensitivity* and *spatial resolution*. Sensitivity involves signal and noise levels including the signals from objects of interest along with noise signals that can make it difficult to see objects. Noise has a large variety of sources originating from both the sensor design and the environment. Sensitivity is especially important when viewing objects with small image signals that can be drowned out by large noise sources. This is a major design issue during sensor concept evaluation. Radiometry is a discipline that describes the amount of light that leaves the object and ends up on the sensor detector. Radiometry, optical design, detector performance characteristics, and detector sample times are of primary importance in sensor sensitivity analysis.

If a sensor has sufficient sensitivity, intelligent decisions on object detection, recognition, or identification can only be performed with the appropriate resolution. Resolution is influenced by every stage of the process: the atmosphere, sensor optics, sensor detector, sensor electronics, and the display/observer. Important considerations are atmospheric turbulence, the diffraction or aberration limits of the optical system, and the detector size and shape with respect to the optical focal length of the sensor. Electronic response, display resolution, and many other also parameters contribute to the resolution of the overall system.

In most cases, resolution and sensitivity are conflicting parameters. Certain design parameters cause this phenomenon. For example, at a given optics diameter, an increase in a sensor's focal length may increase resolution and decrease sensitivity. Sensitivity and resolution issues usually provide the most important sensor trade studies. Requirements analyses address the design of a sensor that has sufficient sensitivity and resolution for a given application.

There are also some generalizations in the comparison of EO and infrared sensors. The detectors that respond to the visible and near-visible wavelengths are typically higher performance than those of I^{2}R sensors. The shorter wavelength photons of the visible light provide a higher energy in the electron conversion process. Also, the development of visible detectors has been the subject of much research for a longer period of time. Therefore, the higher performance EO detector in both sensitivity and size gives EO sensors better characteristics than I^{2}R systems. In general, EO systems have plenty of sensitivity even with high resolution. Typical EO systems are resolution limited. Infrared systems are usually more sensitivity limited than EO sensors, so more attention must be paid to the sensitivity parameters in I^{2}R system design. In fact, many I^{2}R systems are background noise limited where other-than-target sources drown out the target signal (recall that all objects are emitting).

1.7 LINEAR SYSTEMS APPROACH

The linear systems approach to sensor analysis is convenient in determining the response of an imaging system. Imaging systems can usually be considered linear shift-invariant (LSI) systems, where the LSI system is defined as having the properties

$$L\{af(x-c)+bg(x-d)\} = aL\{f(x-c)\} + bL\{g(x-d)\} \quad (1.1)$$

where, a and b are multiplicative constants and c and d are shifting constants. $f(x)$ and $g(x)$ are functions of the independent variable x, and L denotes the LSI operator.

In simple terms, the definition above is one of superposition, linear scaling, and linear shifting. The response of an imaging system can be considered the summation of a set of point-source responses. For example, the image of a point-source object provided by an EO or I^2R system is desired to be a point-like image. Two point-source objects would produce two point-like images. The superposition aspect implies that the sum of two separately imaged point-source objects would produce the same two point-like images. Also, when an object is shifted, the image is shifted, but unchanged in appearance. Finally, a brighter point-source object would produce a brighter image.

Imaging systems can be treated as LSI systems in most cases, where any object can be represented as an infinite number of weighted point sources. The collective response of the sensor to these point sources yields an accurate representation of the sensor image. Again, there are two very important aspects of LSI sensor analysis: sensitivity and resolution.

Sensitivity is typically addressed through radiometric analysis. Superposition holds here as a characteristic of flux, or radiometric power (for noncoherent optical systems). Resolution is addressed in a manner very similar to complex circuit and signal analysis. An impulse response is determined for the system and applied to the input signal by way of two-dimensional convolution to produce an output image. This approach can also be performed in the spatial frequency domain. The imaging system transfer function is multiplied by the input object spectrum to produce the output image spectrum.

Each system contributor or component has its own impulse response and transfer function including the atmosphere, optics, detector, electronics, mechanical aspects, display, and human vision. The system impulse response can be determined by the convolution of all the component impulse responses and the system transfer function can be determined by the multiplication of all the component transfer functions (just like circuit analysis). Chapter 3 provides a detailed description of this approach.

While the LSI approach gives good results, not all components provide LSI responses. For example, the impulse response of the human eye is a nonlinear function of display brightness. These nonlinearities are treated by fixing parameters within a range such that the behavior of the component can be assumed as linear.

An LSI sensor analysis can result in a characterization by any number of parameters. Sensitivity parameters are described by system intensity transfer functions (SITF) and noise equivalent temperature differences (NETD) or noise equivalent irradiance (NEI). Resolution performance can be given by an impulse response or a modulation transfer function (MTF) for the entire system. Sensitivity and resolution parameters can be combined to give an overall performance indication of minimum resolvable temperature differences (MRTD or just MRT) for I^2R systems or minimum resolvable contrast (MRC) for EO systems. MRT and

MRC curves are provided as a function of spatial frequency (i.e., sensitivity plotted as a function of resolution).

The MRT and MRC are important parameters because sensitivity and resolution are not independent. The MRT and MRC curves give a sensor analyst a quantitative performance measure of a sensor in terms of both sensitivity and resolution.

A sensor *user* may want to know how far away a particular target can be detected, recognized, or identified. Because the sensor performance curves are known, the target size and contrast are needed along with the viewing path atmospheric characteristics. Johnson's criterion is used to provide the minimum number of cycles across a target in order to detect, recognize, or identify the target. The spatial frequency corresponding to one of these tasks coupled to the atmospheric transmission and the target-to-background contrast can be used to determine the probability of detection, recognition, or identification of the target as a function of range (distance from the sensor to the target).

1.8 SUMMARY

The material presented in this book is provided in three sections as shown in Figure 1.5. Part 1 provides a background review of mathematics, LSI systems, and diffraction principles necessary to perform sensor analysis. Part 2 describes LSI system component modeling associated with the targets and backgrounds, atmospheric path, each of the sensor components, and the human visual response. Emphasis here is on introductory modeling of these components. Finally, Part 3 combines the LSI system methods and the component models to provide overall system level performance estimates for I^2R and EO sensors. I^2R systems are presented first since many of the principles that apply to EO systems were developed for I^2R systems. Design issues are discussed where they affect the sensor component performances. Examples of real systems are used throughout the text in order to illustrate analysis and design principles.

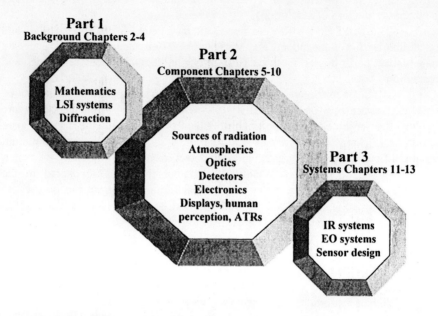

Figure 1.5 Text organization.

REFERENCES

[1] Hecht, E., and A. Zajac, *Optics*, Reading, MA: Addison-Wesley, p.138, 1979.
[2] Waldman, G., and J. Wooten, *Electro-Optical Systems Performance Modeling,* Norwood, MA: Artech House, p. 2, 1993.
[3] Wolfe, W., and G. Zissis, *The Infrared Handbook,* Office of Naval Research, Washington, DC, pp. 5 - 91, 1978.
[4] Lloyd, J., *Thermal Imaging Systems,* New York: Plenum Press, p. 8, 1975.

Part 1

Background

Chapter 2

Mathematics

Mathematical representation of sensor components is of primary importance in any sensor design or performance analysis. The accuracy of the mathematical expressions determines the quality of the overall performance estimates. While the very basics of spectral frequency analysis are presented in this chapter, Goodman [1] and Gaskill [2] can be reviewed for a more in-depth discussion on complex numbers, functions, and transforms of applied optical systems. Goodman states that "optics has gradually developed ever stronger ties with communications and information sciences." The commonality corresponds to the information-gathering nature of imaging and communications systems. Even the mathematical tools of the two disciplines are similar.

We assume that the reader has some background in Fourier analysis and communications theory. The emphasis here is to transition the corresponding principles into two dimensions, as imaging systems tend to be characterized with two-dimensional functions. The transition presented here is not a rigorous one; however, it will allow the sensor analyst to develop many useful models and perform various design analyses.

This mathematics review is intended to provide the necessary background and reference material to perform I^2R and EO analysis. Functions, Fourier transforms, and linear operators are required in the modeling of components such as the optics, detectors, and displays. These mathematics also provide the basis for LSI I^2R and EO system principles (LSI systems principles are covered in Chapter 3, I^2R systems are covered in Chapter 11, and EO systems are covered in Chapter 12). Finally, diffraction effects (Chapter 4) cannot be calculated without the mathematical background provided here. We begin with a review of functions.

2.1 COMPLEX FUNCTIONS

Complex functions are similar to the *phasors* [3] used in engineering circuit analysis and can be represented in the form

$$g(x) = v(x) + jw(x) \tag{2.1}$$

or in the form

$$g(x) = a(x)e^{j\phi(x)} \tag{2.2}$$

(2.1) gives the complex function in Cartesian coordinates where $v(x)$ is the real part of the function and $w(x)$ is the imaginary part of the function. (2.2) gives the function in polar form, where $a(x)$ is the nonnegative amplitude of the function and $\phi(x)$ is the argument or the phase of the function. The complex conjugate of the function is denoted $g^*(x)$ and is found by changing the sign on the imaginary part of 2.1 or the phase of 2.2. The relationships between the Cartesian and the polar forms of the function are given in Table 2.1.

Table 2.1
Cartesian and polar relationships

Conversions
$a(x) = \|g(x)\| = \sqrt{v^2(x) + w^2(x)}$
$\phi(x) = \arg[g(x)] = \tan^{-1}[\frac{w(x)}{v(x)}]$
$v(x) = Re\{g(x)\} = a(x)\cos\phi(x)$
$w(x) = Im\{g(x)\} = a(x)\sin\phi(x)$

The *Re* and *Im* notation corresponds to taking the real part and the imaginary part of the complex function. The polar-to-Cartesian coordinate conversion is determined using Euler's [4] relationship

$$e^{j\phi(x)} = \cos\phi(x) + j\sin\phi(x) \tag{2.3a}$$

where $\cos\phi(x)$ is the real part of the function and $\sin\phi(x)$ is the imaginary part of the function. Euler's other forms are

$$\sin\phi(x) = \frac{e^{j\phi(x)} - e^{-j\phi(x)}}{2j} \tag{2.3b}$$

and

$$\cos\phi(x) = \frac{e^{j\phi(x)} + e^{-j\phi(x)}}{2} \tag{2.3c}$$

A function $f(x) = v(x) + jw(x)$ whose real part is even (i.e., $v(x)=v(-x)$) and whose imaginary part is odd ($w(x)=-w(-x)$) is called *Hermitian*. Also, a function whose real part is odd and whose imaginary part is even is described as *anti-Hermitian*.

Manipulations of complex functions are necessary in sensor analysis with the majority of manipulations involving addition, subtraction, multiplication, division, transforms, and convolutions. Addition and subtraction of complex functions are generally accomplished in Cartesian coordinates with the real parts adding or subtracting directly and the imaginary parts adding or subtracting directly. Multiplication and division are more tractable when taken in polar coordinates, where

$$[a_1(x)e^{-j\phi_1(x)}]/[a_2(x)e^{-j\phi_2(x)}] = \frac{a_1(x)}{a_2(x)}e^{-j[\phi_1(x)-\phi_2(x)]} \tag{2.4}$$

$$a_1(x)e^{-j\phi_1(x)}a_2(x)e^{-j\phi_2(x)} = a_1(x)a_2(x)e^{-j[\phi_1(x)+\phi_2(x)]} \tag{2.5}$$

Note that while vector division is not defined, complex function division is defined for $a_2 \neq 0$. Transform and convolution operations are addressed later in this chapter.

2.2 ONE-DIMENSIONAL FUNCTIONS

There are a number of one-dimensional functions that must be understood before the extension of functions into two dimensions. These functions are limited to those that are useful in I^2R and EO sensor analysis. Table 2.2 shows these functions along with their definitions. The functions shown are used in various sensor models such as apertures, detectors, and analog-to-digital samplers. For example, the *Gaus(x)* function may depict the spatial distribution of the intensity in a cathode ray tube (CRT) display spot.

The successful analyst must be able to manipulate these functions through scaling and shifting to represent real systems. There are three basic mechanisms for shaping and moving these functions. Consider the function $f(x) = 2rect(\frac{x-1}{4})$ shown in Figure 2.1. Compare it with the definition of the *rect* function given in Table 2.2.

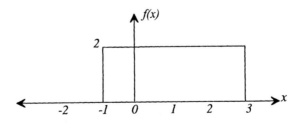

Figure 2.1 $f(x) = 2rect\left(\frac{x-1}{4}\right)$.

The multiplicative constant 2 is multiplied by each of the function points to adjust the height, or amplitude, of the function. The center of the function has been shifted to $x = 1$, where the argument of the rect function goes to zero. The x value where the argument goes to zero will always be the new origin of the function. Finally, the width of the function is adjusted by the constant, 4, where now the width of the rectangle is four units. Note that when x is set to 3, the argument of the rect function becomes 1/2, a discontinuous, transition point for the *rect* function. This example shows that the function definition still holds for $(x-1)/4$ as a replacement for x in the rect function argument of Table 2.2. Use these definitions to generate simple "lookup tables" when difficult arguments are involved.

To summarize the scaling and shifting properties of one-dimensional functions, the multiplicative constant should be multiplied by each defined value of a function. Given that the function arguments can be written in the form $(x-x_o)/b$, the origin reference of the new function is shifted to x_o and the function width is spread by a factor of b. Also note that functions like $f(x) = 2rect(3x - 3)$ can be written as $f(x) = 2rect(\frac{x-1}{1/3})$. Finally, functions with a $-x$ in the argument are flipped around the vertical axis; however, the lookup table approach still holds true.

There is no substitute for practice in the manipulation of functions, so a number of problems are given at the end of this chapter. It should become obvious that the *rect(x)* function can be represented as *rect(x)=step(x+1/2)step(1/2-x)* or as *rect(x)=step(x+1/2)-step(x-1/2)*. Be very careful in manipulating functions. Representation in one form may cause a great deal of unnecessary mathematics (e.g., when transformations are required), whereas representation in a different way may provide a straightforward evaluation. Another worthwhile exercise is to represent the *tri(x)* function with a number of *ramp(x)* functions.

The *delta* function, sometimes called the *impulse* or the *Dirac* function, is one of considerable discussion. It is used widely by both engineers and mathematicians. The *impulse* function can be described by its attributes of infinite height, zero width, and an area of 1. In fact, the definition given in Table 2.2 could be modified with the use of a *rect* or *tri* function instead of the *Gaus* function given. The representation in the graph is used to give the area of the *delta* function as 1. Three very important properties of delta functions are

$$\delta(x - x_o) = 0, \quad x \neq x_o \tag{2.6}$$

$$\int_{x_1}^{x_2} g(\alpha)\delta(\alpha - x_o)d\alpha = g(x_o), \quad x_1 < x_o < x_2 \tag{2.7}$$

$$\delta(\tfrac{x-x_o}{b}) = |b|\delta(x - x_o) \tag{2.8}$$

Table 2.2
One-dimensional functions

Function	Definition	Graph
Step $step(x) =$	$\begin{aligned} 0, & \quad x < 0 \\ 1/2, & \quad x = 0 \\ 1, & \quad x > 0 \end{aligned}$	
Signum $sign(x) =$	$\begin{aligned} 1, & \quad x > 0 \\ 0, & \quad x = 0 \\ -1, & \quad x < 0 \end{aligned}$	
Rectangle $rect(x) =$	$\begin{aligned} 1, & \quad |x| \le 1/2 \\ 0, & \quad otherwise \end{aligned}$	
Ramp $ramp(x) =$	$\begin{aligned} 0, & \quad x \le 0 \\ x, & \quad x > 0 \end{aligned}$	
Triangle $tri(x) =$	$\begin{aligned} & 1 - |x|, \\ & |x| \le 1 \\ & 0, \quad otherwise \end{aligned}$	
Sinc $sinc(x) =$	$[sin(px)]/(px)$	

Table 2.2
One-dimensional functions (continued)

Function	Definition	Graph
Sinc² $sinc^2(x) =$	$\{[sin(\pi x)]/(\pi x)\}^2$	
Gaussian $Gaus(x) =$	$e^{-\pi x^2}$	
Delta $\delta(x) =$	$\lim\limits_{b \to 0} \dfrac{1}{|b|} Gaus(\dfrac{x}{b})$	
Even impulse pair $\delta\delta(x) =$	$\delta(x+1) + \delta(x-1)$	
Odd impulse pair $\delta_\delta(x) =$	$\delta(x+1) - \delta(x-1)$	
Comb $comb(x) =$	$\sum\limits_{n=-\infty}^{\infty} \delta(x-n)$	

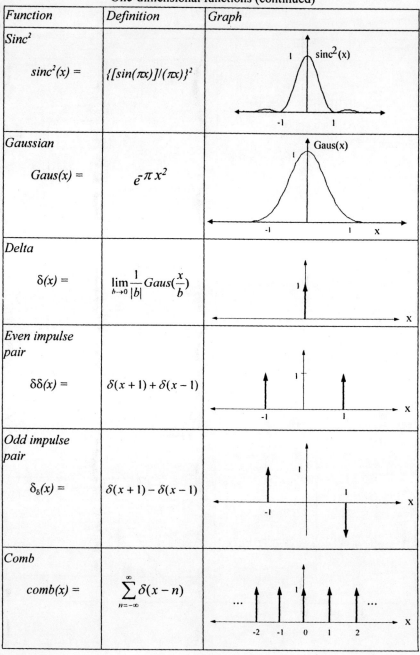

There are three related functions that are composed of *delta* functions. The first two are the even impulse pair and the odd impulse pair as shown in Table 2.2. These functions are simply the summation of two impulse functions, where the first is an even function configuration and the second is an odd function configuration. These functions are extremely useful in the representation of the Fourier transforms for cosines and sines. Finally, the *comb* function is an infinite sum of *delta* functions that can represent the sampling nature of discrete detectors in space or a digital sampling process in the time domain.

2.3 TWO-DIMENSIONAL FUNCTIONS

Two-dimensional functions play a key role in the modeling and evaluation of I^2R and EO sensors. Most I^2R and EO systems form an image at a two-dimensional plane (e.g., a detector array or film). The complex wave propagating through the atmosphere and the sensor can be represented in a two-dimensional (transverse to the direction of propagation) plane. Also, sensor components can usually be represented as two-dimensional functions that have some symmetry in either Cartesian or polar coordinates. Symmetry reduces the complexity of both the problem formulation and the mathematics necessary to evaluate the expression.

A special class of two-dimensional functions is those that are *separable* in some particular coordinate system. A two-dimensional function is separable in Cartesian coordinates if

$$\mathbf{g}(x,y) = \mathbf{g}_x(x)\mathbf{g}_y(y) \qquad (2.9)$$

and a function is separable in polar coordinates if

$$\mathbf{g}(r,\theta) = \mathbf{g}_r(r)\mathbf{g}_\theta(\theta) \qquad (2.10)$$

In simple terms, a separable function is one that can be written as the product of one-dimensional functions of orthogonal independent variables. Separable functions make the analysis of two-dimensional systems much simpler. For example, the two-dimensional Fourier transform of a separable function is the product of the one-dimensional Fourier transforms.

An example of a separable two-dimensional function is shown in Figure 2.2. The top graph shows the function $f_x(x) = 5tri(\frac{x-9}{7})$, and the second graph shows $f_y(y) = 5tri(\frac{y-13}{5})$. The two functions multiplied give $f(x,y) = 25tri(\frac{x-9}{7}, \frac{y-13}{5})$ shown in the bottom graph. Be careful about making generalizations about separable function shapes. The product of two triangle functions may, at first thought, be conceived as a pyramid. The product of the two triangle function values at every point along the x and y axes cause the unexpected curved shape along the diagonal. Only when viewed as slices parallel to the coordinate axes is the true shape of a triangle present because the multiplier of the triangles along each line is a constant.

As one can imagine, an infinite number of separable functions exist. Just using the functions shown in Table 2.2, there are 144 different combinations of functions where a function in the x-direction is multiplied by a function in the y-direction. In fact, sums and differences of functions in one direction multiplied by sums and differences of functions in the other direction give two-dimensional functions that are separable. Shifting and scaling of functions provide even more combinations of separable functions.

There are three significant two-dimensional functions that are separable in polar coordinates. These functions are the *cylinder, Gaussian*, and *sombrero* functions or *cyl(r), Gaus(r)*, and *somb(r)*. Despite the single argument, these functions are two-dimensional because $f(r, \theta) = f_R(r)$ or $f(\theta) = 1$. That is, they are circularly symmetric, where r is the radial variable. The three functions are shown and defined in Figure 2.3. The *cyl(r)* function is useful in representing circular aperture stops, pupils, and mirrors. The *Gaus(r)* function is useful in modeling laser spot intensities and electronic beam written display spots. Finally, the *somb(r)* function is similar to the *sinc(x)* function, but in two dimensions and has the useful attribute of being the Fourier transform of the *cyl(r)* function. The J_1 shown in the definition of the sombrero function is a first-order Bessel function of the first kind, as given by Andrews [5].

In many cases, an entire EO or I^2R system cannot be represented in only Cartesian or polar coordinates. In these cases, some conversion is needed in the function arguments to a single coordinate system. These coordinate transformations are typical and are represented with the following notation:

$$r = \sqrt{x^2 + y^2} \qquad (2.11)$$
$$\theta = \tan^{-1}(\tfrac{y}{x}) \qquad (2.12)$$
$$x = r\cos\theta \qquad (2.13)$$
$$y = r\sin\theta \qquad (2.14)$$

Finally, one may encounter functions that are not separable. For Cartesian coordinates, these are functions that cannot be written in terms of $g(x,y) = g_x(x)g_y(y)$, for example $g(x,y) = rect(\tfrac{x-3}{3}, \tfrac{y-2}{2}) + 2rect(\tfrac{x+3}{4}, \tfrac{y-2}{3})$. While these functions tend to complicate the mathematics and may sometimes provide nontractable solutions, the analytical techniques and equations are the same and can, if necessary, be solved through numerical means. Finally, a function that is separable in polar coordinates does not mean the function is separable in rectangular coordinates (they usually are not) and vice versa.

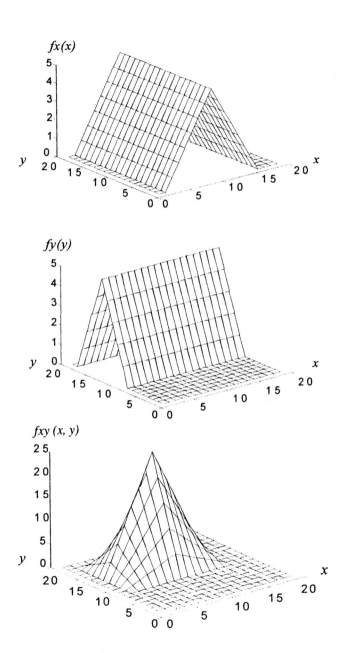

Figure 2.2 Two-dimensional triangle function.

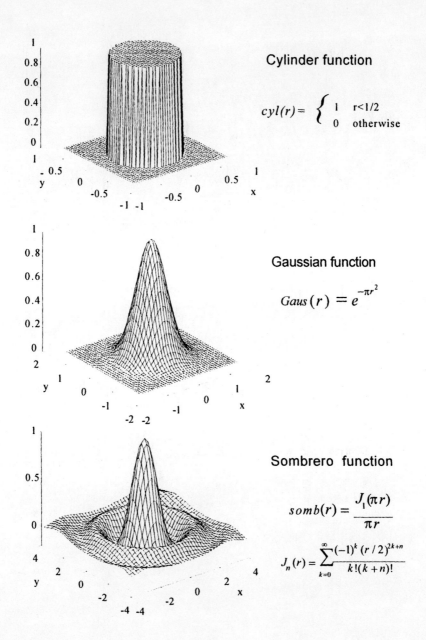

Cylinder function

$$cyl(r) = \begin{cases} 1 & r < 1/2 \\ 0 & \text{otherwise} \end{cases}$$

Gaussian function

$$Gaus(r) = e^{-\pi r^2}$$

Sombrero function

$$somb(r) = \frac{J_1(\pi r)}{\pi r}$$

$$J_n(r) = \sum_{k=0}^{\infty} \frac{(-1)^k (r/2)^{2k+n}}{k!(k+n)!}$$

Figure 2.3 Circularly symmetric functions.

2.4 CONVOLUTION AND CORRELATION

The convolution [6] of two functions $f(x)$ and $h(x)$ can be described by the process of "*flip, slip, multiply,* and *integrate.*" Pick one function as stationary, usually the more complex of the two. Then, the *flip* is an inversion from left to right (around the $f(x)$ or $h(x)$ axis), the *slip* is the moving of one function along the x-axis with respect to the other, the *multiply* is a point-by-point multiplication of the slipped function by the stationary function, and the *integrate* is the summation of all multiplied points. This is shown in Figure 2.4, where $f(x) = h(x) = rect(x)$.

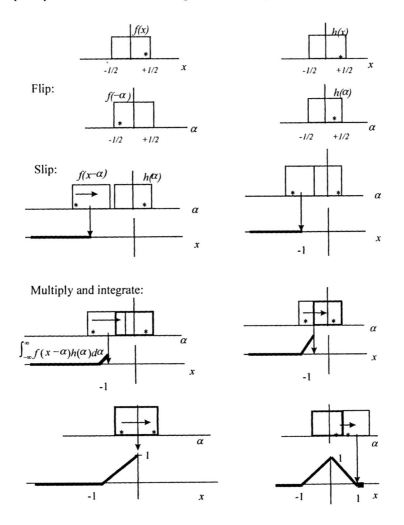

Figure 2.4 The process of convolution.

The shorthand for convolution is $g(x) = f(x) * h(x)$ where

$$g(x) = f(x) * h(x) \equiv \int_{-\infty}^{\infty} f(\alpha)h(x - \alpha)d\alpha \tag{2.15}$$

The properties of the convolution integral include

commutative: $f(x) * h(x) = h(x) * f(x)$ $\hspace{2cm}$ (2.16)

distributive: $[af(x) + bh(x)] * g(x) = a[f(x) * g(x)] + b[h(x) * g(x)]$ $\hspace{1cm}$ (2.17)

associative: $[f(x) * g(x)] * g(x) = f(x) * [h(x) * g(x)]$ $\hspace{1.5cm}$ (2.18)

shift invariance: $f(x - x_o) * h(x) = g(x - x_o)$ $\hspace{2cm}$ (2.19)

delta function: $f(x) * \delta(x) = f(x)$ $\hspace{3cm}$ (2.20)

In general, the result of a convolution tends to be smooth compared with the original functions (with the exception of convolutions involving *delta* functions). Convolution is useful in representing many physical phenomena, including the scanning of a rectangular shaped detector across an inverted, or flipped, image. The convolution of complex functions is found in the same manner as that of (2.15), where the equation for the complex polar form is

$$f_3(x) = f_1(x) * f_2(x) = \int_{-\infty}^{\infty} a_1(\alpha)e^{j\phi_1(\alpha)}a_2(x - \alpha)e^{j\phi_2(x-\alpha)}d\alpha$$

$$= \int_{-\infty}^{\infty} a_1(\alpha)a_2(x - \alpha)e^{j[\phi_1(\alpha)+\phi_2(x-\alpha)]}d\alpha \tag{2.21}$$

In the complex Cartesian form

$$f_3(x) = f_1(x) * f_2(x) = [v_1(x) + jw_1(x)] * [v_2(x) + jw_2(x)]$$

$$= [v_1(x) * v_2(x) - w_1(x) * w_2(x)] + j[v_1(x) * w_2(x) + w_1(x) * v_2(x)$$

$$= v_3(x) + jw_3(x) \tag{2.22}$$

Two-dimensional convolution in Cartesian coordinates is given by

$$g(x,y) = \int_{-\infty}^{\infty} \int_{-\infty}^{\infty} f(\alpha, \beta)h(x - \alpha, y - \beta)d\alpha d\beta \tag{2.23}$$

where the shorthand notation is $g(x,y) = f(x,y) ** h(x,y)$. A nice convolution property of separable two-dimensional functions is

$$g(x,y) = [f_X(x)f_Y(y)] * *[h_X(x)h_Y(y)] = [f_X(x) * h_X(x)][f_Y(y) * h_Y(y)] \qquad (2.24)$$

The convolution of two-dimensional functions in polar coordinates is limited here to those functions that are circularly symmetric. The convolution integral for two circularly symmetric functions in polar coordinates is

$$g_R(r) = f_R(r) * *h_R(r) = \int_0^\infty \int_0^{2\pi} f_R(r')h_R(\sqrt{r^2 + r'^2 - 2rr'\cos\theta'}\,)r'dr'd\theta' \qquad (2.25)$$

A close cousin of the convolution is the correlation where the "flip" operation is eliminated from the process. The result of a correlation operation can be thought of as a measure of how similar one signal or function is to another. The shorthand notation for cross-correlation, or the correlation of two different functions is *g(x)=f(x) ★h(x)* where

$$g(x) = \int_{-\infty}^\infty f(\alpha)h(\alpha - x)d\alpha \qquad (2.26)$$

The cross correlation is not convolution, but *g(x)=f(x) ★h(x)=f(x)*h(-x)*. Due to the symmetry of the functions in Figure 2.4, here (with even functions) the convolution is the same as correlation. Also, there is a *complex* cross-correlation that is defined as

$$\gamma_{fh}(x) \equiv f(x) ★h^*(x) \qquad (2.27)$$

where *h*(x)* denotes the complex conjugate of *h(x)*. Finally, the complex autocorrelation is defined as

$$\gamma_f(x) \equiv f(x) ★f^*(x) \qquad (2.28)$$

Correlation is taken to two dimensions in a manner similar to convolution with

$$g(x,y)=f(x,y) ★★h(x,y)= \int_{-\infty}^\infty \int_{-\infty}^\infty f(\alpha, \beta)h(\alpha - x, \beta - y)d\alpha d\beta$$

$$= \int_{-\infty}^\infty \int_{-\infty}^\infty f(\alpha + x, \beta + y)h(\alpha, \beta)d\alpha d\beta \qquad (2.29)$$

The two-dimensional cross-correlation is not commutative but can be expressed as

$$f(x,y) ★★h(x,y)=f(x,y)** h(-x,-y) \qquad (2.30)$$

The complex cross-correlation is defined as

$$\gamma_{fh}(x,y) \equiv f(x,y) ★★h^*(x,y) \qquad (2.31)$$

The complex autocorrelation can also be calculated in two dimensions:

$$\gamma_f(x,y) \equiv f(x,y) \star \star f^*(x,y) \tag{2.32}$$

In two-dimensional polar coordinates, we again limit the correlations to circularly symmetric functions, which causes the correlation to give the same results as that of a convolution. That is

$$f_R(r) \star \star f_R(r) = f_R(r) ** f_R(r) \tag{2.33}$$

With the lack of the flip operator, the correlation is used to model actions such as a noninverted image that is scanned by a detector. The complex autocorrelation is used in operations such as the determination of the optical transfer function of a sensor. Both the convolution and the correlation functions provide measures of likeness between two functions, where the convolution likeness involves one function that is flipped.

2.5 THE FOURIER TRANSFORM

A mathematical tool of great importance in I²R and EO system analysis is the Fourier transform [7]. This particular tool describes the *frequency* or *spectral* content of spatial variations in the image and can describe the throughput characteristics of the I²R/EO system. An object that comprises many small features that are closely spaced with good contrast has some high spatial frequency content, whereas large objects that are spaced far apart have significant low spatial frequency content. The Fourier transform of an object space or an image space describes their corresponding small and large spatial variations. Fourier transforms are useful in the modeling of sensors and describing the spatial frequency content of an image that traverses through each of the sensor components. Sensor optics, detectors, electronics, and displays can be represented by the Fourier transform of their spatial models. Exceptions are those electronics that cause signals to increase or decrease exponentially; these must be represented with the *Laplace transform*. Many electronics, however, can be adequately described by use of the Fourier transform.

The Fourier transform of some complex function $f(x)$ is

$$F(\xi) \equiv \int_{-\infty}^{\infty} f(x)e^{-j2\pi\xi x}dx \tag{2.34}$$

where the existence of the Fourier transform is met by the requirement that it be applied to physically realizable systems. The spatial frequency ξ is given in cycles per milliradian or cycles per meter depending on the units of x. Gaskill [2] states that a few functions that are generally used by engineers, such as the impulse and infinite periodic functions, are not physically realizable; however they can still be useful in the analysis of systems because they are good approximations. Many of these functions such as the *delta* function do have generalized Fourier transforms that will be used throughout this book.

Given a Fourier transform, the inverse Fourier transform can be determined by

$$f(x) \equiv \int_{-\infty}^{\infty} F(\xi)e^{j2\pi\xi x}d\xi \qquad (2.35)$$

where this function definition completes what is called the *Fourier transform pair*. Note that the only difference between these two transforms is the sign of the exponential kernel within the integrals.

We are not interested in writing the above integrals each time we want to express the Fourier transform operation, so a standard shorthand for the Fourier transform operation is used:

$$F(\xi) = \Im\{f(x)\} \text{ and } f(x) = \Im^{-1}\{F(\xi)\} \qquad (2.36)$$

The first operation is the Fourier transform, and the second operation is the inverse Fourier transform.

The extension of Fourier transforms to two dimensions is a simple one in Cartesian coordinates. The forward Fourier transform is

$$\Im\Im\{f(x,y)\} = F(\xi,\eta) \equiv \int_{-\infty}^{\infty}\int_{-\infty}^{\infty} f(x,y)e^{-j2\pi[x\xi+\eta y]}dxdy \qquad (2.37)$$

and the inverse Fourier transform is

$$\Im\Im^{-1}\{F(\xi,\eta)\} = f(x,y) \equiv \int_{-\infty}^{\infty}\int_{-\infty}^{\infty} F(\xi,\eta)e^{j2\pi[\xi x+\eta y]}d\xi d\eta \qquad (2.38)$$

Separable functions, again, have a nice property regarding the forward and reverse Fourier transforms

$$\Im\Im\{f(x,y)\} = \Im\{f_X(x)\}\,\Im\{f_Y(y)\} \qquad (2.39)$$

so that the individual one-dimensional transforms can be calculated separately and then multiplied. The inverse transforms of separable functions can be determined in the same manner.

In two-dimensional polar coordinates, the equivalent Fourier transform is called the *Fourier-Bessel transform*, or the *Hankel transform* of zero order:

$$G(\rho) \equiv 2\pi \int_{0}^{\infty} r\mathbf{g}_R(r)J_o(2\pi r\rho)dr \qquad (2.40)$$

The function $g_R(r)$ is a two-dimensional polar function that is circularly symmetric (recall that $g_\theta(\theta) = 1$). The J_o term is the zero-order Bessel function of the first kind. The inverse transform can be found by

$$g_R(r) = 2\pi \int_0^\infty \rho G(\rho) J_o(2\pi r\rho) d\rho \qquad (2.41)$$

Note that the inverse transform is identical to the forward transform. The shorthand notations for the Fourier-Bessel transform and corresponding inverse transform are $\mathcal{BB}\{g_R(r)\}$ and $\mathcal{BB}^{-1}\{G(\rho)\}$.

2.6 PROPERTIES OF THE FOURIER TRANSFORM

There are a number of properties that are useful in the evaluation and manipulation of Fourier transforms. These properties are not just for academic interest, but are used widely in the analysis of I^2R and EO systems. The mathematics are shown as the following theorems and, where applicable, the theorems assume that $\mathcal{JJ}\{f(x,y)\}=F(\xi,\eta)$ and $\mathcal{JJ}\{h(x,y)\} = H(\xi,\eta)$:

Linearity theorem. The transform of the sum of two functions is the sum of their individual transforms:

$$\mathcal{JJ}\{af(x,y) + bh(x,y)\} = a\mathcal{JJ}\{f(x,y)\}+b\mathcal{JJ}\{h(x,y)\} = aF(\xi,\eta) + bH(\xi,\eta) \qquad (2.42)$$

where a and b are constants.

Similarity theorem. "Wide" functions in the space domain correspond to "narrow" functions in the frequency domain and vice versa. This width characteristic is coupled to a change in amplitude in order to conserve energy (i.e., see Parseval's theorem below):

$$\mathcal{JJ}\{f(ax,by)\} = \frac{1}{|ab|}F(\frac{\xi}{a},\frac{\eta}{b}) \qquad (2.43)$$

Shift theorem. The shifting of a function in space corresponds to a phase shift in the frequency domain:

$$\mathcal{JJ}\{f(x-a,y-b)\} = F(\xi,\eta)e^{-j2\pi(\xi a+\eta b)} \qquad (2.44)$$

Parseval's theorem. Energy is conserved in both the space and frequency domains:

$$\int_{-\infty}^\infty \int_{-\infty}^\infty |f(x,y)|^2 dxdy = \int_{-\infty}^\infty \int_{-\infty}^\infty |F(\xi,\eta)|^2 d\xi d\eta \qquad (2.45)$$

Convolution theorem. The convolution of two functions in the space domain corresponds to the multiplication of the transforms in the frequency domain:

$$\Im\{\int_{-\infty}^{\infty}\int_{-\infty}^{\infty}f(\alpha,\beta)h(x-\alpha,y-\beta)d\alpha d\beta\} = \Im\{f(x,y)**h(x,y)\}= F(\xi,\eta)H(\xi,\eta)$$

(2.46)

Correlation theorem. The transform of the complex autocorrelation is the square of the transforms magnitude:

$$\Im\{\int_{-\infty}^{\infty}\int_{-\infty}^{\infty}f(\alpha,\beta)f^*(\alpha-x,\beta-y)d\alpha d\beta\} = \Im\{\gamma_f(x,y)\} = |F(\xi,\eta)|^2$$

(2.47)

Fourier integral theorem. The transform of an inverse transform and the inverse transform of a transform yield the original function:

$$\Im[\Im^{-1}\{f(x,y)\}]=\Im^{-1}[\Im\{f(x,y)\}]=f(x,y)$$

(2.48)

The properties described here are very basic, and each property has a duality characteristic. That is, each one of the properties can be applied to not only the forward transform, but also to the inverse transform. These properties are also applicable to the polar two-dimensional functions, where the similarity theorem is modified to conserve energy and the shifting theorem is held in Cartesian coordinates. Table 2.3 lists a summary of the Fourier transform properties.

2.7 TRANSFORM PAIRS

Each of the functions described in Sections 2.2 and 2.3 has a corresponding Fourier transform. The function and its corresponding Fourier transform are called a transform pair. Take, for example, the *rect(x)* function of Table 2.2. The Fourier transform can be applied to the function to yield

$$F(\xi) = \int_{-\infty}^{\infty} rect(x)e^{-j2\pi\xi x}dx = \int_{-1/2}^{1/2} 1e^{-j2\pi\xi x}dx$$
$$= \frac{1}{j2\pi\xi}[e^{j2\pi\xi/2} - e^{-j2\pi\xi/2}]$$

(2.49)

From Euler's equation of (2.3b), the transform becomes

$$F(\xi) = \frac{\sin\pi\xi}{\pi\xi} =\text{sinc}(\xi)$$

(2.50)

the function that completes the transform pair of *f(x)=rect(x)*. In two dimensions, the transform pair becomes *f(x)=rect(x,y)* and $F(\xi,\eta) = \text{sinc}(\xi,\eta)$.

Another important transform is that of the *delta* function. The transform can be found by the Fourier integral

$$F(\xi) = \int_{-\infty}^{\infty} \delta(x)e^{-j2\pi\xi x}dx \qquad (2.51)$$

however, the $\delta(x)$ function is equal to zero at locations other than x = 0, so the integral becomes

$$F(\xi) = \int_{-\infty}^{\infty} \delta(0)e^{-j2\pi\xi 0}dx = \int_{-\infty}^{\infty} \delta(0)dx = 1 \qquad (2.52)$$

In a similar fashion, $\delta(x,y)$ gives a corresponding transform of $F(\xi,\eta) = 1$.

The Fourier transform integral is not usually evaluated to determine a function's transform pair. This procedure has already been performed for most of the common functions and has been tabulated. In some cases, it is necessary to perform the integral, but when possible use the pairs provided in Table 2.4. The transform pair table along with the transform properties can be used to determine a function that adequately describes the EO and I²R component or sensor of interest.

Table 2.4 can be considered a lookup table where the transform pairs can be taken and used directly. The pairs are given only in the forward transform direction; however, the concept of duality where $\mathcal{F}\{F(\xi)\} = f(-x)$ doubles the size of the transform pair table. The table given includes a limited number of transform pairs that are useful in I²R or EO sensor analysis. There are a large number of transform pair libraries and tables if further mathematics are necessary.

2.8 IMPORTANT EXAMPLES

To illustrate the importance of the mathematical techniques described in this chapter, a few examples are given that have been instrumental in sensor analysis.

Example 1: A linear detector array with 128 elements can be modeled in one dimension (the lengthwise dimension) to determine its voltage response to a particular image pattern. The detectors are uniform in response across their entire surface (say, 1V), square in shape, 20 μm in height, and 40 μm center-to-center spacing. The analyst must write a response function. A simple sketch is shown in Figure 2.5.

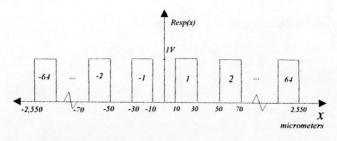

Figure 2.5 Detector response function.

Table 2.3
Fourier transform properties

Space domain	Frequency domain
$f(\pm x, \pm y)$	$F(\pm \xi, \pm \eta)$
$f^*(\pm x, \pm y)$	$F^*(\mp \xi, \mp \eta)$
$f_X(x)f_Y(y)$	$F(\xi)F(\eta)$
$f(\frac{x}{a}, \frac{y}{b})$	$\|ab\|F(a\xi, b\eta)$
$f(x \pm x_o, y \pm y_o)$	$F(\xi, \eta)e^{\pm j2\pi x_o \xi}e^{\pm j2\pi y_o \eta}$
$f(x,y)e^{\pm j2\pi \xi_o x}e^{\pm j2\pi \eta_o y}$	$F(\xi \mp \xi_o, \eta \mp \eta_o)$
$af(x,y) + bh(x,y)$	$aF(\xi, \eta) + bH(\xi, \eta)$
$f(x,y) * *h(x,y)$	$F(\xi, \eta)H(\xi, \eta)$
$f(x,y)h(x,y)$	$F(\xi, \eta) * *H(\xi, \eta)$
$f(x,y) \star \star h(x,y)$	$F(\xi, \eta)H(-\xi, -\eta)$
$f(x,y)h(-x, -y)$	$F(\xi,, \eta) \star \star H(\xi,, \eta)$
$\gamma_{fh} = f(x,y) \star \star h^*(x,y)$	$F(\xi, \eta)H^*(\xi, \eta)$
$f(x,y)h^*(x,y)$	$\gamma_{FH} = F(\xi,, \eta) \star \star H^*(\xi,, \eta)$
$\gamma_f = f(x,y) \star \star f^*(x,y)$	$\|F(\xi, \eta)\|^2$
$\|f(x,y)\|^2$	$\gamma_F = F(\xi,, \eta) \star \star F^*(\xi,, \eta)$
$\int_{-\infty}^{\infty} \int_{-\infty}^{\infty} f(\alpha, \beta)d\alpha d\beta = F(0,0)$	$\int_{-\infty}^{\infty} \int_{-\infty}^{\infty} F(\alpha, \beta)d\alpha d\beta = f(0,0)$
$g_R(r)$	$G(\rho)$
$g_R(\frac{r}{a})$	$\|a\|^2 G(a\rho)$
$ag_1(r) + bg_2(r)$	$aG_1(\rho) + bG_2(\rho)$
$g_1(r) **g_2(r) = g_1(r) \star \star g_2(r)$	$G_1(\rho)G_2(\rho)$
$g_1(r)g_2(r)$	$G_1(\rho) **G_2(\rho) = G_1(\rho) \star \star G_2(\rho)$
$\gamma_{g1g2}(r) = g_1(r) \star \star g_2{}^*(r)$	$G_1(\rho)G_2^*(\rho)$
$g_1(r)g_2^*(r)$	$\gamma_{G1G2}(\rho) = G_1(\rho) \star \star G_2{}^*(\rho)$
$\gamma_g(r) = g(r) \star \star g^*(r)$	$\|G(\rho)\|^2$
$\|g_R(r)\|^2$	$\gamma_G(\rho) = G(\rho) \star \star G^*(\rho)$
$g_R(\sqrt{x^2 + y^2})$	$G(\sqrt{\xi^2 + \eta^2})$
$\int_0^{\infty} g_R(r)r dr = G(0)$	$\int_0^{\infty} G(\rho)\rho d\rho = g_R(0)$

Table 2.4
Fourier transform pairs

Space domain	Frequency domain
1	$\delta(\xi)$
$\delta(x)$	1
$rect(x)$	$sinc(\xi)$
$sinc(x)$	$rect(\xi)$
$\delta\delta(x)$	$2cos(2\pi\xi)$
$\delta_\delta(x)$	$2sin(2\pi\xi)$
$\delta(x,y) = \delta(x)\delta(y)$	1
$\delta(x \pm x_o, y \pm y_o) = \delta(x - x_o)\delta(y - y_o)$	$e^{\pm j2\pi x_o\xi}e^{\pm j2\pi y_o\eta}$
$e^{\pm j2\pi\xi_o x}e^{\pm j2\pi\eta_o y}$	$\delta(\xi \mp \xi_o, \eta \mp \eta_o) = \delta(\xi \mp \xi_o)\delta(\eta \mp \eta_o)$
$cos(2\pi\xi_o x)$	$\dfrac{1}{2|\xi_o|}\delta\delta(\dfrac{\xi}{\xi_o})\delta(\eta)$
$sin(2\pi\eta_o y)$	$\dfrac{j}{2|\eta_o|}\delta(\xi)\delta_\delta(\dfrac{\eta}{\eta_o})$
$rect(x,y) = rect(x)rect(y)$	$sinc(\xi,\eta) = sinc(\xi)sinc(\eta)$
$tri(x,y) = tri(x)tri(y)$	$sinc^2(\xi,\eta) = sinc^2(\xi)sinc^2(\eta)$
$Gaus(x,y) = Gaus(x)Gaus(y)$	$Gaus(\xi,\eta) = Gaus(\xi)Gaus(\eta)$
$comb(x,y) = comb(x)comb(y)$	$comb(\xi,\eta) = comb(\xi)comb(\eta)$
$sgn(x,y) = sgn(x)sgn(y)$	$\dfrac{1}{j\pi\xi}\dfrac{1}{j\pi\eta}$
$cyl(r)$	$somb(\rho)$
$\dfrac{\delta(r)}{\pi r}$	1
$\delta(r - r_o)$	$2\pi r_o J_o(2\pi r_o\rho)$
$Gaus(r)$	$Gaus(\rho)$

The function can be represented as a *rect* function convolved with a suitably constructed *comb* function. The useful format of the *comb* function is

$$\frac{1}{|a|}comb(\frac{x-x_o}{a}) = \sum_{n=-\infty}^{\infty} \delta(x - x_o - na) \tag{2.53}$$

such that the *comb* function is shifted by 20 µm and scaled to 40 µm center-to-center spacing. The appropriate voltage response model of the array is then

$$Resp(x) = [\frac{1}{40}comb(\frac{x-20}{40}) * rect(\frac{x}{20})]rect(\frac{x}{5620}) \tag{2.54}$$

where x is given in µm. The *rect* multiplier is the limiting window function that allows only 128 detectors to exist. The response beyond this array is zero due to the definition of the *rect(x)* function. This type of model can easily be extended to two dimensions because most detector arrays can be described by separable functions.

Example 2: The optical transfer function (in the frequency domain) of any I²R or EO sensor with a particular circular limiting aperture can be described by the autocorrelation of a *cyl* function model of the aperture. The autocorrelation of a *cyl* function with unity diameter yields

$$\gamma_{cyl}(\rho) = cyl(\rho) \star\star cyl(\rho) = \frac{2}{\pi}[\cos^{-1}(\rho) - \rho(1 - \rho^2)^{1/2}]cyl(\rho/2) \tag{2.55}$$

where a good approximation has been shown to be

$$\gamma_{cyl}(\rho) \approx 0.25[5tri(\rho) - 1 + \rho^4]cyl(\rho/2) \tag{2.56}$$

Shifting and scaling of these two functions is performed in the same manner as previously shown. Note that the complex autocorrelation of the *cyl* function is the same as the autocorrelation because there is no imaginary part or non-zero phase associated with the function. Also, the cross-correlation of two cylinder functions of different diameters is much more complicated than the function described above, and the corresponding analysis and functions can be found in Gaskill [2].

Example 3: The electron beam impact on the phosphorus coating of a CRT display causes photoluminescence that is modeled by a Gaussian intensity. The smaller the Gaussian spot diameter, the higher the spatial resolution (i.e., higher spatial frequencies can be passed) the CRT provides. The transfer function that describes the passage of spatial frequencies is represented by the Fourier transform of the Gaussian spot. For example, the transfer function of a 0.25-mm spot CRT can be described by

$$\mathfrak{I}\mathfrak{I}\left\{Gaus\left(\frac{r}{0.25}\right)\right\} = \frac{1}{(0.25)^2}Gaus(0.25\rho) \qquad (2.57)$$

where r is in millimeters and ρ is in cycles per millimeter.

  The three examples shown here provide insight to functional modeling, correlation, and the Fourier transform. None of these examples appears to be difficult, but a good deal of the analytical work has already been performed and we are using the results. There are not many models within the realm of EO and I^2R sensor analysis that are difficult to use or derive. It is still important to understand the basic mathematical concepts such that when modifications are necessary, they can be performed correctly. The mathematics described in this chapter will be used extensively throughout the sensor analysis techniques of this book.

EXERCISES

2.1 Give $f(x)$ in polar form:

 a) $f(x) = 20e^{j110^{\circ}} - 8e^{j40^{\circ}}$

 b) $f(x) = 6.1x - j3.82$

2.2 Give $f(x)$ in rectangular form:

 a) $f(x) = \dfrac{j}{6.3 - j9.7}$

 b) $f(x) = jx^2 + jx + xe^{-j45^{\circ}}$

2.3 Draw the following functions:

 a) $f(x) = 2rect\left(\frac{x-3}{5}\right)$

 b) $f(x) = Gaus(3x - 2)$

 c) $f(x) = 4rect\left(\frac{x-4}{4}\right) - 2rect\left(\frac{x-4}{2}\right)$

 d) $f(x) = 4tri\left(\frac{x-5}{2}\right) - 2tri\left(\frac{x-5}{1}\right)$

2.4 Write a function for the following signals:

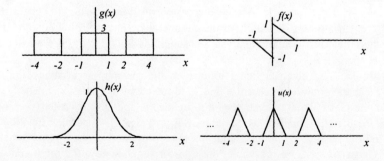

Figure 2.6

2.5 From problem 2.4, sketch $v(x) = 4f(\frac{2-x}{3})$:

2.6 Sketch the following functions:
a) $f(x,y) = rect(\frac{x}{2}, \frac{y}{4})$
b) $f(x,y) = sinc(\frac{x}{2}, y)$
c) $f(x,y) = cyl(\frac{\sqrt{x^2+y^2}}{2}) - cyl(\sqrt{x^2+y^2})$
d) $f(x,y) = somb(\sqrt{x^2 + (\frac{y}{2})^2})$
e) $f(x,y) = rect(x-2)\delta(y)$
f) $f(x,y) = \delta(x)\delta(2-y)$

2.7 Sketch the following functions:
a) $f(x) = rect(x) * rect(x-2)$
b) $g(x) = \delta\delta(x) * \delta\delta(x)$
c) $h(x) = step * rect(\frac{x}{4})$
d) $u(x) = rect(x) * rect(\frac{x}{3})$
e) $v(x) = \frac{1}{4}comb(\frac{x}{4}) * rect(\frac{x}{2})$

2.8 Perform the following convolutions or correlations and sketch the results:
a) $f(x,y) = rect(x,y) * *rect(\frac{x}{2}, \frac{y}{2})$
b) $f(x,y) = rect(x,y) * *\delta(x-3, y-2)$
c) $f(x,y) = sinc(\frac{x}{2}, \frac{y}{4}) * *\delta\delta(\frac{x}{4})$
d) $f(x,y) = cyl(2r) \bigstar\bigstar cyl(2r)$

2.9 Find the Fourier transform of the following functions:
a) $f(x) = |x|$
b) $f(x) = e^{-x^2}$
c) $f(x) = rect(\frac{x}{5})$
d) $f(x) = rect(x-3)e^{j2\pi x}$
e) $f(x) = rect(x-1) * rect(x)$
f) $f(x) = sinc(4x) * sinc(2x)$
g) $f(x) = \frac{1}{2}comb(x - \frac{1}{2}) * tri(x)$

2.10 Find the Fourier transform of the following two-dimensional functions:
a) $f(x,y) = rect(\frac{x}{2}, y)$
b) $f(x,y) = \frac{1}{5}comb(\frac{x}{5}) * *rect(\frac{x}{2}, y)$
c) $g(r) = cyl(\frac{r}{2}) \bigstar\bigstar cyl(\frac{r}{2})$

REFERENCES

[1]   Goodman, J. W., *Introduction to Fourier Optics*, San Francisco: McGraw-Hill, 1968.

[2]   Gaskill, J. D., *Linear Systems, Fourier Transforms, and Optics*, New York: Wiley, 1978.

[3]   Hayt, W., and J. Kemmery, *Engineering Circuit Analysis*, New York: McGraw-Hill, p. 285, 1978.

[4]   Saff, E. B., and A. D. Snider, *Fundamentals of Complex Analysis for Mathematics, Science, and Engineering,*, New Jersey: Prentice Hall, p. 65, 1976.

[5]   Andrews, L., *Special Functions for Engineers and Applied Mathematicians*, New York: McMillan, 1985.

[6]   Ross, S. L., *Introduction to Ordinary Differential Equations*, New York: Wiley, p. 454, 1966.

[7]   Stremler, F. G., *Introduction to Communication Systems*, Reading, MA: Addison-Wesley, p. 81, 1982.

[8]   Tzannes, N. S., *Communication and Radar Systems*, New Jersey: Prentice Hall, pp. 41 - 52, 1985.

Chapter 3

Linear Shift Invariant I^2R and EO Systems

Linear operators and processes are a key part of an engineer's or scientist's formal education in analytical mathematics. Integration, derivatives, and Fourier transforms are linear operations. As a starting point, most systems are assumed to be linear, and a model is developed using the mathematics of Chapter 2. In actuality, most systems are linear over a restricted region of their application. Investigations into nonlinear mathematics and systems have consumed many lifetimes in the study of chaos, weather, and other distinctly nonlinear fields, resulting in few useful generalizations or analytical techniques.

LSI principles apply to imaging systems in a manner that is identical to LSI circuits. Consider the similarities shown in Figure 3.1. Circuits are shown with an independent variable of time, and imaging systems are shown with an independent variable of two-dimensional space. Both the circuit and the imaging system are shown in the frequency domain where the circuit frequency is in cycles per second, or Hertz, and the imaging system frequency is given in cycles per meter (or cycles per milliradian). Both systems are characterized by the impulse response. A voltage spike is used on the input of the circuit, and a tiny point of light is used on the input of the imaging system. The output of the circuit gives a voltage impulse response, and the output of the imaging system gives the spatial impulse response (equal to the blur image of the point source). Once the impulse response is determined, the output of the system with any input function is simply the input function convolved with the impulse response.

In the frequency domain, the spectrum of the spike is a uniform value (one-dimensional transform for circuits and two-dimensional transform for imaging systems). This uniform input spectrum is multiplied by the circuit or imaging system transfer function to give an output spectrum. This output spectrum is the transfer function of the system. With circuits, this is simply the transfer function with a magnitude and phase. With imaging systems, the transfer function is described by the modulation transfer function (MTF) that is similar to the magnitude of the circuit transfer function.

Once the transfer function is determined, the output spectrum, given any input spectrum, can be found by multiplying the input spectrum by the transfer function. In summary, there are two methods for LSI analysis: (1) the time or space domain where the input function is convolved with the impulse response to give an output, and (2) the frequency domain where the input spectrum is multiplied by the system transfer function to give an output spectrum. The transform of the impulse response gives the transfer function, and the inverse transform of the transfer function gives the impulse response.

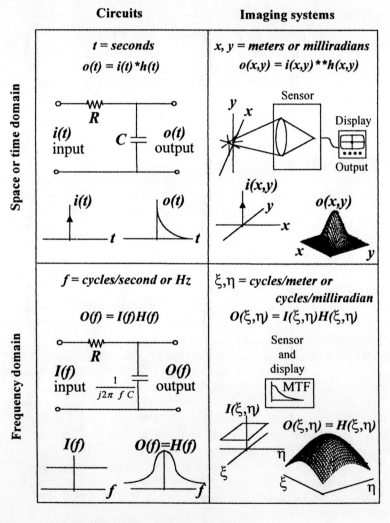

Figure 3.1 Circuit and imaging system LSI analysis.

3.1 LINEAR SYSTEMS

Linearity requires two properties [1, 2]: superposition and scaling. Many scientists and engineers study temporal systems such as circuits, where the independent variable is time t. There is no difference in the mathematics if the spatial variables, x and y, are defined as the independent variables instead. To illustrate this concept, we use a one-dimensional analysis. Consider the input $i(x)$ to a system $L\{\}$ with an output $o(x)$. So we can write

$$o(x) = L\{i(x)\} \tag{3.1}$$

The system is said to provide a superposition characteristic if

$$o(x) = L\{i_1(x) + i_2(x)\} = L\{i_1(x)\} + L\{i_2(x)\} \tag{3.2}$$

Such a system behaves as though the inputs were present by themselves and the output is simply the sum of the individual responses. The property of superposition is important for analysis of linear systems. It allows us to determine the output for a simple basis (linearly independent) function input and to use the results to predict the output for a input signal composed of a sum of the basis functions. Common basis functions are sinusoids (and their close cousins, the complex exponentials) and *delta* (or impulse) functions.

The system output for a set of sinusoidal input functions is sometimes termed the *sinewave response*. For optical systems, the sinewave response is sometimes called the *modulation transfer function MTF* [3]. The frequency for sinusoids of spatial variables x and y, for example, is expressed in cycles per millimeter or some other appropriate scaled dimension. The response to a *delta* function is called the *impulse response*. In an optical system, the response can also be called a *point-spread function (psf)*.

We can observe the *psf* easily by looking at the stars on a clear night. Virtually all the visible stars will appear to be about the same size, in spite of the vast differences in the actual size and distances from Earth. What is really being sensed is the *psf* of the eye because the stars are too small to be resolved. That is, the stars are point sources, or *delta* functions, for the human eye. In mechanical systems, a sudden input (or impulse) might be achieved by striking the system. Camera flashes viewed by video cameras (as frequently seen at nighttime bowl games for college football) provide impulses both in time and space.

The second property required for a system to be linear is the scaling property. Briefly, if the system is linear, doubling the input will only result in a doubling of the output. "Doubling" is simply an arbitrary chosen scale factor to illustrate the property. Whatever scale factor is applied to the input, the same scale factor must result at the output. Using our previous notation, this is expressed in equation form as

$$o(x) = L\{ai(x)\} = aL\{i(x)\} \qquad\qquad (3.3)$$

A common feature in I²R and EO systems that defeats this property is the presence of automatic gain control (AGC). If the gain of the system adjusts depending on the input, then the scaling property does not hold for the system. EO test engineers must be aware of any AGC function in the sensor electronics. For tests requiring linearity, the AGC must be controlled, either by disabling it or by presenting a very bright input in a part of the field-of-view (FOV). The bright input drives the AGC to its minimal gain condition and holds it there so that responses to test objects obey the scaling property. Also, saturation must be avoided or the scaling property will not hold. Saturation occurs when the input signal is large enough to cause the output signal to reach its maximum. Under this condition, changes seen on the input signal are not seen on the output signal.

3.2 SHIFT INVARIANCE

Shift invariance [4, 5] in a temporal system implies that the system is not changing with time. The response to an input applied now is the same as the response to that input applied an hour from now. It will simply be shifted in time by an hour. In temporal systems, the property is often referred to as *time invariance*. *Shift invariance* in an optical system implies that an input at one point in the FOV produces a response identical to that of the same input at a different location in the FOV, just shifted to a different location. In optical systems, this is frequently a marginally fulfilled condition. Most optical systems perform better "on-axis" than they do "off-axis," where "on-axis" and "off-axis" refer to the optical axis of the system. The optical axis of the system is usually the axis of symmetry of the optical elements, although sometimes the optical elements themselves are off-axis elements. Thus, shift invariance is considered a first-order assumption for most optical systems. It is approximately true over small regions in the FOV.

The property of shift invariance can be stated in equation form. Let $o_1(x)$ represent the output resulting from an input located at x; that is, $i(x)$. Then, the output in response to the same input shifted to x_o is

$$o(x) = L\{i(x - x_o)\} = o_1(x - x_o) \qquad\qquad (3.4)$$

for shift invariance to hold.

Shift invariance allows the techniques of linear systems analysis to be applied to I²R and EO systems. In effect, the system responds to identical inputs the same regardless of where they occur in the FOV. Without shift invariance, the system would require characterization at every location within its FOV. Characterization at a single location is sufficient for a LSI system.

3.3 BASICS OF LSI SYSTEMS

Sections 3.1 and 3.2 revealed the approach used to analyze LSI systems. An arbitrary input is considered to be composed of a sum (i.e., integral) of appropriately weighted and shifted basis functions (*delta* functions, mostly). The response (output) of the system to a single *delta* function can then be used along with superposition to determine the output of the system to this arbitrary input. So, all we need to completely characterize the input-output behavior of an LSI system is its impulse response.

We begin with a brief review of *delta* functions. *Delta* functions, $\delta(x)$, are considered to have infinite height, zero width, and an area of one. It is perhaps clearer to picture them as the limit of a process of shrinking the width and increasing the height at the same rate to retain the unit area. Convenient functions to shrink in width are Gaussian, rectangle, and sinc functions, although others will also yield *delta* functions in the limit of zero width. The infinite height is sometimes troublesome to the practical-minded analyst or engineer. In the real world, only the integration properties of the of *delta* functions are used. The most fundamental of these is the sifting property (2.7). It states that multiplying a function by a delta function and integrating across the *delta* function sifts out the value of the function at the location of the *delta* function. Recall from Chapter 2 that the sifting property was written as

$$f(x_o) = \int_{x_1}^{x_2} f(x)\delta(x - x_o)dx \quad \text{for} \quad x_1 \leq x_0 \leq x_2 \tag{3.5}$$

Briefly stated, we multiplied by a *delta* function located at x_o, integrated across the *delta* function and obtained the value of $f(x)$ at the location of x_o (i.e., $f(x_o)$).

An equation such as this does not conform to our usual use of equations in engineering. Usually, the left side corresponds to some value that we seek. The right side usually corresponds to given quantities. The above equation can be thought of as being ridiculous. If one has a function, $f(x)$, all you need to do to get $f(x_o)$ is to evaluate $f(x)$ at x_o. It seems pointless to multiply by a *delta* function and integrate to achieve what you already have. However, the sifting property has some very powerful ramifications, so it is worth learning. Perhaps its greatest value is seen from the following discussion.

We can change variables so that x is replaced by the dummy variable α, and x_o is replaced by x. Changing the limits to $+/-\infty$ yields

$$f(x) = \int_{-\infty}^{\infty} f(\alpha)\delta(\alpha - x)d\alpha \tag{3.6}$$

The beauty of this equation is that any function can be written as a sum (integral) of appropriately weighted and shifted *delta* functions. Thus, *delta* functions can be the basis functions for our arbitrary input. This allows a simple characterization of the input-output properties of LSI systems, because all we need is the response to a *delta* function. As it turns out, and as shown below, the output of an LSI system is the convolution of the input and the impulse response.

Once again, we let the output be related to the input by

$$o(x) = L\{i(x)\} \qquad (3.7)$$

where $L\{\}$ is a linear system operator. The input can be written as a sum of weighted and appropriately located *delta* functions. That is:

$$i(x) = \int_{-\infty}^{\infty} i(\alpha)\delta(x - \alpha)d\alpha \qquad (3.8)$$

In these terms, the output is

$$o(x) = L\{\int_{-\infty}^{\infty} i(\alpha)\delta(x - \alpha)d\alpha\} \qquad (3.9)$$

The linear operator operates only on functions of x, so the operator can be moved inside the integral to yield

$$o(x) = \int_{-\infty}^{\infty} i(\alpha)L\{\delta(x - \alpha)\}d\alpha \qquad (3.10)$$

$L\{\delta(x - \alpha)\}$ is, by definition, the response of the system to a delta function located at α. The shift invariance property indicates the response to an impulse at α is the same as the response to an impulse at 0, just shifted to α. Letting $h(x)$ represent the system response to an impulse at $x=0$, the response to an impulse at α is $h(x - \alpha)$. Substitution yields the desired result

$$o(x) = \int_{-\infty}^{\infty} i(\alpha)h(x - \alpha)d\alpha \qquad (3.11)$$

This is just the convolution of the input with the system's impulse response. It is convenient to use the notation

$$o(x) = i(x) * h(x) \qquad (3.12)$$

to represent the convolution integral. This notation has no meaning until it is replaced by the integral it represents. It is best thought of as shorthand for the integral representing the convolution.

3.4 IMPULSE RESPONSE

The concept of the impulse response [6] can best be shown through an example. Consider the RC circuit shown in Figure 3.2(a). The impulse response of the circuit can be found using circuit theory as

$$h(t) = \frac{1}{RC}e^{-t/(RC)} \quad \text{for } t \geq 0 \tag{3.13}$$

The graphic representation is shown in Figure 3.2(b). We are interested in determining the output voltage $v_o(t)$, given the step input function shown in Figure 3.2(c). The output corresponds to the charging of the capacitor through the resistor given some applied dc voltage $v_i(t)$. The convolution of the input with the impulse response gives the output. Recall that the convolution involves the flip, slip, multiply, and integrate process, where $h(t)$ is the function that is flipped (remember that convolution is commutative). The flipped function and the stationary function plotted on the α axis are shown in Figure 3.2(d). These two functions are multiplied and integrated. The integration from $-\infty$ to ∞ can be broken into three sections of limits: $(-\infty, 0), (0, t), (t, \infty)$. Note that multiplication of the two functions (point-by-point) yields a zero product unless $t \geq 0$ as shown in Figure 3.2(e). The only section that yields a non-zero product of the two functions is $(0, t)$. Therefore the convolution integral becomes

$$v_o(t) = \int_0^t (1)(\frac{1}{RC}e^{-(t-\alpha)/(RC)})d\alpha \tag{3.14}$$

Evaluation of this integral gives

$$v_o(t) = \frac{1}{RC}e^{-t/(RC)}\int_0^t e^{\alpha/(RC)}d\alpha = e^{-t/(RC)}[e^{t/(RC)} - e^0] = 1 - e^{-t/(RC)} \tag{3.15}$$

for arguments greater than or equal to 0. The output is shown in Figure 3.2(f). The output appears to be reasonable in that we expect the charging voltage of a capacitor to have a limit approaching that of the charging voltage (i.e., 1V) at a rate related to the resistance and capacitance.

It is worth showing a simple impulse response example of an optical system, where the output can be determined for some well-defined input. Consider the imaging system shown in Figure 3.3. The optical system shown by the box could be a series of lenses or a single lens that reimages two points of light onto an image plane. The input plane is denoted by x_i, y_i and the output plane is denoted x_o, y_o. The two points of light are small enough in spatial extent to be unresolvable by the system and, therefore, can be considered impulses. For this example, we assume that the light is monochromatic (single frequency) and that the system can be considered spatially coherent. Coherence is discussed in Chapter 4. The important point here is that we want to find the electromagnetic field output for the given input. From Chapter 2, the shifting and scaling of the even impulse pair given by

$$\frac{1}{|a|}\delta\delta(\tfrac{x-x_o}{a}) = [\delta(x-x_o+a) + \delta(x-x_o-a)] \qquad (3.16)$$

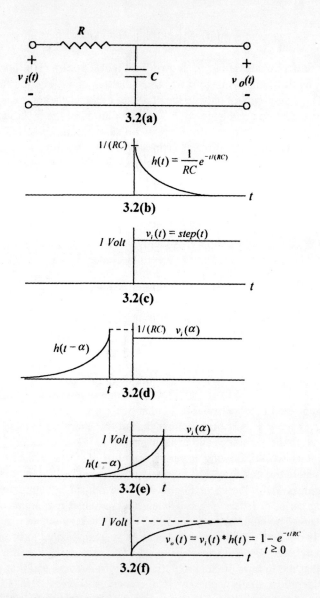

Figure 3.2 Impulse response example.

Therefore, the electromagnetic field for the two points of light located at $\pm a$ from the optical axis in the input plane can be represented with an even impulse pair function with $x_0 = 0$:

$$U_i(x,y) = \frac{1}{|a|}\delta\delta(\frac{x}{a}) \qquad (3.17)$$

The impulse response or *psf* for the perfect optical system in this example has been determined to be

$$h(x,y) = psf(x,y) = \frac{1}{b^2}somb(\frac{r}{b}) \qquad (3.18)$$

where b is λ/d, the wavelength of the monochromatic light (λ) over the diameter of the optical lens (d), and r is $\sqrt{x^2+y^2}$. Recalling the shift invariance property of (2.19) and the *delta* function convolution property of (2.20), the output of the system is

$$U_o(x,y) = U_i(x,y) * h(x,y) = \frac{1}{ab^2}[somb(\frac{\sqrt{(x+a)^2+y^2}}{b}) + somb(\frac{\sqrt{(x-a)^2+y^2}}{b})] \qquad (3.19)$$

It is important to convince yourself that this is correct. While the result is obviously two shifted and scaled impulse responses, the tools of linear systems are shown to work in the optical case. Substitution of λ/d for b shows that the diameter of the *somb* function, sometimes called the *Airy disc* (after the gentleman who originally derived it) increases with an increased wavelength or a decreased optical lens diameter (or limiting aperture). This simple example contains several important concepts that occur again and again.

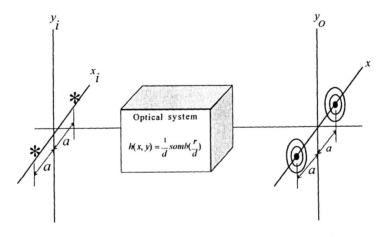

Figure 3.3 Optical system response.

The field magnitude derived here is the system output. It is not sensed by vision or by optical detectors. The square of the field magnitude is defined as the *irradiance* and is the parameter that is actually sensed in imaging systems. It corresponds to optical power. Also, most I^2R and EO systems are not monochromatic and operate in a "nonspatially coherent" environment. The usual noncoherent impulse response is proportional to the square of the coherent impulse response (i.e., the *somb* function). This noncoherent impulse response is the *psf.* The relationship causes noncoherent systems to be LSI systems of the irradiance variable instead of the electromagnetic field quantity. *In simple terms, the input irradiance is convolved with the psf to determine system output irradiance.*

The impulse response, or *psf*, of an entire system is the convolution of the individual impulse responses of the optics, detectors, electronics, processor, display, and, if appropriate, human vision. This is due simply to the fact that the output of each component is the input of the next. The result is a more *Gaus*-like system *psf* as shown in Figure 3.4(a). The *x*-axis cross-section is shown in Figure 3.4(b).

It is sometimes difficult to measure the *psf* of an I^2R and EO system because it requires the illumination of a tiny pinhole as the object (much smaller than the optical system resolution capability). The amount of light exiting the pinhole is limited and begins to impinge on system sensitivity. An alternative is the knife-edge response, or *edge response,* of the system. A long, straight blade is uniformly illuminated from behind, and the sensor image transition from dark to bright is measured as shown in Figure 3.4(c). The *x*-axis cross section is shown in Figure 3.4(d). The relationship between the impulse response (*psf*) and the edge response ($e_x(x)$) is simply

$$e_x(x) = \int_{-\infty}^{x} psf(\alpha)d\alpha \qquad (3.20)$$

As can be easily seen from a mathematical viewpoint, the *psf* is the spatial derivative of the edge response (in the direction normal to the blade edge). The edge response provides a method of obtaining the impulse response of the system without the problem of signal limitations.

We consider a final example here to firm up the impulse response concept. It is typical, in imaging systems, to evaluate the performance of an imaging system by placing a four-bar target in front of the imager as the object and to evaluate the quality of the four-bar target image as shown in Figure 3.5. The four-bar target is simply a transparency with four rectangular holes so that light (visible or infrared) can pass. The image of the four-bar target is always a degraded rendition of the original object. The system is the optical system shown where the transparency is the input and the image is the output.

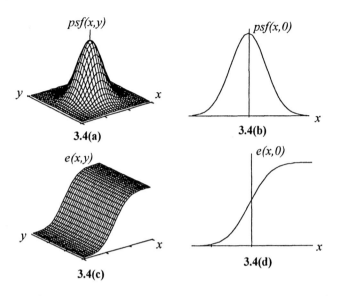

Figure 3.4 *psf* and edge response.

Because the system is an LSI system, from (3.12) we know that the output is the input convolved with the system impulse response (or *psf*). The output (the four-bar target image) is also shown in Figure 3.5.

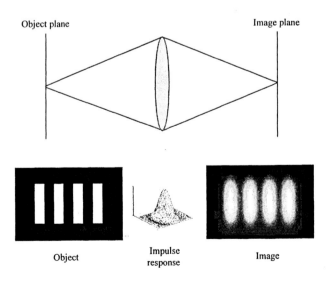

Figure 3.5 Four-bar target, imaging system, and image.

3.5 TRANSFER FUNCTION

The system transfer function [4 - 6] defines the system frequency throughput. In temporal systems, a wide transfer function allows high frequencies through the system. High temporal frequencies correspond to very rapid changes in some parameter such as voltage or current with respect to time. In space, a wide transfer function allows high *spatial* frequencies through a system. High spatial frequencies correspond to the irradiance of an object changing dramatically over short distances in space. For example, leaves on a tree produce higher spatial frequency signals than the trunk of the tree.

It is usually convenient to evaluate the response of LSI systems to some input in the frequency domain. In EO and I²R systems, the input spectrum is determined by the Fourier transform of the input irradiance. The input spectrum is then multiplied by the system transfer function to determine output spectrum. *The inverse transform of the output spectrum yields the resulting system output image.* The analysis in the space domain requires the input space to be convolved with the system impulse response to produce a spatial output (an image). Note that the duality of convolution in the space domain corresponds to multiplication in the frequency domain. Also, *the transfer function is simply the Fourier transform of the impulse response.*

The transfer function determines the weighting of the output spectrum relative to the input spectrum. Consider the circuit mathematically defined in Figure 3.6(a). The transfer function of the circuit is shown in Figure 3.6(b). To determine the output for given inputs, the input spectrum is multiplied by the transfer function. This means that each frequency component of the input is assigned a weighting factor as determined by the transfer function. The result is then inverse-transformed to yield the output. Consider the inputs given in Figures 3.6(c), 3.6(d), and 3.6(e). The Fourier transform of a constant 1V input, a dc signal, is an impulse located at the origin (see Table 2.5). This impulse is multiplied by the unity throughput of the transfer function for dc signals. The output is the inverse transform of the unaltered impulse (i.e., a 1V constant signal). The second signal, shown in Figure 3.6(d), is a cosine function of 50 Hz. The transform of this signal is an even impulse pair, where the two impulses are located at +/- 50 Hz. Note from Figure 3.6(b) that the transfer function has an attenuation of 0.5 here, so the multiplication of the impulse pair by the signal spectrum yields a signal of one-half the amplitude. The output is inverse-transformed to give the temporal signal shown. Finally, a 100-Hz signal is input to the system and is multiplied by the transfer function weighting of zero. Therefore, 0V is seen on the system output as a result of this input. What is the output of this system if the input is a 100-Hz oscillation on top a 50-Hz cosine wave with a dc offset of 1V? Remember the principle of *superposition*.

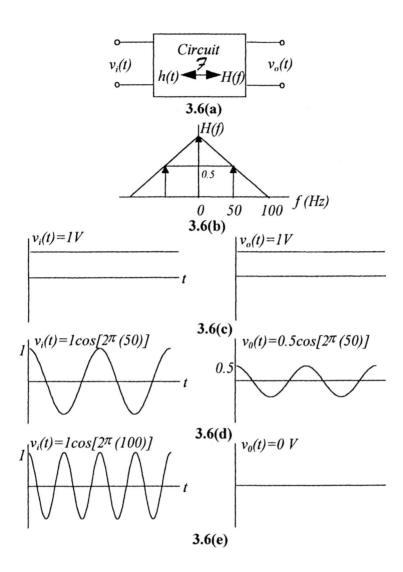

Figure 3.6 Transfer function example.

In this chapter, we limit our optical transfer function discussion to broadband noncoherent optical systems (i.e., the system is linear with irradiance, not EM field strength). A more general discussion is reserved for Chapter 4. Consider the space domain of Figure 3.7. The system can be characterized by providing an impulse, or point-source, irradiance to the input of the optical system. The output of the system is simply an image of the impulse response, or psf, because the convolution of any function with an impulse is that function. In the frequency domain, the transform of the impulse function is a uniform frequency distribution across the spectrum. The system output spectrum is the uniform spectrum (i.e., a constant 1) multiplied by the system transfer function. Therefore, the output is simply the system transfer function. Note that the transfer function is simply the transform of the impulse response and that narrow impulse responses correspond to wide transfer functions, and vice versa.

The transfer function of a noncoherent system is called the *optical transfer function (OTF)*. The OTF is complex and has both magnitude and phase. The magnitude is called the *modulation transfer function (MTF)* and the phase is called the *phase transfer function (PTF)*. MTF is often a circularly symmetric function, so it is plotted as a one-dimensional function. The OTF is the Fourier transform of a real function (the psf) and so the OTF is hermitian (the MTF is even and the PTF is odd). The PTF can be ignored if the psf is symmetrical, because the PTF goes to zero. Ideally, one could use a point source to obtain a psf and then obtain the OTF by transforming the psf. Practically, this approach can suffer from signal-to-noise limitations so other approaches, such as the edge response, are used.

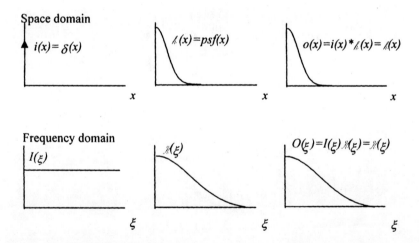

Figure 3.7 LSI optical systems.

3.6 SPATIAL SAMPLING

It is common to represent a function $f(x,y)$ by an array of sampled values. Not only is this the case with I^2R and EO systems, but it is also true for synthetic aperture radar (SAR), magnetic resonance imaging (MRI), and other imaging sensors. It is well known that the spatial samples must be taken sufficiently close to each other to obtain an accurate representation of the function. Also, for *bandlimited* functions, the original function can be reconstructed exactly with the sampled array information provided that the spacings are within particular limits. Bandlimited functions are those whose corresponding Fourier transforms are nonzero over some finite frequency band. All frequency components outside the finite frequency band are zero. The reconstruction theory of these band-limited functions is known as the *Whittaker-Shannon sampling theorem.*

Consider a function that is sampled by a Cartesian lattice of samples to give a sampled function

$$f_s(x,y) = |\tfrac{1}{a}|comb(\tfrac{x}{a})|\tfrac{1}{b}|comb(\tfrac{y}{b})f(x,y) = |\tfrac{1}{ab}|comb(\tfrac{x}{a},\tfrac{y}{b})f(x,y) \qquad (3.21)$$

The sampled function is an array of delta functions spaced in the x direction by intervals a and spaced in the y direction by intervals b and that are weighted (area-wise) by the values of the original function. Using the convolution theorem, the spectrum of the sampled function is

$$F_s(\xi,\eta) = comb(a\xi, b\eta) * *F(\xi,\eta) \qquad (3.22)$$

The convolution of *delta* functions (2.20) along with the shift invariant property (2.19) gives the spectrum of (3.22) that is simply the spectrum of the original function located at each of the *delta* functions

$$F_s(\xi,\eta) = |\tfrac{1}{ab}| \sum_{n=-\infty}^{\infty} \sum_{m=-\infty}^{\infty} F(\xi-\tfrac{n}{a},\eta-\tfrac{m}{b}) \qquad (3.23)$$

Note that the sampled spectrum is replications of the original function located at intervals of $1/a$ and $1/b$, as shown in Figure 3.8.

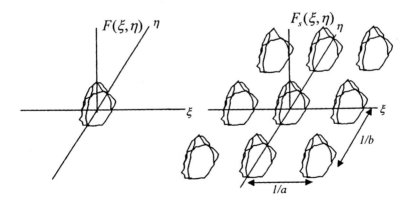

Figure 3.8 Spectra of (1) the original function and (2) the sampled function.

The scaling theorem relates the sample distances a and b to the spectrum spacing of (3.23). Note that if a and b are small, then the spacing in the frequency domain is large and vice versa. Therefore, a and b must be small enough to ensure that the frequency domain spacing does not allow overlap of the replicated spectrums. Overlap corresponds to information corruption that cannot be recovered. The requirements on a and b can be determined in the frequency domain such that the frequency spacing is twice the function's spectrum widths. Let $2\xi_{max}$ and $2\eta_{max}$ be the bandlimited widths of the original function's spectrum. Therefore:

$$a \le \frac{1}{2\xi_{max}} \qquad \text{and} \qquad b \le \frac{1}{2\eta_{max}} \qquad (3.24)$$

These are the maximal spacings of the samples for exact recovery of the original function. The sampled spectrum must be filtered to recover the original spectrum. A number of filters accomplish this task; however, the simpler function is

$$H(\xi, \eta) = rect(\frac{\xi}{2\xi_{max}}, \frac{\eta}{2\eta_{max}}) \qquad (3.25)$$

When this transfer function is multiplied by the sampled function spectrum, the original function spectrum is obtained:

$$F(\xi, \eta) = F_s(\xi, \eta) rect(\frac{\xi}{2\xi_{max}}, \frac{\eta}{2\eta_{max}}) \qquad (3.26)$$

This recovery of the original signal can also be seen in the spatial domain

$$f(x,y) = [f(x,y)|\frac{1}{ab}|comb(\frac{x}{a})comb(\frac{y}{b})] ** 4\xi_{max}\eta_{max} sinc(2\xi_{max}x, 2\eta_{max}y) \qquad (3.27)$$

The sampled function $f_s(x,y)$ can be written as

$$f_s(x,y) = f(x,y)|\frac{1}{ab}|comb(\frac{x}{a})comb(\frac{y}{b}) = \sum_{n=-\infty}^{\infty}\sum_{m=-\infty}^{\infty} f(na, mb)\delta(x - na, y - mb) \qquad (3.28)$$

Note that the sampled function is a weighted collection of *delta* functions and that the convolution of the *sinc* function with these delta functions, as given in equation 3.27, results in weighted *sinc* functions located at the *delta* functions. The reconstructed original signal is

$$f(x,y) = 4\xi_{max}\eta_{max}\sum_{n=-\infty}^{\infty}\sum_{m=-\infty}^{\infty} f(na, mb) sinc[2\xi_{max}(x - na), 2\eta_{max}(y - mb)] \qquad (3.29)$$

If the sampling intervals are taken to be the maximum allowable spacing within the limits of (3.24), then (3.29) becomes

$$f(x,y) = \sum_{n=-\infty}^{\infty} \sum_{m=-\infty}^{\infty} f(\frac{n}{2\xi_{max}}, \frac{m}{2\eta_{max}}) sinc[2\xi_{max}(x - \frac{n}{2\xi_{max}}), 2\eta_{max}(y - \frac{m}{2\eta_{max}})] \qquad (3.30)$$

This identity is known as the Whittaker-Shannon [2] sampling theorem. It states that exact replication of a bandlimited image function can be performed simply by applying a *sinc* interpolation function to the sampled image. Goodman [2] points out that this is not the only sampling theorem. It applies to the Cartesian sampling array and the rectangular transfer function. These choices could be altered to give a number of sampling theorems. In fact, other transfer functions have been shown to give better results while limiting the number of samples required per unit area to reconstruct an exact image.

3.7 SPATIAL SAMPLING AND RESOLUTION

A sensor's resolution characteristics depend on a number of variables, but can be discussed using two general parameters: the *system transfer function* and the *sampling function*. The system transfer function [7] includes optical degradation (diffraction and aberrations), detector size and shape, electronics and processing, display, and the human visual transfer function. The individual transfer functions can be cascaded to obtain a system transfer function (i.e., system MTF) that can be multiplied by an input spectrum to give the output spectrum. The sampling function (for sampled systems) corresponds to the discrete nature of spatial sampling. The sampling function has no transfer function but can definitely affect the spatial resolution of the system [8, 9].

Consider the sampled imaging system shown in Figure 3.9. A target is imaged onto a discrete detector array (a *staring* array) by imaging optics. We assume that the detector responses are uniform over the detector surfaces, the output light is the integrated light on the detectors, and the imaged surface is a large array of detectors. The image samples, or voltage, provided by the output of the detector array can be written as

$$i(x,y) = K[o(\frac{x}{c}, \frac{y}{c}) * *rect(\frac{x}{p}, \frac{y}{p}) * * h(x,y)]\frac{1}{p^2}comb(\frac{x}{p}, \frac{y}{p}) \qquad (3.31)$$

K is a radiometry constant to describe the signal throughput of the system, p is the distance between pixel centers (pixel pitch), c is an image magnification constant equal to the focal length over the object range f/R and h is the optical impulse response or psf. The GSD acronym is known as the *ground sampled distance* (derived for ground-looking sensors on airborne platforms). The GSD is the projection of the pixel pitch onto the ground or target of interest at the object range. This is the absolute limit to the spatial resolution of the system. Many performance parameters such as the National Imagery Interpretation Rating System (NIIRS) [10] have been developed based on the GSD. Systems can have less resolution than the GSD because of the transfer function and corresponding psf. Projection of a psf onto the ground in the same manner as the sample function gives a feel for the associated resolution. If the projected psf is smaller than twice the GSD, then the resolution is limited by the sampling function. If the psf is larger than twice the GSD, then the resolution is limited by the transfer function. For example, ground resolved distance (GRD) is a photo reconnaissance parameter that corresponds to the minimum test target size that can be resolved on the ground by an experienced photointerpreter. This parameter can be equivalent to the GSD if the psf is smaller than twice the pixel pitch. Optimal design gives a psf at twice the pixel pitch.

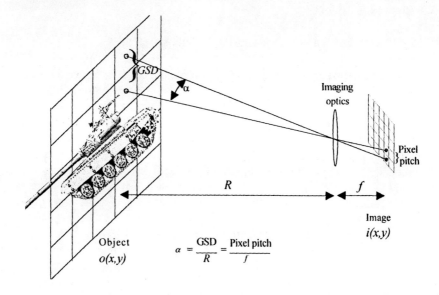

Figure 3.9 Sampled imaging system.

The samples image in the frequency domain can be expressed

$$I(\xi, \eta) = Kc^2 p^2 \{O(c\xi, c\eta) sinc(p\xi, p\eta) \mathcal{H}(\xi, \eta)\} * *comb(p\xi, p\eta) \quad (3.32)$$

where $\mathcal{H}$ is the incoherent transfer function of the optics (i.e., the transform of the psf). The width of the *sinc* function is twice the width (distance between samples) of the *comb* function. From the Whittaker-Shannon sampling theorem, any function to be convolved with the sampling spectrum has to be less than half the sampling spacing in the frequency domain to retain all spatial frequency information. Therefore, the product $O(c\xi, c\eta) sinc(p\xi, p\eta) \mathcal{H}(\xi, \eta)$ must have a width less than half the *comb* spacing to retain information with no overlap of the convolved functions. If not, this overlap causes high-frequency information to mix with low-frequency information resulting in low-frequency artifacts. This effect is known as *aliasing*. Noting that the *sinc* function does not provide the necessary spectral limit to prevent aliasing; the transfer function must be designed to provide this requirement. In fact, most detectors do not completely fill the array and are smaller in width than the pixel pitch causing the size of the *rect* function to be smaller than that of (3.31). The smaller detector corresponds to a wider *sinc* in the frequency domain. Another solution, but not a practical one, is for the sampling system to view only low-frequency images with no significant high frequency characteristics.

Finally, the spatial frequency of the object space can be given in a number of parameters. In the most basic form, irradiance can be written as a function of space, where x and y are in meters, so the spatial frequency parameters are in cycles per meter. A more common approach is to give x and y in radians or milliradians. That is, x and y in meters are divided by the range from the sensor to the object yielding a new x and y in radians (for small angles). To get milliradians, radians are multiplied by 1,000. The object irradiance as a function of x and y in milliradians gives ξ and η in cycles per milliradians. Because these spatial frequencies are range independent, they are easier to apply in sensor performance calculations.

EXERCISES

3.1 The Fourier transform can be considered as a system that maps a function into its transform.
a) Is this system linear?
b) Is this system shift invariant?

3.2 A system is specified by the operator:

$$S\{f(x)\} = 0.5 \int_{-\infty}^{x} f(\alpha)d\alpha$$

a) Is the system linear?
b) Is the system shift invariant?
c) Sketch the output for $f(x) = rect(\frac{x-2}{2})$.
d) Sketch the output for $f(x) = rect(\frac{x+2}{2})$.

3.3 A system is specified by the operator:

$$S\{f(x)\} = [f(x)]^3 + [f(x)]^2 + 3f(x)$$

a) Is the system linear?
b) Is the system shift invariant?

3.4 Use the convolution integral to determine the output of a circuit if the voltage input is shown in the figure below and the circuit impulse response is $h(t) = 10e^{-3t}, t \geq 0$:

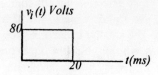

Figure 3.10

3.5 An LSI system has an impulse response:

$$h(x) = 4\,\text{sinc}^2(2x) - 2\,\text{sinc}^2(x)$$

The input of the system is $f(x) = 1 + \cos(2\pi\xi_o x)$. Sketch the output for
a) $\xi_o = 0.5$
b) $\xi_o = 1.0$
c) $\xi_o = 2.5$

3.6 The image irradiance formed by an incoherent optical system is given by

$$I(x,y) = |h(x,y)|^2 * * |f(x,y)|^2 = h(x,y) * * |f(x,y)|^2$$

where $h(x,y)$ is the coherent impulse response, $h(x,y)$ is the incoherent impulse response (or psf), and $f(x,y)$ is the input image field amplitude. That is, the system is linear in irradiance. The output amplitude formed by a coherent system is

$$g(x,y) = h(x,y) * * f(x,y)$$

where the corresponding irradiance is $I(x,y) = |g(x,y)|^2$. The system is linear with field amplitude. For $f(x,y) = rect(\frac{x}{\Delta x})$ and $h(x,y) = rect(\frac{x}{\Delta x}) - rect(\frac{x-\Delta x}{\Delta x})$:

a) Find the system output irradiance formed by the coherent system.
b) Find the system output irradiance formed by the incoherent system.

3.7 A system with a transfer function shown is stimulated with input signals described by
a) $f(x) = 1 + \cos[2\pi(0.5)x]$
b) $f(x) = 1 + \cos[2\pi(0.75)x]$
c) $f(x) = 1 + \cos[2\pi x]$
Determine and sketch the output signal for each case.

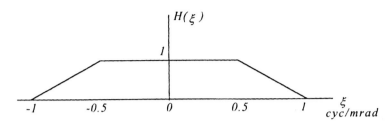

Figure 3.11

REFERENCES

[1] Gaskill, J. D., *Linear Systems, Fourier Transforms, and Optics,* New York: Wiley, p. 139, 1978.

[2] Goodman, J. W., *Introduction to Fourier Optics,* San Francisco: McGraw-Hill, p. 17, 1968.

[3] Holst, G. C., *Electro-Optical Imaging System Performance*, Orlando, FL: JCD Publishing, p. 130, 1995.

[4] Hayt, W., and J. Kemmerly, *Engineering Circuit Analysis*, New York: McGraw-Hill, p.641, 1978.

[5] Cogdell, J. R., *Foundations of Electrical Engineering,* Englewood Cliffs, NJ: Prentice-Hall, 1990.

[6] Nilsson, J. W., *Electric Circuits*, Reading, MA: Addison-Wesley, 1989.

[7] Ratches, J., "Static Performance Model for Thermal Imaging Systems," *Optical Engineering,* Vol. 15, No. 6, pp. 525 - 530, 1976.

[8] Dudzik, M. C., *Electro-Optical Systems Design, Analysis, and Testing From the Infrared and Electro-Optical Systems Handbook*, Bellingham, WA: SPIE Press, p. 45, 1993.

[9] Lloyd, J., *Thermal Imaging Systems,* New York: Plenum Press, p. 369, 1975.

[10] "Imagery Interpretation Rating Scale," *Air Standard Agreement*, AID STD 101/11A, Jan. 1980.

Chapter 4

Diffraction

The performance of I²R and EO systems is fundamentally limited by the blur spot produced with the diffraction of light. In the case of circular entrance and exit apertures, a closed-form diffraction equation presented in Chapter 7 represents the transfer of spatial frequencies through incoherent systems and thus, this chapter is not required in the analysis of those systems. This chapter is necessary for those who must deal with complex system apertures or who simply desire a better understanding of this basic limitation to sensor performance.

Diffraction is a phenomenon [1-3] that was discovered in the 1700s and studied by many great scientists of the time such as Young, Fresnel, Fraunhofer, Poisson, and Arago. Fresnel won the French national optics award for predicting a bright spot behind an illuminated disc that required the curving of light. This theory was considered beyond belief by Poisson, Laplace, Biot, and Gay-Lussac, so Arago (a judge at the competition) arranged for an immediate experimental demonstration in the basement of the conference hall. It was shown to be true and Fresnel's historical contribution became famous. In fact, this demonstration provided a significant shift in the Newtonian light paradigm of particle theory to a more wavelike characterization of light.

The essence of diffraction is that light spreads (or curves) around obstructions. The spreading increases with longer light wavelengths and smaller obstructions. The spreading makes it impossible to reconstruct an infinitesimal point source in the image plane of a sensor. The light curves around the collecting aperture of a sensor, thus producing a "spread" point source rather than the original infinitesimal source. The spreading is greater for smaller apertures. The spreading is also less for short wavelengths and more for longer wavelengths. Diffraction occurs even if the optic is geometrically perfect residing in a vacuum.

Diffraction is one of the primary reasons that large telescope apertures are desired. An optical system considered to perform to its physical limit is called *diffraction-limited.* Large, ground-based astronomical telescopes are sometimes limited by optical disturbances in Earth's atmosphere. Prime locations for telescopes are high altitudes where the atmospheric effects are reduced.

Space-based systems such as the Hubble telescope are either diffraction-limited or limited by the imperfections in the imaging paths of the optics (i.e., aberrations). The large apertures of these systems are designed to reduce the diffraction effects.

This chapter provides the fundamentals of diffraction analysis where the student or analyst can determine diffraction effects for a particular sensor. The material here is limited to the very basics needed to perform general sensor analysis, and more specific information can be found in the references.

4.1 TEM WAVES

The term "waves" is usually slang for transverse electro-magnetic (TEM) waves. TEM simply means that the electric field is normal to the magnetic field and both fields are normal to the direction of wave propagation. We usually keep track of the electric field distribution because given one, the other is known. For simplicity, the electric field distribution is described as a *complex amplitude*. The electric field irradiance is the squared absolute value of the complex amplitude.

The polarization of a wave indicates the direction of the electric field vector oscillation with respect to the direction of propagation. A linearly polarized wave is one in which this oscillation can be described on a single axis. For example, a wave propagating down the z-axis of Figure 4.1 might be linearly polarized in the y-direction. In this case, there would be no electric field oscillating in the x-direction (i.e., only the magnetic field). There are a number of other polarization types, such as circularly polarized in the clockwise or counterclockwise directions, where the electric field vector changes as the wave propagates. Also, a random polarized wave would have an equal amount of electric field amplitude in all directions normal to the direction of propagation.

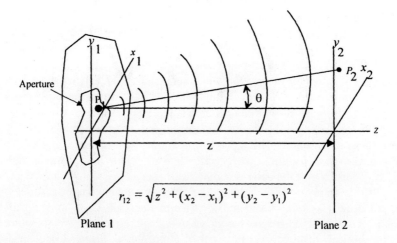

$$r_{12} = \sqrt{z^2 + (x_2 - x_1)^2 + (y_2 - y_1)^2}$$

Figure 4.1 Diffraction geometry.

We can represent a monochromatic light wave using the scalar function

$$u(x,y,z,t) = a(x,y,z)\cos(2\pi vt - \phi(x,y,z)) \qquad (4.1)$$

where v is the temporal frequency of the wave, $a(x,y,z)$ is the amplitude of the wave, and the argument of the cosine is the phase. The surfaces over which $\phi(x,y,z)$ is a constant are wavefronts. The wavefronts can take on planar, quadratic, spherical, cylindrical, and more complicated shapes. We use the phasor form, or complex amplitude, of the wave

$$u(x,y,z) = a(x,y,z)e^{j\phi(x,y,z)} \qquad (4.2)$$

where the temporal representation of the wave can be retrieved by

$$u(x,y,z,t) = Re\{u^*(x,y,z)e^{j2\pi vt}\} \qquad (4.3)$$

Because detectors, including the human eye, are power sensitive, the irradiance is

$$E(x,y,z) = |u(x,y,z)|^2 = u(x,y,z)u^*(x,y,z) \qquad (4.4)$$

A plane wave traveling down the z-axis of Figure 4.2 can be described as

$$u(x,y,z) = Ae^{jkz} \qquad (4.5)$$

where k is the phase propagation constant $k = 2\pi/\lambda$. The wavefronts are perpendicular to the z-axis as shown in Figure 4.2. The wavefronts correspond to constant amplitudes of the electric field and are separated by λ. Any phase change from z_1 to z_2 can be found by

$$\Delta\phi = (z_2 - z_1)k = z_{12}k \qquad (4.6)$$

Direction cosines are applied to plane waves that are tilted with respect to the propagation axis. Usually, we try to orient the coordinate axis such that the wave propagates down the z-axis. If tilting is necessary, however, direction cosines are used. A tilted plane wave can be expressed by

$$u(x,y,z) = Ae^{jk(\gamma_x x + \gamma_y y + \gamma_z z)} \qquad (4.7)$$

where

$$\gamma_x^2 + \gamma_y^2 + \gamma_z^2 = 1 \qquad (4.8)$$

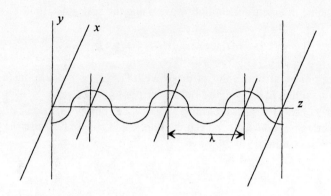

Figure 4.2 Plane wave propagation.

The direction cosines are the cosines of the angles from some Cartesian axes to the direction of wave propagation. Consider the wave propagation shown in Figure 4.3, where the wave propagates in the x-z plane (i.e., $y = 0$). The y-direction cosine is zero and the x- and z-direction cosines are shown. In two dimensions, the wave is propagating at angles α and β from the z and x axes, respectively. Recall that the direction of wave propagation is always normal to the wavefronts. The phase change from some z_1 to some z_2 is now $k\gamma_z z_{12}$.

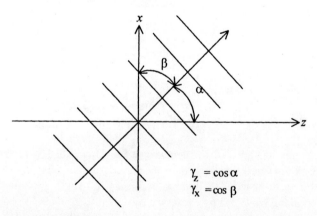

$$\gamma_z = \cos \alpha$$
$$\gamma_x = \cos \beta$$

Figure 4.3 Direction cosines.

In mathematical models, waves are typically set up to propagate down the z-axis and described in a plane (x, y) at some specified z. The wave given at some $z = z_1$ is

$$u(x_1, y_1) = A e^{jk\gamma_z z_1} e^{jk(\gamma_x x + \gamma_y y)}$$
$$= u_1(x, y) = A' e^{jk(\gamma_x x + \gamma_y y)} \tag{4.9}$$

Note that the new complex amplitude, A', takes into account the constant z_1 phase term (sometimes neglected) because this phase is additive and affects the entire field equally over the $z = z_1$ plane. Also, the notation $u_1^-(x,y)$ means just to the left of the z_1 plane and $u_1^+(x,y)$ means just to the right of the z_1 plane, as light (on paper) is usually constructed in most textbooks to travel from left to right.

An expanding spherical wave can be approximated by

$$u_2(x,y) = \frac{A}{j\lambda r_{12}} e^{jkR} \tag{4.10}$$

where the point source is located in plane 1 at (α, β) and the wave is described at plane 2 (x,y). Sometimes spherical waves are approximated by quadratic waves using the Taylor's series expansion

$$R = \sqrt{z_{12}^2 + (x-\alpha)^2 + (y-\beta)^2} \approx z_{12}[1 + \tfrac{1}{2}(\tfrac{x-\alpha}{z_{12}})^2 + \tfrac{1}{2}(\tfrac{y-\beta}{z_{12}})^2] \tag{4.11}$$

So the expanding quadratic wave is written

$$u_2(x,y) = \frac{A}{j\lambda z_{12}} e^{jkz_{12}} e^{j\frac{\pi}{\lambda z_{12}}[(x-\alpha)^2+(y-\beta)^2]} \tag{4.12}$$

Finally, it should be noted that a positive (+) exponential in the later exponential argument of (4.12) corresponds to a diverging, or expanding, wave. A negative (-) exponential corresponds to a converging wave.

4.2 COHERENCE

It is important to understand whether an imaging system is responding to coherent or incoherent light. Coherence defines the manner in which the optical transfer function is calculated. In general, incoherent optical systems can resolve higher spatial frequencies than coherent systems. However, there is a reduction in the modulation of higher spatial frequency signals compared with lower spatial frequency signals.

Coherence can be described as a fixed phase relationship of a field between two points in space or two points in time. The coherence [4] of a source determines the manner in which an irradiance distribution is calculated. At a system level, incoherent systems are linear in irradiance:

$$\mathcal{L}\{aE_1(x,y) + bE_2(x,y)\} = a\,\mathcal{L}\{E_1(x,y)\} + b\,\mathcal{L}\{E_2(x,y)\} \tag{4.13}$$

A coherent system is linear in field distribution:

$$\mathcal{L}\{au_1(x,y) + bu_2(x,y)\} = a\,\mathcal{L}\{u_1(x,y)\} + b\,\mathcal{L}\{u_2(x,y)\} \tag{4.14}$$

Because $E(x,y) = |u(x,y)|^2$, the coherent irradiance from the sum of two fields (a coherent system) is

$$E_{total}(x,y) = u_1(x,y)u_1^*(x,y) + u_2(x,y)u_2^*(x,y) + u_1(x,y)u_2^*(x,y) + u_2(x,y)u_1^*(x,y)$$

$$= E_1(x,y) + E_2(x,y) + u_1(x,y)u_2^*(x,y) + u_2(x,y)u_1^*(x,y) \qquad (4.15)$$

The third and fourth terms in (4.15) describe the interference effects caused by the coherence of the source. Note that in an incoherent system, these terms become negligible. There are varying degrees of coherence, from no measurable phase relationship to a strong coherence. The term *partial coherence* is used to describe systems that are between coherent and incoherent. The degree of coherence is determined by the source characteristics.

Two types of coherence are *spatial* and *temporal* coherence; however, both measure the same type of phenomenon. Spatial coherence is a measure of the phase correlation of the wave between two points in space. That is, it is a measure of how constant the phase relationship is between two points in space. Spatial coherence is driven by the size of the light source. A large light source with large variations in the phase across the source provides for a less coherent system than a small point source. It makes sense that the phase of the light emitted from a tiny source will be more closely linked as it propagates through space. If we think of a large source as a huge collection of point sources, the coherence is reduced by the mixing of all the phases associated with the point sources.

Temporal coherence is related to the spectral width of the source. Coherent systems comprise monochromatic (single wavelength) sources. The system becomes partially coherent as wavelengths are added and incoherent as a large number of wavelengths are added. Lasers are examples of temporal coherent sources because they are very narrow spectral bandwidth systems. A coherence length sometimes describes the propagation distance (i.e., related to time by the speed of light) over which a source is temporally coherent. The coherence length is related to the spectral bandwidth, $\Delta\omega$:

$$l \approx \frac{2\pi c}{\Delta\omega} = \frac{\lambda^2}{\Delta\lambda} \qquad (4.16)$$

Laser coherence lengths can be hundreds of meters, whereas the coherence length for a broadband source may be on the order of microns.

It should be noted that the imaging systems presented within the scope of this text can be considered to be incoherent systems. Sources are large areas with objects scattered throughout a typical scene. Bandwidths include a considerable number of wavelengths and extremely small coherence lengths. In fact, the majority of practical imaging systems can be considered to be incoherent systems with the exception of those with extremely small sources or laser-illuminated systems. The development of incoherent system theory, however, is better presented in terms of coherent systems. We will keep in mind that the square magnitude relationship between field and irradiance can transform into a correlation in the frequency domain. This becomes apparent in the following sections.

4.3 DIFFRACTION

We introduce diffraction first in terms of the *coherent* optical system response. The *incoherent* response function is then presented as the autocorrelation of the coherent optical system response. Diffraction [5,6] is a general phenomenon that applies not only to the field of light wave propagation, but also to sound and radio waves. The importance here is that diffraction must be understood to comprehend the properties of optical systems. Diffraction is defined by Sommerfeld as "any deviation of light rays from rectilinear paths which cannot be interpreted as reflection or refraction." Diffraction theory as we know it allows one to calculate the light pattern caused by light as it passes through obstacles, patterns, or apertures.

We consider here a very brief history of the current diffraction models, but will not present a mathematical derivation of the models used in this text. References [5, 6] at the end of this chapter are provided if the reader is interested. One such model starts with the application of Green's theorem to the Helmholtz wave equation in order to determine a complex field quantity in terms of its boundary values. The result was the integral theorem of Helmholtz and Kirchhoff. The Kirchhoff boundary conditions were then applied to this theorem to derive the first diffraction model, the Fresnel-Kirchhoff diffraction formula. This model provided very accurate results except where field quantities approached the obstruction boundaries. The inconsistencies were resolved by Sommerfeld with a shift in boundary phase terms and the current Rayleigh-Sommerfeld diffraction formula became the fundamental model to describe diffraction. Finally, the Huygens-Fresnel principle extended the diffraction theory to a superposition integral that generalized diffraction with the important linearity property. The reader is directed to Goodman [5] as a reference for these derivations. We begin here with the result of the Huygens-Fresnel principle.

Consider the diffraction geometry shown in Figure 4.1. An aperture is illuminated by a uniform field where the aperture can be considered a collection of point sources. A point of light located at P_1 produces a field amplitude and a corresponding impulse response at P_2 of

$$h(x_2y_2;x_1,y_1) = \frac{1}{j\lambda}\frac{e^{jkr_{12}}}{r_{12}}\cos\theta \qquad (4.17)$$

where $k = \frac{2\pi}{\lambda}$ and r_{12} is the distance between P_1 and P_2. This can be considered the impulse response of the spatial system because it is the response in plane 2 to an impulse of light in plane 1. If θ is held to less than 18 deg, the cos θ term can be set to 1 and the accuracy of the field calculation results in an error of less than 5%. Also, r_{12} can be replaced with z_{12}, the distance between plane 1 and plane 2. This replacement is only good for the amplitude term and not the phase term, as very small distances can change the phase significantly because of the large k term.

The Huygens-Fresnel principle states that the field distribution in plane 2 from some field distribution leaving plane 1 (through the aperture shown) is

$$u_2(x_2,y_2) = \int_{-\infty}^{\infty} \int_{-\infty}^{\infty} h(x_2,y_2;x_1,y_1)u_1(x_1,y_1)dx_1dy_1 \qquad (4.18)$$

$u_1(x_1,y_1)$ can be considered a collection of point sources that are within the aperture shown and no point sources are "on" outside the aperture. The integration only needs to be performed over the aperture as the contributions outside the aperture are zero.

Fresnel Diffraction

The wave given by the point source of light for (4.1) is spherical in nature. A helpful simplification can be accomplished if the spherical wave geometry is approximated with a parabolic shape. The distance r_{12} can be rewritten using a Taylor series expansion of the spherical radius

$$r_{12} = \sqrt{z^2 + (x_2 - x_1)^2 + (y_2 - y_1)^2} \approx z[1 + \tfrac{1}{2}(\tfrac{x_2-x_1}{z})^2 + \tfrac{1}{2}(\tfrac{y_2-y_1}{z})^2] \qquad (4.19)$$

where the higher order terms have been dropped. The condition for the use of this approximation is satisfied by

$$z^3 >> \tfrac{\pi}{4\lambda}[(x_2 - x_1)^2 + (y_2 - y_1)^2]_{max} \qquad (4.20)$$

The max notation corresponds to the largest distances between possible plane 1 source locations and possible plane 2 observation points. Using the Fresnel approximation, the impulse response of the system shown in Figure 4.1 becomes

$$h(x_2y_2;x_1,y_1) = \tfrac{e^{jkz}}{j\lambda z}e^{j\frac{k}{2z}[(x_2-x_1)^2+(y_2-y_1)^2]} \qquad (4.21)$$

Goodman states that this Fresnel approximation can be viewed in two different ways. First, the complex field $u_2(x_2,y_2)$ can be found by the convolution of $u_1(x_1,y_1)$ with $h(x_2y_2;x_1,y_1)$, which we now represent as $h(x,y)$ for convenience:

$$u_2(x_2,y_2) = \tfrac{e^{jkz}}{j\lambda z}\int_{-\infty}^{\infty}\int_{-\infty}^{\infty} u_1(x_1,y_1)e^{j\frac{k}{2z}[(x_2-x_1)^2+(y_2-y_1)^2]}dx_1dy_1 = u_1(x_1,y_1) **h(x,y) \qquad (4.22)$$

A second form of the Fresnel diffraction approximation can be written as

$$u_2(x_2,y_2) = \frac{e^{jkz}}{j\lambda z}e^{j\frac{k}{2z}(x_2^2+y_2^2)}\int_{-\infty}^{\infty}\int_{-\infty}^{\infty}\{u_1(x_1,y_1)e^{j\frac{k}{2z}(x_1^2+y_1^2)}\}e^{-j\frac{2\pi}{\lambda z}(x_1x_2+y_1y_2)}dx_1 dy_1 \qquad (4.23)$$

Note that this equation is the Fourier transform of the quantity inside the {} brackets. The spatial frequencies are scaled in terms of plane 2 with $\xi = \frac{x_2}{\lambda z}$ and $\eta = \frac{y_2}{\lambda z}$ with units of cycles per meter.

The convolution approach can be transformed to provide a transfer function. This is accomplished by the transform of the impulse response, $h(x,y)$

$$H(\xi,\eta) = e^{jkz}e^{-j\pi\lambda z(\xi^2+\eta^2)} \qquad (4.24)$$

This transfer function is used in the same manner as with any linear system. It can be considered the transfer function for a Fresnel approximation of spatial propagation from one plane to another.

Fraunhofer Diffraction

The Fraunhofer approximation is a further simplification of the diffraction model when more strict requirements are met. This simplification corresponds to the approximation of the spherical or quadratic (in the Fresnel case) wavefront as a planar wavefront. It is common sense that this requires that the observation point be further from the source and the transverse source distance be limited. Therefore, the following condition is more stringent than those for Fresnel diffraction:

$$z \gg \frac{k(x_1^2+y_1^2)_{max}}{2} \qquad (4.25)$$

The Fraunhofer diffraction approximation is

$$u_2(x_2,y_2) = \frac{e^{jkz}}{j\lambda z}e^{j\frac{k}{2z}(x_2^2+y_2^2)}\int_{-\infty}^{\infty}\int_{-\infty}^{\infty}\{u_1(x_1,y_1)\}e^{-j\frac{2\pi}{\lambda z}(x_1x_2+y_1y_2)}dx_1 dy_1 \qquad (4.26)$$

Note that if $\frac{x_2}{\lambda z}$ and $\frac{y_2}{\lambda z}$ are substituted with ξ and η, then the approximation becomes the Fourier transform of the field distribution leaving the aperture. Again, the spatial frequencies ξ and η are in cycles per meter. Typically, the above substitution is performed and the transform is obtained. Then the reverse substitution is performed to give a scaled transform. Finally, the magnitude squared field distribution is obtained to provide the spatial irradiance.

Example

Consider a rectangular transparency placed in plane 1 of the system shown in Figure 4.1. The transparency is illuminated with a monochromatic, uniform amplitude plane wave, $u_1^-(x_1,y_1) = A$ (the negative superscript means just to the left of the transparency). Assuming that Fraunhofer conditions are met, determine the irradiance distribution at plane 2.

The transmittance of the rectangular aperture can be expressed as

$$t_1(x_1,y_1) = rect(\tfrac{x_1}{a}, \tfrac{y_1}{b}) \tag{4.27}$$

Once the uniform plane wave propagates through the aperture, the field distribution to the right of the transparency is

$$u_1^+(x_1,y_1) = A rect(\tfrac{x_1}{a}, \tfrac{y_1}{b}) \tag{4.28}$$

(4.26) can be written in terms of the two-dimensional Fourier transform operator:

$$u_2(x_2,y_2) = \frac{e^{jkz}}{j\lambda z} e^{j\frac{k}{2z}(x_2^2+y_2^2)} \mathcal{FF}\,\{u_1^+(x_1,y_1)\}\big|_{\xi=\frac{x_2}{\lambda z}, \eta=\frac{y_2}{\lambda z}} \tag{4.29}$$

Because the transform of $u_1^+(x_1,y_1)$ is

$$\mathcal{FF}\,\{A rect(\tfrac{x_1}{a}, \tfrac{y_1}{b})\} = A ab\, sinc(a\xi, b\eta) \tag{4.30}$$

the field distribution becomes

$$u_2(x_2,y_2) = A\frac{abe^{jkz}}{j\lambda z} e^{j\frac{k}{2z}(x_2^2+y_2^2)}\, sinc(\tfrac{ax_2}{\lambda z}, \tfrac{by_2}{\lambda z}) \tag{4.31}$$

The irradiance distribution across plane 2 can be found by $E_2(x_2,y_2) = |u_2(x_2,y_2)|^2$, or

$$E_2(x_2,y_2) = A^2 \frac{a^2 b^2}{\lambda^2 z^2}\, sinc^2(\tfrac{ax_2}{\lambda z}, \tfrac{by_2}{\lambda z}) \tag{4.32}$$

4.4 EFFECTS OF LENSES ON DIFFRACTION

A topic of considerable importance is the effect of diffraction on optical systems. The traditional approach in the analysis of optical systems is to represent the lens as a transmittance function. Consider the lens shown in Figure 4.4, where the lens is positioned in some plane 1. The field distribution to the left of the lens is represented as $u_1^-(x,y)$ and the field distribution to the right of the lens will be represented as $u_1^+(x,y)$. The relationship between the two field distributions is

$$u_1^+(x,y) = u_1^-(x,y)t_l(x,y) \tag{4.33}$$

where $t_l(x,y)$ is the transmittance function of the lens. Given that the field is limited to propagate inside the pupil function shown, the transmittance for a thin lens approximation is

$$t_l(x,y) = e^{jkn\Delta_o} e^{-j\frac{k}{2f}(x^2+y^2)} \tag{4.34}$$

where n is the index of refraction, f is the lens focal length, and k is the propagation constant. Note that a positive focal length focuses, or converges, a plane wave to a small point and that a negative focal length disperses, or diverges, a plane wave to a larger pattern. It is also interesting that the transmittance given is entirely a phase term.

The finite extent of the lens aperture must be accounted for if the illuminating field distribution is larger than the lens pupil using the pupil function

$$u_1^+(x,y) = u_1^-(x,y)p(x,y)e^{-j\frac{k}{2f}(x^2+y^2)} \tag{4.35}$$

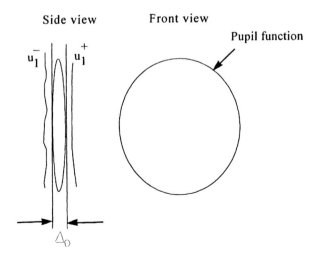

Figure 4.4 Lens transmittance.

where $p(x,y) = 1$ inside the lens and $p(x,y) = 0$ outside the lens. A $cyl(x,y)$ function from Chapter 2 is sufficient for this representation. The constant phase delay has been omitted because it does not affect the result. Consider the thin lens system shown in Figure 4.5. $u^-_{lens}(x,y) = At(x,y)$ depicts that the transparency has a transmission function $t(x,y)$ that is illuminated by a uniform plane wave of amplitude A. The field to the right of the lens is

$$u^+_{lens}(x,y) = At(x,y)p(x,y)e^{-j\frac{k}{2f}(x^2+y^2)} \tag{4.36}$$

Assuming that the system from plane 1 to plane 2 is in the Fresnel region (quadratic approximation), the field at plane 2 is

$$u_2(x,y) = \frac{Ae^{jkf}}{j\lambda f}e^{j\frac{\pi}{\lambda f}(x^2+y^2)} \, \mathcal{J}\mathcal{J} \, \{u^+_{lens}(x,y)e^{j\frac{\pi}{\lambda f}(x^2+y^2)}\}|_{\xi=\frac{x}{\lambda f},\eta=\frac{y}{\lambda f}}$$
$$= \frac{Ae^{jkf}}{j\lambda f}e^{j\frac{\pi}{\lambda f}(x^2+y^2)} \, \mathcal{J}\mathcal{J} \, \{At(x,y)p(x,y)\}|_{\xi=\frac{x}{\lambda f},\eta=\frac{y}{\lambda f}} \tag{4.37}$$

Finally, if the transparency is smaller than the pupil, (4.37) can be further simplified:

$$u_2(x,y) = \frac{Ae^{jkz}}{j\lambda z}e^{j\frac{\pi}{\lambda f}(x^2+y^2)} \, \mathcal{J}\mathcal{J} \, \{At(x,y)\}|_{\xi=\frac{x}{\lambda f},\eta=\frac{y}{\lambda f}} \tag{4.38}$$

Note that u_2 and u^+_1 are not quite related by an exact transform of the transparency because the $e^{j\frac{\pi}{\lambda f}(x^2+y^2)}$ multiplier is present in the result.

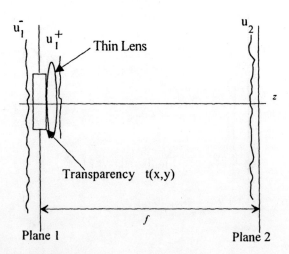

Figure 4.5 Thin lens system.

It is worth stopping to briefly discuss the results of (4.37) and (4.38). The system given in Figure 4.5 is the typical long-range imaging system, where the transparency is really the field function resulting from some distant object and the pupil function cannot be neglected. If $t(x,y)$ were replaced with $p(x,y)$ in (4.38), a distant point source would be imaged by such a system with a limiting pupil aperture (i.e., no transparency). We would then obtain the corresponding point source response in plane 2.

Even though there is a quadratic phase effect by the multiplier, the field distribution is related to the Fourier transform of the pupil. That is, the impulse response of the system is related to the Fourier transform of the limiting pupil. If this pupil is a $rect(\frac{x}{a}, \frac{y}{b})$ function, then the psf would be a $ab\operatorname{sinc}(a\xi, b\eta) = ab\operatorname{sinc}(\frac{ax}{\lambda f}, \frac{by}{\lambda f})$ function. Note that a larger pupil in plane 1 gives a smaller point spread in plane 2. Also, a small wavelength and a small focal length make for a small psf. Finally, most pupils are circular in nature, so a $cyl(\frac{r}{b})$ is more appropriate.

4.5 F-F SYSTEM

An exact Fourier transform of a field at a plane can be obtained with the *f-f system* as shown in Figure 4.6. The f-f system is one where a known field is located one focal length in front of a lens and a screen is placed one focal length behind the lens. The field distribution at plane 3 can be expressed as

$$u_3(x,y) = \frac{e^{jkf}}{j\lambda f} e^{j\frac{\pi}{\lambda f}(x^2+y^2)} \, \mathscr{J}\mathscr{J} \, \{u_2^-(x,y)\}|_{\xi=\frac{x}{\lambda f}, \eta=\frac{y}{\lambda f}} \qquad (4.39)$$

$u_3^-(x,y)$ is the field given in the lens effect section by (4.38). We could provide the expression for $u_2^-(x,y)$ and calculate $u_3(x,y)$ by longhand; however, it is easier to perform this evaluation in the transform domain. We know the following:

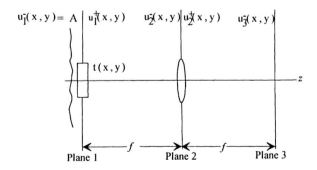

Figure 4.6 f-f optical system.

$$U_1^+(\xi, \eta) = \mathcal{FF}\{At(x,y)\} = AT(\xi, \eta) \tag{4.40}$$

$$U_2^-(\xi, \eta) = \mathcal{FF}\{u_2^-(x,y)\} \tag{4.41}$$

and

$$U_2^-(\xi, \eta) = U_1^+(\xi, \eta)e^{-j\pi\lambda f(\xi^2+\eta^2)} \tag{4.42}$$

The field distribution at plane 3 is now

$$u_3(x,y) = \frac{e^{jkf}}{j\lambda f}e^{j\frac{\pi}{\lambda f}(x^2+y^2)}U_1^+(\xi, \eta)e^{-j\pi\lambda f(\xi^2+\eta^2)}|_{\xi=\frac{x}{\lambda f}, \eta=\frac{y}{\lambda f}} \tag{4.43}$$

Substitution of $\xi = \frac{x}{\lambda f}$ and $\eta = \frac{y}{\lambda f}$ into the exponential allows cancellation of the $e^{j\frac{\pi}{\lambda f}(x^2+y^2)}$ term. Also, e^{jkf} is again neglected as the constant phase because given some f, it does not affect the result. Therefore, the field distribution at plane 3 becomes

$$u_3(x,y) = \frac{1}{j\lambda f}U_1^+(\xi, \eta)|_{\xi=\frac{x}{\lambda f}, \eta=\frac{y}{\lambda f}} \tag{4.44}$$

where the ξ and η substitution can be performed only after the transform of $u_1^+(x,y)$. Note that the field distribution at plane 3 is an exact, but scaled, transform of the $u_1^+(x,y)$ field.

4.6 FF-FF SYSTEM

Another common system that is considered to study the imaging effects of diffraction is the *ff-ff system* shown in Figure 4.7. We can begin with a simplified (4.44) that describes the field distribution at the new $u_2^-(x,y)$:

$$u_2^-(x,y) = \frac{e^{j2kf}}{j\lambda f}U_1^+(\frac{x}{\lambda f}, \frac{y}{\lambda f}) \tag{4.45}$$

The field distribution to the right of plane 2 is modified by a pupil function, $p_2(x,y)$:

$$u_2^+(x,y) = u_2^-(x,y)p_2(x,y) = \frac{e^{j2kf}}{j\lambda f}p_2(x,y)U_1^+(\frac{x}{\lambda f}, \frac{y}{\lambda f}) \tag{4.46}$$

In the same manner as (4.45), we can find the field distribution at plane 3:

$$u_3(x,y) = \frac{e^{j2kf}}{j\lambda f}U_2(\frac{x}{\lambda f}, \frac{y}{\lambda f}) \tag{4.47}$$

but the transform of $u_2^+(x,y)$ can be found by

$$U_2^+(\xi,\eta) = \mathcal{FF} \{u_2^+(x,y)\} = \mathcal{FF} \{\frac{e^{j2kf}}{j\lambda f}P_2(x,y)U_1^+(\frac{x}{\lambda f},\frac{y}{\lambda f})\} \tag{4.48}$$

Recall that the transform of a product is the convolution of the spectra and that the transform of a transform is a flipped original function:

$$U_2^+(\xi,\eta) = \frac{e^{j2kf}}{j\lambda f}[P_2(\xi,\eta) * *(\lambda f)^2 u_1^+(-\lambda f\xi,-\lambda f\eta)] \tag{4.49}$$

Finally, we can determine the field distribution at plane 3:

$$u_3(x,y) = -\frac{e^{j4kf}}{(\lambda f)^2}[P_2(\xi,\eta) * *(\lambda f)^2 u_1^+(-\lambda f\xi,-\lambda f\eta)]|_{\xi=\frac{x}{\lambda f},\eta=\frac{y}{\lambda f}} \tag{4.50}$$

It turns out that convolving before substitution differs from convolving after substitution by a scale factor. An extra $(\lambda f)^2$ appears as a result of the $\xi = \frac{x}{\lambda f}, \eta = \frac{y}{\lambda f}$ substitution:

$$u_3(x,y) = -\frac{e^{j4kf}}{(\lambda f)^2}[P_2(\frac{x}{\lambda f},\frac{y}{\lambda f}) * *u_1^+(-x,-y)] \tag{4.51}$$

As seen by the convolution of the pupil transform with the original system input, the pupil function is a smoothing function that blurs the field distribution. In fact, the impulse response of the system is

$$h_{13}(x,y) = \frac{1}{(\lambda f)^2}P_2(\frac{x}{\lambda f},\frac{y}{\lambda f}) \tag{4.52}$$

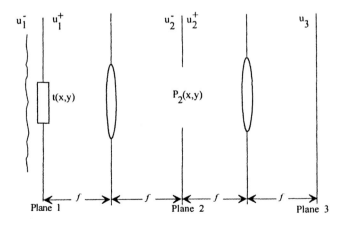

Figure 4.7 ff-ff system.

Note that the input convolved with this coherent impulse response gives the output field. The coherent transfer function of the system can be found by taking the Fourier transform of the impulse response:

$$H_{13}(\xi, \eta) = p_2(-\lambda f \xi, -\lambda f \eta) \tag{4.53}$$

It is important to note that the transfer function of the coherent system is simply the pupil function scaled. The aperture size in plane 2 determines the spatial frequencies that can pass through the system. A low-pass or high-pass filter can be placed in this plane just by modifying an aperture to pass or block certain frequencies. The ff-ff system has been the subject of a great deal of optical filtering study.

4.7 TRANSFER FUNCTIONS

Both the f-f and ff-ff system analyses that have been presented assumed spatially and temporally coherent sources. A coherent transfer function is associated with each system. For the ff-ff system case, the output spectrum is related to the input spectrum by the coherent transfer function

$$U_3(\xi, \eta) = U_1^+(\xi, \eta) H_{13}(\xi, \eta) = U_1^+(\xi, \eta) p_2(\lambda f \xi, \lambda f \eta) \tag{4.54}$$

As an example, if the transfer function is a circular pupil:

$$H_{13}(\xi, \eta) = p_2(\lambda f \xi, \lambda f \eta) = cyl(\frac{\rho \lambda f}{d}) \tag{4.55}$$

where the focal length of the system is 20 cm, the circular diameter is 1 cm, and the wavelength is 0.5 μm, then the width of the circular aperture in the Fourier domain is 100 cycles per millimeter as shown in Figure 4.8. The cutoff frequency is the distance from the transform plane origin or 50 cycles per millimeter. Therefore, the coherent cutoff frequency is

$$\rho_c = \frac{d}{2\lambda f} \tag{4.56}$$

Any frequency less than this cutoff frequency passes the system unaltered at full amplitude. Any frequency greater than the cutoff frequency is blocked and has a transfer of essentially zero. Also note that more frequency (and resolution) content passes for larger diameter pupils, shorter wavelengths, and shorter focal lengths.

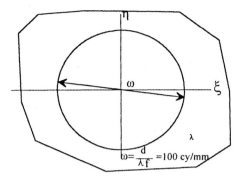

Figure 4.8 Circular aperture and transfer function.

Most systems that view broadband objects, such as the world in general, are incoherent. FLIRS, video cameras, telescopes, and some microscopes are all incoherent optical systems. Such systems are still linear but are linear in irradiance instead of field amplitude. That is, the output irradiance is related to the input irradiance by the convolution of the incoherent impulse response:

$$E_3(x,y) = E_1(x,y) ** h_{13}(x,y) \tag{4.57}$$

where

$$h_{13}(x,y) = \frac{1}{K}|h_{13}(x,y)|^2 \tag{4.58}$$

and K is the area under $|h_{13}(x,y)|^2$. For the case of the ff-ff system, the incoherent impulse response becomes

$$h_{13}(x,y) = \frac{1}{K}(\frac{1}{\lambda f})^4 |P_2(\frac{-x}{\lambda f}, \frac{-y}{\lambda f})|^2 \tag{4.59}$$

Recalling that the absolute value of a function squared gives a correlation in the alternate domain, we can find the equivalent incoherent transfer function. The incoherent transfer function is usually referred to as the *optical transfer function (OTF)*. The OTF has two components: the *modulation transfer function (MTF)* and the *phase transfer function (PTF)*. The OTF can be expressed in terms of the coherent impulse response and coherent transfer function

$$\mathcal{H}_{13}(\xi,\eta) = OTF = MTF\angle PTF = \mathcal{JJ}\{h_{13}(x,y)\}$$

$$= \mathcal{JJ}\{\frac{1}{K}h_{13}(x,y)h_{13}^*(x,y)\} = \frac{1}{K}H_{13}(\xi,\eta)\star\star H_{13}^*(\xi,\eta) = \frac{\gamma_{HH}(\xi,\eta)}{\gamma_{HH}(0,0)} \tag{4.60}$$

Note that the magnitude of the result describes the MTF and the phase describes the PTF.

The incoherent transfer function can be found as the normalized correlation function of the coherent transfer function. For the ff-ff case:

$$\gamma_{HH}(\xi, \eta) = p_2(-\lambda f\xi, -\lambda f\eta) \star\star p_2^*(-\lambda f\xi, -\lambda f\eta) \tag{4.61}$$

where

$$H_{13}(\xi, \eta) = p_2(-\lambda f\xi, -\lambda f\eta) = cyl(\frac{\lambda f\rho}{d}) \tag{4.62}$$

Again, f is the focal length of the lenses and d is the diameter of the circular pupil function in plane 2. The normalized correlation function is the result of two cyl functions of the same size in the process of slip, multiply, and integrate as depicted in Figure 4.9. A slice of the result of the normalized correlation is also shown in Figure 4.9. The exact solution to the correlation is given by (7.36); however, it is frequently approximated as

$$\mathcal{H}_{13}(\rho) \approx 0.25[5tri(\frac{\lambda f\rho}{d}) - 1 + (\frac{\lambda f\rho}{d})^4]cyl(\frac{\lambda f\rho}{2d}) \tag{4.63}$$

where $\rho = \sqrt{\xi^2 + \eta^2}$. A few characteristics to note here are (1) any input frequency other than the dc component are degraded in magnitude (unlike the coherent transfer case), and (2) the cutoff frequency is twice that of the coherent transfer case, $\rho_c = d/\lambda f$. The good news is that for a given aperture size, we can obtain much higher spatial resolution (i.e., frequencies). The bad news is that all signals other than the dc component are reduced in amplitude.

4.8 GENERALIZED OPTICAL SYSTEMS

Optical systems are extremely complex components of electro-optical and I²R systems. They usually include multiple lenses, real images, virtual images, aberrations, mounting tolerances, apertures, filters, and pupils. Many of these aspects of optical systems are discussed in Chapter 7. However, a large number of optical systems (especially those that image far away objects) can be modeled as a simplified system containing a single imaging lens with a sensing medium located in the image plane as shown in Figure 4.10. Sensing elements such as film, scanning detectors, or staring arrays are placed in the image plane of the optical system. The field-of-view (FOV) of the system is the sensing element size divided by the focal length of the system (for small angles):

$$FOV \approx b/f \tag{4.64}$$

Objects that are viewed at distances much larger than the focal length are imaged onto the sensing element. The image is not perfect even if the optical system has negligible aberrations and imaging artifacts (i.e., the system is diffraction-limited). The system closely resembles the system shown in Figure 4.5 and follows the performance of (4.38) if the object illumination is coherent. The only difference here is that the object is far away and the transparency or the pupil, whichever is smaller, is the limiting aperture of the system. The system, however, is incoherent, and the magnitude of the incoherent transfer function (i.e., MTF) is the normalized autocorrelation of the pupil function. The pupil function is typically a *cyl* function that describes the diameter of the collecting/imaging lens. The object irradiance spectrum is multiplied by the MTF of the system (like the one shown in Figure 4.9) to provide an image spectrum. The MTF describes the system performance and is typically expressed in angular resolution with a cutoff frequency $\rho_c = d/\lambda$:

$$MTF(\xi, 0) = 0.25[5tri(\tfrac{\lambda\xi}{d}) - 1 + (\tfrac{\lambda\xi}{d})^4]cyl(\tfrac{\lambda\xi}{2d}) \qquad (4.65)$$

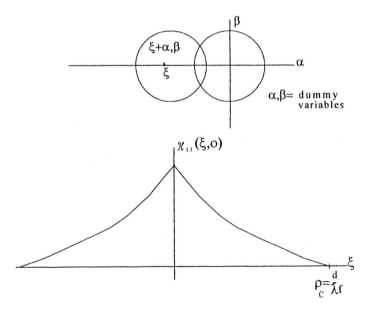

Figure 4.9 Optical transfer function.

Note that the MTF is written as a function of horizontal spatial frequency, where ξ is in cycles per radian. This function is identical in any radial direction. The MTF would require recalculation as the normalized autocorrelation of the pupil shape if the pupil is noncircular. It should be noted that the MTF is degraded if aberrations are present or if there is a central obstruction in the optical path. Aberrations are included with a separate transfer function and central obstruction would require recalculation of the diffration-limited MTF with the central obstruction in the pupil function.

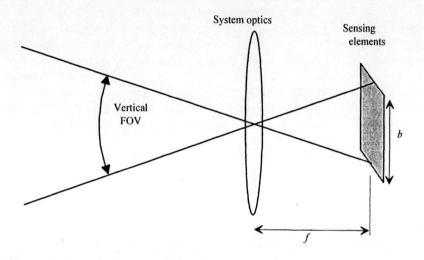

Figure 4.10 Generalized optical system.

Finally, it is worth discussing the alternative approach to a diffraction-limited transfer function. Sometimes a psf is convolved with a perfect image to give the diffraction degraded image. The diffraction-limited psf for a generalized optical system with a circular pupil can be found by the inverse Fourier transform of the normalized autocorrelation of the two pupil *cyl* functions:

$$psf(r) = \mathcal{J}\mathcal{J}^{-1}\{\frac{1}{\gamma_{IIH}(0,0)}cyl(\frac{\lambda\rho}{d}) \star\star cyl(\frac{\lambda\rho}{d})\}$$

$$= \frac{\pi}{4}(\frac{d}{\lambda})^2 somb^2(\frac{dr}{\lambda}) \qquad (4.66)$$

Note that the diffraction spot, or psf, is circularly symmetric and that r must be specified in angular space (radians).

The material covered in this chapter is intended to summarize the physical limitations of optical systems because of the nature of diffraction. Other characteristics and limitations of optical systems are covered in Chapter 7. Diffraction is the last topic of analytical tools necessary to address the analysis and design of I²R and EO systems. The next chapters provide characterizations of system components.

EXERCISES

4.1 Assuming the Fraunhofer diffraction region, find the irradiance distribution of the double slit shown, given that it is illuminated by a coherent, unit amplitude, normally incident plane wave, $u_1^-(x,y) = 1$.

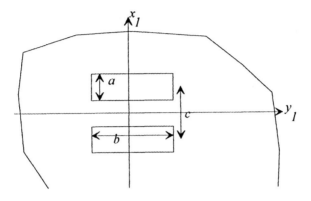

Figure 4.11

4.2 Find the Fresnel diffraction irradiance pattern caused by the aperture $t(x,y) = circ(\frac{\sqrt{x_1^2+y_1^2}}{a})$. Assume a coherent, unit amplitude, normally incident plane wave, $u_1^-(x,y) = 1$ and $\lambda = \lambda_o$.

4.3 A slit is illuminated by light of wavelength 0.5 μm. A diffraction pattern is formed on a screen 50 cm away from the aperture where the distance between the first and third minima is 2 mm. Determine the width of the slit.

4.4 A circular aperture 5 mm in diameter is illuminated by light of wavelength 0.5 μm. How far away must a screen be placed from the aperture to give the Fraunhofer diffraction pattern?

4.5 The spectral width of an argon laser is $\Delta\lambda = 0.2$ nm and its wavelength is 0.488 μm. Compute the coherence length of the laser light.

4.6 Consider an ff-ff optical system with a transparency described by $t(x,y) = 0.5 + 0.25 \sin(2\pi ax) + 0.25 \sin(2\pi bx)$, where a is 5 cycles per mm and b is 10 cycles per mm. The transparency is illuminated with $u_1^-(x,y) = 1$ of coherent light with a wavelength of 0.5 μm. The focal lengths of all lenses are 20 cm. Design a $p_2(x,y)$ filter such that the first sine term passes the system and the second sine term does not pass throughout the system.

4.7 An incoherent, generalized optical system has a broadband (λ =8 to 12 μm) infrared filter, an effective focal length of 20 cm, and a circular pupil (limiting aperture) of 10 cm. Determine the diffraction-limited MTF of the system. Also determine the psf of the system.

4.8 A generalized diffraction-limited optical system has a focal length of 40 cm and the limiting aperture entrance pupil is shown in Figure 4.8. Assuming the central wavelength of the broadband system to be 4 μm, determine the OTF.

REFERENCES

[1] Gillespie, C., *Dictionary of Scientific Biography,* New York: Scribner, 1972.

[2] Williams, T., *Biographical Dictionary of Scientists,* New York: Wiley, 1982.

[3] Hecht, E., and A. Zajac, *Optics,* Reading, MA: Addison-Wesley, 1979.

[4] Yu, F. T. and I. C. Khoo, *Principles of Optical Engineering,* New York: Wiley, p. 169, 1990.

[5] Goodman, J. W., *Introduction to Fourier Optics,* San Francisco: McGraw-Hill, p. 30, 1968.

[6] Gaskill, J. D., *Linear Systems, Fourier Transforms, and Optics,* New York: Wiley, p. 321, 1978.

Part 2

Components

Chapter 5

Sources of Radiation

Now that the necessary mathematical, linear systems, and diffraction analytical tools have been covered, we turn our attention to the analysis of the system shown in Figure 5.1. The system comprises the radiation sources (targets and backgrounds), the atmosphere, and the sensor. The sensor includes optics, scanner (if required), detectors, electronics, display, and human perception. If an automated target processor is used, the display and human perception are not required. We return to this diagram frequently as a component roadmap to our analysis. The first component in the system is the objects that are viewed by the sensor. Objects are defined [1] as "figures seen through or imaged by an optical system." Objects, as seen by sensors, include targets and backgrounds. The objects of interest are targets, where backgrounds and clutter are those objects that reduce the system capacity to obtain accurate target information.

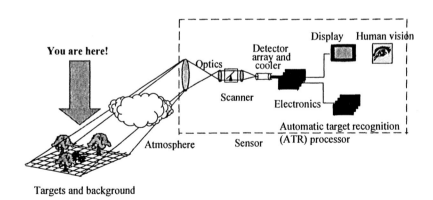

Figure 5.1 Targets and backgrounds are the first component in the overall system.

The goal of an observer is to distinguish the target from the background. Therefore, the sensor response to the target is frequently considered a signal and the sensor response to the background is considered a form of noise. Targets include people, buildings, ground vehicles, ships, aircraft, missile hardbodies, and missile plumes. The background and clutter include all the other radiation signals that enter the sensor aperture including signals from objects near the target, terrain or space behind the target, and the atmosphere. Atmospheric backgrounds can include clouds or other radiation variances that reduce the ability to discriminate the target signal. The atmospheric characteristics that affect sensor analysis are addressed in Chapter 6. Finally, clutter describes the background objects that are similar to the target in size and shape. Clutter makes the search process and discrimination of targets more difficult.

This chapter is organized to satisfy two goals: (1) present the necessary background and material to characterize both infrared and electro-optical signals originating from a target and background, and (2) present the background and material to spatially describe a target. These signal and spatial characteristics can be combined with the two basic imaging system characteristics of sensitivity and resolution to determine the performance of an imaging system against a particular target and background.

Both infrared and electro-optical signal characterization require a knowledge of radiometry, so this chapter begins with a radiometry/photometry section. Infrared signals are characterized by a "delta T," or a differential temperature between the target and the background. Even though this quantity sounds like a thermal temperature, it is really an optical power quantity that is related to an equivalent blackbody differential temperature. The fundamentals of blackbody radiation are presented in the infrared signal section. Electro-optical signals are described by a target-to-background contrast in the electro-optical sensor band. Finally, the spatial characteristics of both infrared and electro-optical systems are described in the last section along with the bar-target representation of targets.

5.1 RADIOMETRY AND PHOTOMETRY

Sensor design and analysis revolve around some operational requirement that includes a target under some background conditions. A typical requirement for a military I^2R system is similar to the following:

The sensor shall provide a 90% recognition probability of a T-62 tank at a range of 2 km under mid-latitude summer weather conditions.

In a different application, an EO system may be designed around the recognition of people at an airport for security reasons. Both these examples give a system requirement that is based on targets and must be translated into parameters that are meaningful for the sensor designer. The first step to understanding targets and backgrounds is to be fluent in radiometry.

Four photonic actions can occur at an object's surface. The quantities that characterize these actions are absorptance (α), reflectivity (ρ), transmissivity (τ), and emissivity (ε). The definitions of the first three quantities involve the ratio of absorbed, reflected, or transmitted energy to that of incident energy. Conservation of energy [2] dictates that

$$\alpha(\lambda) + \rho(\lambda) + \tau(\lambda) = 1 \qquad (5.1)$$

Note that (5.1) is a function of wavelength. The majority of materials are not transmissive in the infrared wavelengths. A few exceptions are zinc selenide and germanium. Most of the materials that are transmissive in the EO wavelengths such as glass, Plexiglas, plastic, and so forth are not transmissive in the infrared. For materials that are opaque ($\tau(\lambda) = 0$):

$$\alpha(\lambda) + \rho(\lambda) = 1 \qquad (5.2)$$

In the EO wavelengths, external light (light from sources other than the target such as the sun, stars, and moon) provides illumination of the target. Here, highly reflective wavelengths (colors) have little absorption as seen in (5.2). In the infrared, the target provides most of the radiant signal seen by the sensor through emission while there is low reflectivity. In fact, for a target at thermal equilibrium (neither gaining nor losing heat), the absorptance and emissivity are identical:

$$\alpha(\lambda) = \varepsilon(\lambda) \qquad (5.3)$$

Using (5.3) in (5.2),

$$\varepsilon(\lambda) + \rho(\lambda) = 1 \qquad (5.4)$$

where it is now easy to see that a highly emissive infrared target has a low reflectivity.

In the infrared, the radiant signals come primarily from the target and background emission of blackbody radiation [3]. All bodies above the temperature of absolute zero (zero degrees Kelvin) emit electromagnetic waves. The heat in the body causes molecular vibrations which, in turn, causes electron vibrations. These electrical vibrations provide the electromagnetic coupling to produce emission. A heated body placed in a vacuum chamber with total darkness (no impinging radiation) eventually loses all of its heat to the process of blackbody radiation. The amount of radiation that is emitted depends heavily on the target temperature and the surface characteristics (emissivity) of the target. A hotter target emits more radiation than a cooler target and a rough-surfaced target emits more radiation than a smooth target. These characteristics are also true for background objects and are discussed in more detail later in the chapter.

Reflected radiation in the infrared is usually small unless the radiation source is extremely bright as in the case of solar radiation. As a general rule, the reflection of solar radiation in the longwave (8 to 12 μm) is much less than reflections in the midwave (3 to 5 μm). Midwave sensors can view a significant amount of reflected solar radiation, so both reflected and emitted radiation must be considered for daytime scenarios.

With the EO sensor, the majority of the useful light in the bandwidth of detector responsivity is provided by the target and background reflectivities and some external (other-than-target) source. Most cases involve the sun as this illuminating source. Other sources include moonlight, starlight, and artificial lighting. Not only is the emission spectrum of the illuminating source important, but the reflectivity of the target is of utmost importance. This is the opposite case from the longwave I^2R sensor. Here, the target radiation seen by the sensor is the illuminating spectrum of the source that is modified by the target reflectivity spectrum. The important contributors to the resulting contrast are the target reflectivity, background reflectivity, and illuminating spectrum.

Figure 5.2(a) shows a tank viewed by a longwave I^2R sensor, and Figure 5.2(b) shows the same tank viewed by a midwave I^2R sensor. The lighter shade of the tank depicts a larger optical radiation signal than the background, and therefore, a higher temperature or surface emission than the objects around the tank. One can quickly determine that a high I^2R target-to-background contrast requires either high-temperature differential, emissivity differential, or a combination of both. Terrestrial targets are normally at temperatures (27 deg C) that contain high radiant power around wavelengths of 10 μm and are best viewed by longwave sensors. Rocket plumes, jet exhausts, and projectiles that are around 600 to 1,000 deg C give high radiant powers that are around 4 μm, suggesting that they are best viewed by the midwave I^2R sensor. Hotter objects (the filament of a lightbulb) can even be seen in the EO wavelengths.

The shadow of the tank in the longwave image is present because the ground in the shade is cooler (less absorbed solar energy) so that the ground emits less radiation. The shadow of the tank in the midwave is a combination of less emission and less reflected solar radiation. Figure 5.2(c) shows the same tank as seen by an EO sensor. The shadow here is provided only by an absence of reflected radiation. Also, notice that the warm tracks are not resolved (here, they are in the shade) and that the image is constructed only by reflected energy from the sun.

(a)

(b)

(c)

Figure 5.2 Longwave (a), midwave (b), and EO (c) tank images (provided by Mr. Ray Deep and Mr. Glenn Vinson of Redstone Technical Test Center, Redstone Arsenal, AL).

Finally, in both EO and I^2R systems, a very important parameter is the target size. Larger targets are obviously easier to detect, recognize, and identify. Smaller targets are difficult to resolve. The performance of a particular sensor in a scenario depends on the target size and target to background contrast. The transition of the operational sensor requirement to meaningful target and background parameters includes the representation of the radiant power leaving the target and background (i.e., contrast) as a function of space (i.e., target size). Once a target-to-background function is written in terms of the radiant power leaving that target as a function of space, the function can be transformed to the spatial frequency domain to determine which target and background spatial characteristics traverse through the sensor.

Radiometric Units

Radiometric concepts are necessary for a quantitative understanding of flux (power) transfer through a sensor. These concepts allow the analyst to determine how much energy is collected on the sensor detector surface. The amount of electromagnetic flux from both the target and the background contributes to the overall signal-to-noise ratio (SNR) of an image. Two important assumptions are made in radiometric analysis: (1) sources are incoherent such that interference can be neglected, and (2) diffraction is ignored so that light travels in straight lines.

The *solid angle* is a parameter that must be discussed because many radiometric units are given with respect to solid angles. A solid angle has units of steradians (sr) and is the angle subtended at the center of a sphere by an area on the surface of the sphere. The numerical value of a solid angle is a given area on the sphere surface divided by the square of the sphere radius. Consider the sphere shown in Figure 5.3.

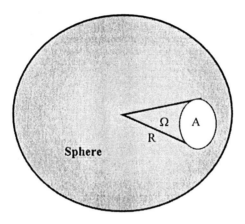

Figure 5.3 Depiction of a steradian.

The steradian is given by

$$\Omega = \frac{A}{R^2} \qquad (5.5)$$

where A is obtained from the curved surface of the sphere. The maximum number of steradians on a spherical surface is $4\pi R^2 / R^2 = 4\pi$ sr. Note that an angle of radians multiplied by an angle of radians does not give steradians. That is, 2π radians times 2π radians gives $4\pi^2$ square radians, a factor of π off from the actual number of steradians in a sphere. Finally, if R is much larger than any dimension of the area, A, then the area on the sphere can be assumed to be flat. Given any flat shape imaginable and a distance to the shape, a steradian can be calculated for the corresponding solid angle using (5.5).

The units of radiometry [4] are shown in Table 5.1, where the basic unit of energy is given in terms of the Joule. The amount of energy per unit time is flux, or power. Intensity is the amount of power a source delivers per unit solid angle. Exitance and irradiance both have the same units of power-per-unit area; however, exitance addresses power leaving a surface and irradiance addresses the amount of power impinging on a surface. One interesting note is that exitance is sometimes called *emittance*, depending on the analytical community. Exitance really describes the total power per unit area leaving an object including the emitted power and the reflected power. Each of the following units is used, whether directly or indirectly, during a source to detector radiometry calculation. Many times the partial differentials yield to simpler calculations if the amount of power leaving or impinging on a surface is constant across the surface.

Table 5.1
Radiometric units

Symbol	Quantity	Definition	Units
Q	Energy	*Fundamental*	Joule
Φ	Flux (Power)	$\dfrac{\partial Q}{\partial t}$	J/sec=Watts
I	Intensity	$\dfrac{\partial^2 Q}{\partial t \partial \Omega} = \dfrac{\partial \Phi}{\partial \Omega}$	W/sr
M	Exitance or emittance	$\dfrac{\partial^2 Q}{\partial t \partial A} = \dfrac{\partial \Phi}{\partial A}$	W/cm^2
E	Irradiance	$\dfrac{\partial^2 Q}{\partial t \partial A} = \dfrac{\partial \Phi}{\partial A}$	W/cm^2
L	Radiance	$\dfrac{\partial^3 Q}{\partial t \partial \Omega \partial A} = \dfrac{\partial^2 \Phi}{\partial A \partial \Omega} = \dfrac{\partial I}{\partial A}$	W/(cm^2-sr)

Example 1

An example of the simplicity of radiometric calculations for uniform sources is illustrated by the following. A 1 mm by 1 mm square emits 1 μW of light uniformly over the area. The corresponding emittance is 1 μW divided by the small area, giving 100 μW per square cm.

Example 2

Frequently, point-source radiation is specified in terms of its intensity. The point source shown in Figure 5.4 provides a uniform 10 W/sr intensity over an entire sphere. The power entering a 1-cm aperture located 10 m from the point source is desired.

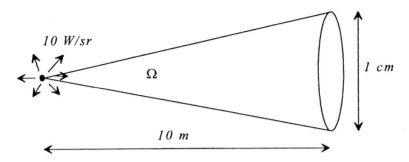

Figure 5.4 Point-source intensity example.

The solution is given by first determining the solid angle of the aperture, Ω. The solid angle is given by the area of the aperture divided by the square of the range (distance from the source to the aperture), or $\Omega = [\pi(0.005)^2]/[10^2]$ giving 7.85×10^{-7} steradians. Because the point source provides uniform illumination over all angles, the amount of power through the aperture is $10W/sr(7.85 \times 10^{-7} sr) = 7.85\ \mu W$.

Radiance is given as the source power per unit area per unit source angle. Radiance is a surface emission quantity that is independent of the source area or solid angle. This is a quality that becomes apparent in the blackbody section.

Example 3

A 1-mm-radius sphere provides 1W of power uniformly in all directions. Find the radiance of the sphere. Assuming a uniform radiance over the sphere, the solution is given by normalizing the power by the sphere surface area $4\pi(0.1)^2$ square cm and the spherical solid angle 4π steradians to give $L = 0.63\ W/[cm^2 - sr]$.

One particular surface quality applies to a majority of natural and human-made surfaces. The Lambertian surface includes most rough (rough on the order of a wavelength) surfaces such as paints, cloths, stones, and wood that is not shiny. Specular, or shiny and mirrored, surfaces are usually not Lambertian. The Lambertian surface follows a decrease in intensity with angle

$$I_\theta = I_n \cos\theta \qquad [\text{W/sr}] \qquad (5.6)$$

as shown in Figure 5.5.

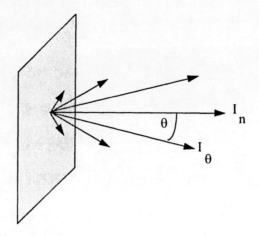

Figure 5.5 Lambertian surface.

I_n is the intensity normal to the surface and the angle θ is taken from the normal direction. The corresponding radiance perceived by a viewer of a tilted Lambertian surface is constant with angle

$$L_\theta = \frac{\partial I}{\partial A} = \frac{I_\theta}{dS_\theta} = \frac{I_n \cos\theta}{dA \cos\theta} = \frac{I_n}{dA} \quad [\text{W/(cm}^2\text{-sr)}] \quad (5.7)$$

The decrease in intensity from the tilt is compensated by the increase in perceived area by the viewer so that the surface appears to remain at a constant brightness. The Lambertian surface is a perfect diffuser that gives a viewer a constant radiance independent of viewing angle. Also, Lambertian [5] surfaces give a radiance that is directly proportional to its emittance:

$$L = \frac{M}{\pi} \quad [\text{W/(cm}^2\text{-sr)}] \quad (5.8)$$

This characteristic proves to be convenient in the manipulation of thermal sources because their radiation characteristics are defined by emittance.

Photometric Units

Photometric units are very similar to radiometric units; however, the radiation is weighted to match the response of the human eye. A luminous efficacy $K(\lambda)$ describes the weighting of the radiation to provide an equivalent photometric response. The photometric, or luminous, flux is found by

$$\Phi_v(\lambda) = K(\lambda)\Phi(\lambda) \quad (5.9)$$

where the v subscript denotes the visual photometric response and K is in units of lumens per watt. A photopic [6] efficiency is the normalized efficacy

$$V(\lambda) = \frac{K(\lambda)}{K_{max}} \tag{5.10}$$

K_{max} is 673 L/W. The photopic response described above is formed primarily by the contributions from cones within the human retina. Cone receptors resemble high-resolution, slow-speed film. The night, or scotopic, response of the human retina is found using $K'(\lambda)$ that was derived by the rod receptors of the human retina. The corresponding $V'(\lambda)$ is given with a normalization K'_{max} of 1,725 L/W. Rod receptors are more like low-resolution, high-speed film. The efficiencies of both photopic and scotopic visions are given in Figure 5.6.

Table 5.2
Photometric units

Symbol	Quantity	Definition	Units
Φ_v	Luminous Flux	Φ_v	Lumens (L)
I_v	Luminous Intensity	$\frac{\partial \Phi_v}{\partial \Omega}$	L/sr
M_v	Luminous Exitance	$\frac{\partial \Phi_v}{\partial A}$	L/m^2
E_v	Illuminance	$\frac{\partial \Phi_v}{\partial A}$	L/m^2 or Lux
L_v	Luminance	$\frac{\partial^2 \Phi_v}{\partial A \partial \Omega} = \frac{\partial I_v}{\partial A}$	L/(m^2-sr)

$K(\lambda)$ and $K'(\lambda)$ can be found in tabular form in the 1970 National Bureau of Standards (NBS). It should be noted that the photometric equivalents to the radiometric quantities radiance, intensity, exitance, or irradiance are found by using the photopic or scotopic efficacy functions multiplied by the fundamental flux $\Phi(\lambda)$. These corresponding photometric quantities are described as luminance, luminous intensity, luminous exitance, and illuminance. All of these quantities can be written as those in Table 5.1 with the v subscript (shown in Table 5.2). Also, the NBS standard is now established as the *candela* [7] that corresponds to a luminous intensity of 1.0 L/sr. Many other photometric units have been defined, such as the Carcel unit, English sperm candle, and the Hefner unit, but are rarely used. Finally, it is only necessary to integrate the efficacy-power product of the photometric quantities from 380 to 780 nm because these are the limits of the human visual response.

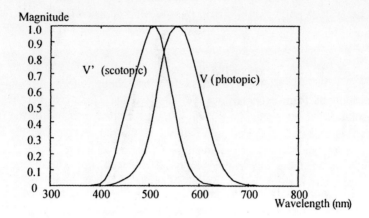

Figure 5.6 Photopic and scotopic efficiencies.

5.2 INFRARED TARGETS AND BACKGROUNDS

Infrared target and background characteristics in the 3- to 5-μm band and the 8- to 12-μm band are of primary interest. These wavelengths correspond to windows in Earth's atmosphere where light propagates with less severe attenuation. Even in these two windows, the attenuation can be significant. The majority of target characterization work has been performed in these bands.

Target characterization is an important part of the overall sensor analysis and design process. Sensor band selection for a scenario begins with the targets and backgrounds. A target-to-background difference in exitance (or emittance) must be present in the band of interest. Exitance is the area-normalized quantity that describes the flux leaving a surface. For infrared systems used during the day, solar reflections must be addressed and exitance must be considered as the sum of emitted and reflected flux. Many tactical systems that include infrared sensors also have electro-optical systems. Because electro-optical systems have higher resolution and more sensitivity than infrared systems during the day, the use of infrared systems is typically reserved for night. Therefore, the focus here is on night use and the emittance of targets and backgrounds.

Blackbody Radiation

In the infrared world, the absorption and the emission characteristics of targets and backgrounds are usually more significant than their reflection and transmission characteristics. This is especially true at night (the usual mode of I^2R system operation), where solar reflection is not present. Daylight hours give solar reflections even in the infrared. However, many natural and human-made objects are low in infrared reflectance and high in emissivity (and absorptance). These objects tend to absorb solar energy with subsequent emission under conditions of thermal equilibrium.

Blackbody radiation is that radiation that is released from bodies that are above the temperature of absolute zero (0 deg Kelvin). The finite temperature of the bodies and their associated heat content provide the energy necessary to emit electromagnetic, or photonic, waves. Two basic concepts hold true for blackbody radiation: (1) a higher temperature body corresponds to a larger emission of flux, and (2) a higher temperature body shifts the flux spectral distribution towards shorter wavelengths. These concepts are true regardless of the emissivity characteristics of the body (including targets and backgrounds).

The spectral distribution and magnitude of an object's radiation are primarily a function of the object's temperature and emissivity. Emissivity, $\varepsilon(\lambda)$, describes an object's emission characteristics; where an emissivity of one, $\varepsilon(\lambda)=1$, indicates a perfect blackbody radiator. Blackbody radiation is described by Planck's blackbody equation. The spectral emittance of an object is

$$M(\lambda, T) = \varepsilon(\lambda) \frac{c_1}{\lambda^5} \frac{1}{[e^{c_2/\lambda T}-1]} \qquad [\text{W/cm}^2\text{-}\mu\text{m}] \qquad (5.11)$$

where

λ = the wavelength in micrometers (μm),

T = absolute temperature in degrees Kelvin (Kelvin = Celsius + 273),

c_1 = 3.7418x10^4 Watts-μm^4/cm,^{2}

c_2 = 1.4388x10^4 μm-Kelvin.

The units show a distinction between the integration over wavelength and the spatial normalization of the emittance (i.e., cm^2-μm). Figure 5.7 shows the emission spectrum of a perfect blackbody at a number of temperatures. Note the dramatic increase in the overall emittance with temperature and the corresponding shift in the peak emission wavelength. The peak wavelength of emission for a given blackbody temperature is given by Wien's law:

$$\lambda_{peak} = \frac{2897.8}{T} \qquad [\mu\text{m}] \qquad (5.12)$$

where the temperature is given in degrees Kelvin.

The total emittance within a spectral band is found by summing, or integrating, the emittance over the appropriate wavelengths

$$M(T) = \int_{\lambda_1}^{\lambda_2} \varepsilon(\lambda) \frac{c_1}{\lambda^5} \frac{1}{[e^{c_2/\lambda T}-1]} d\lambda \qquad [\text{W/cm}^2] \qquad (5.13)$$

This equation is usually integrated numerically or found using lookup tables.

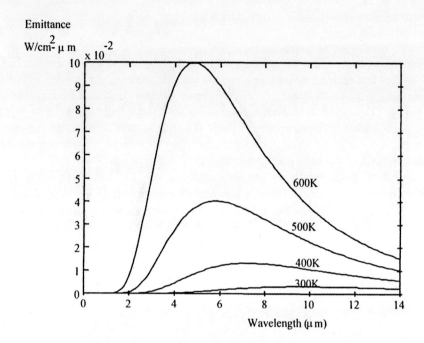

Figure 5.7 Planck's blackbody emission curves.

An object with a constant emissivity over all wavelengths is called a *graybody*. Blackbodies and graybodies exhibit an interesting property called the Stephan-Boltzmann Law. This law provides simple flux calculations when the emission over the entire spectrum is desired:

$$M(T) = \varepsilon\sigma T^4 \qquad [W/cm^2] \qquad (5.14)$$

Stephan-Boltzmann's constant σ is 5.67×10^{-12} W/(cm^2-K^4). The equation applies only to blackbody and graybody sources. Objects that emit as a function of wavelength, where they do not follow blackbody or graybody characteristics, are described as *spectral emitters*. The total or bandlimited emittance of a spectral emitter and the bandlimited emittance of blackbodies and graybodies must be evaluated using (5.13). Finally, blackbodies, graybodies, and the majority of spectral emitters can be considered Lambertian sources. The radiances of these sources are found simply by using (5.8).

Example

A flat, 500 deg C (773 deg K) blackbody source is considered Lambertian. Determine the peak emittance of the source along with the corresponding wavelength. Determine the emittance and radiance of the source in the 3- to 5-μm band. Finally, determine the total emittance and radiance of the source (over all wavelengths). The solution is given using Figure 5.8 as a guide.

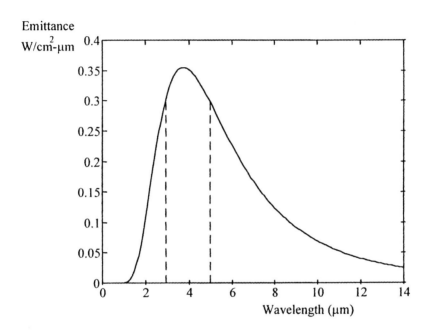

Figure 5.8 Midwave example with 500 deg C blackbody.

The peak emission wavelength is determine to be 3.75 μm using Wien's law given by (5.12). The peak emission (at 3.75 μm) is calculated using Planck's blackbody (5.11) to give 0.355 W/(cm^2-μm). In the 3- to 5-μm band, Planck's equation is integrated over these wavelengths, which gives an emittance of 0.21 W/cm^2. Assuming a Lambertian source, (5.8) gives a radiance of 0.068 W/cm^2-sr. Stephan-Boltzmann's law gives the total emittance of the source at 2.02 W/cm^2 and a total radiance of 0.64 W/cm^2-sr.

Example

A 20 deg C (293 deg K) graybody source is flat and is considered Lambertian. The emissivity is 0.5 over all wavelengths. Determine the emittance and radiance of the source in the 8- to 12-μm band. Also, determine the total emittance and radiance of the source (over all wavelengths). The solution can be seen with Figure 5.9.

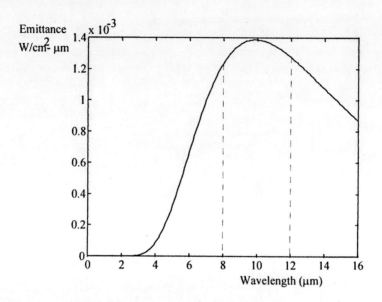

Figure 5.9 Longwave example with 20 deg C graybody.

The peak wavelength of emission is 9.89 μm, in the center of the 8- to 12-μm band. The band emittance is calculated to be 5.3 x 10^{-3} W/cm^2 and the band radiance is 1.7 x 10^{-3} W/cm^2-sr. The total emittance over all wavelengths is 21x10^{-3} W/cm^2 and the total radiance is 6.7 x 10^{-3} W/cm^2-sr.

The spectral emittance of a target or background is described by Planck's (5.11). Note that the surface emittance of an object depends on object temperature, wavelength, and emissivity. Given that an object is viewed by a sensor with a limiting spectral bandwidth, the emittance of the object is integrated over the band to determine the object's emittance seen by the sensor. This bandwidth integration must include atmospheric, sensor optics, and detector spectral responses. A common and incorrect analysis method includes a band-averaged target emittance propagated through a band-averaged atmospheric attenuation and a band-averaged sensor transmission and collected by a band-averaged detector response. This analysis method is used frequently by many analysts and gives a result that includes a level of error. FLIR92 and the NVL TV model are examples of analytical tools that use this technique, where their associated errors are determined to be acceptable. The errors decrease with object emissivities, atmospheric transmissions, and detector responses that do not vary much over the integration band. Smaller bands also give smaller errors.

Whether we use an exact solution or a band-averaged estimate, it is useful to band-average an object's emittance to get a feel for the differences in target-to-background emittance. Given a particular spectral band, the emittance of an object can be found through the integration of (5.13) using the object's temperature and emissivity. This integration is simple if the object is a blackbody (emissivity = 1) or a graybody (emissivity = constant). Lookup tables for the emittance of objects at different temperatures have been compiled and can be found in a number of the references. The emittance must be calculated numerically for objects that are considered spectral emitters.

Emissivity

Emissivity can be described in a number of ways, one of which is the spectral, hemispherical emissivity:

$$\varepsilon(\lambda) = \frac{M_{object}(\lambda)}{M_{BB}(\lambda)} \qquad \text{[unitless]} \qquad (5.15)$$

where the emission of an object is normalized by the emission of a blackbody source at the same temperature. Blackbody sources are readily available and widely used in the infrared community. They are typically cavities or flat surfaces that have been treated to provide an extremely high emissivity over all infrared wavelengths. Blackbodies are also used as references in the measurement of object-emission or sensor-response characteristics.

There are different techniques for measuring object emissivity. One of the more straightforward techniques involves the use of a blackbody positioned next to the object, where the blackbody temperature is set to match that of the object. The object temperature is measured with a high-resolution thermocouple in a manner that does not change the object's temperature. An infrared spectral radiometer collects flux from the object as a function of wavelength (i.e., a spectral scan) and then collects flux from the blackbody source as a function of wavelength. Each flux measurement in the object spectral scan is divided by the corresponding flux measurement of the blackbody spectral scan to give the emissivity as a function of wavelength. Figure 5.10 shows the spectral emissivity for a number of objects.

Another representation of emissivity is that of total emissivity. This is a single emissivity value over all wavelengths. That is, the infinite integral of an object's exitance spectrum relative to that of a blackbody:

$$\varepsilon = \frac{\int_0^\infty M_{object}(\lambda)d\lambda}{\sigma T^4} \qquad (5.16)$$

Note that the wavelength dependence of emissivity has been dropped. This type of emissivity is useful if the object is a graybody because the emission spectrum of the object can then be determined. Care should be used, however, when a single emissivity value is used to represent the emission of a spectral emitter over wide spectral bands where the actual emissivity would vary significantly. For example, the emissivity of olive-drab uniform material could be considered a graybody over an 8- to 10-µm spectral band with an emissivity value of around 0.96 to 0.97. This is a poor assumption for white paint over the 3- to 5-µm spectral band. The multiplication and integration of this emissivity curve by a 3- to 5- µm blackbody emission would give significantly different results than would a constant emissivity approximation. As a rule, most objects are closer to a graybody source in the 8- to 12-µm spectral band than in the 3- to 5-µm spectral band. Analysts find frequently that approximations in the 3- to 5-µm spectral band yield significant errors.

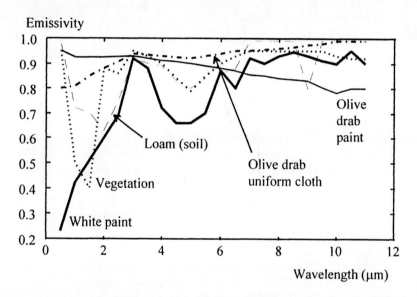

Figure 5.10 Spectral emissivity for various objects (targets and backgrounds).

Some common examples for total emissivities [8] are shown in Table 5.3. Note that shiny metal objects are usually less emissive and more reflective, where rough metal objects are more emissive and less reflective. Also, while water and glass have smooth surfaces, their emissivities are high. Rough, or diffuse, objects can usually be considered Lambertian sources. Shiny objects are considered special cases of reflectors (sometimes called specular objects). Finally, a very interesting emissivity is that of human skin, which provides an outstanding infrared source. Humans are almost perfect radiators.

Table 5.3

Total emissivities

Material	Emissivity
Polished aluminum	0.05
Anodized aluminum	0.55
Polished brass	0.03
Oxidized brass	0.61
Polished gold	0.02
Polished steel	0.07
Oxidized steel	0.79
Tin plate	0.07
Brick	0.93
Graphite	0.98
Polished glass	0.94
Oil paint (average of 10 colors)	0.94
Paper	0.93
Sand	0.90
Human skin	0.98
Soil	0.92
Snow	0.98
Water	0.96
Oak wood (planed)	0.90

Equivalent Differential Temperature (Delta T)

Target-to-background contrast is described in the infrared with the equivalent differential temperature, or "Delta T." While this quantity may appear as though it were a thermal quantity, it is really a radiometric quantity. It is the equivalent differential temperature (at some prescribed background temperature) of two blackbody sources, target and background, required to provide the differential flux as that of the actual target and actual background. This equivalence is, of course, in the band of the sensor. Consider the blackbody source and infrared sensor shown in Figure 5.11.

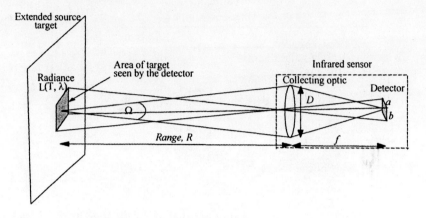

Figure 5.11 Differential temperature geometry.

Using Figure 5.11 as a guide, the radiance of the target is given and the source area seen by a single detector is

$$A_{src} = \frac{abR^2}{f^2} \qquad [\text{cm}^2] \qquad (5.17)$$

where a and b are the dimensions of the detectors in centimeters, f is the focal length of the sensor in centimeters, and R is the distance from the sensor to the target in centimeters. The solid angle of the sensor as seen from the source is given as

$$\Omega = \frac{\pi D^2}{4R^2} \qquad [\text{sr}] \qquad (5.18)$$

where D is the diameter of the entrance aperture in centimeters. The total target flux falling on the detector is given by

$$\Phi_{tgt} = \frac{abR^2}{f^2}\frac{\pi D^2}{4R^2}\int_{\lambda_1}^{\lambda_2} L_{tgt}(T,\lambda)d\lambda = \frac{\pi abD^2}{4f^2}\int_{\lambda_1}^{\lambda_2} L_{tgt}(T,\lambda)d\lambda \quad [\text{W}] \qquad (5.19)$$

If the detector were receiving flux from the background, the amount of flux would be

$$\Phi_{bg} = \frac{\pi abD^2}{4f^2}\int_{\lambda_1}^{\lambda_2} L_{bg}(T,\lambda)d\lambda \qquad [\text{W}] \qquad (5.20)$$

The differential flux between a detector viewing the target and a detector viewing the background is

$$\Delta\Phi = \frac{\pi abD^2}{4f^2}\int_{\lambda_1}^{\lambda_2}[L_{tgt}(T,\lambda) - L_{bg}(T,\lambda)]d\lambda \qquad [\text{W}] \qquad (5.21)$$

(5.21) can be extended to give a differential voltage on the output of the detector from the difference in flux between the target and the background. Using the transmission of the optics $\tau_{optics}(\lambda)$ and the responsivity of the detector in V/ W, $R(\lambda)$:

$$\Delta V = \frac{\pi a b D^2}{4f^2} \int_{\lambda_1}^{\lambda_2} [L_{tgt}(T,\lambda) - L_{bg}(T,\lambda)]\tau_{optics}(\lambda)R(\lambda)d\lambda \quad [V] \qquad (5.22)$$

Now, given some background reference temperature T_{bg}, an equivalent blackbody ΔT can be calculated, which causes the same differential voltage:

$$\Delta V = \frac{\pi a b D^2}{4f^2} \int_{\lambda_1}^{\lambda_2} [L_{bb}(\Delta T + T_{bg},\lambda) - L_{bb}(T_{bg},\lambda)]\tau_{optics}(\lambda)R(\lambda)d\lambda \quad [V] \qquad (5.23)$$

where $L_{bb}(T,\lambda)$ is the radiance of a blackbody source. Equating the two differential voltages (equations 5.22 and 5.23) gives the solution for the delta T:

$$\int_{\lambda_1}^{\lambda_2} [L_{tgt}(T,\lambda) - L_{bg}(T,\lambda)]t_{optics}(\lambda)R(\lambda)d\lambda$$
$$= \int_{\lambda_1}^{\lambda_2} [L_{bb}(\Delta T + T_{bg},\lambda) - L_{bb}(T_{bg},\lambda)]\tau_{optics}(\lambda)R(\lambda)d\lambda \qquad (5.24)$$

Note that the target radiance, background radiance, optical transmission, and detector responsivity must be known. Also, there is no closed-form solution for the delta T, so the solution is usually obtained using numerical methods.

Apparent Differential Temperature (Apparent Delta T)

A more important quantity than delta T is the *apparent delta T*, or the equivalent blackbody differential temperature that would cause the same differential voltage as that of the target and background *as seen through some atmospheric path* (Figure 5.12). A simple way to describe the apparent delta T is that a differential voltage is seen on the output of a detector corresponding to the differences in flux of the target and the background seen through some atmospheric path. The apparent delta T would be the differential temperature (with respect to some background temperature) of two nearby (through negligible atmospheric path) blackbody sources that produce the same differential voltage. There are a number of methods for calculating apparent delta T.

The following techniques are used to determine the apparent target-to-background differential temperature at the entrance aperture of an infrared sensor. All these techniques have been used in analyses. We assume that the apparent temperature corresponds to the actual target-to-background radiance reduced by the atmospheric transmission between the target and the infrared sensor.

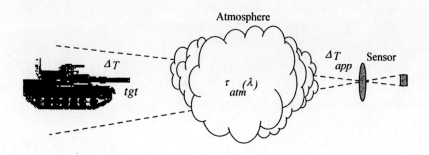

Figure 5.12   Apparent delta T.

The apparent temperature is an equivalent blackbody target temperature differential (above an ambient background ... 300 deg K) that creates an identical differential voltage as that of the target and background through the atmosphere. The real apparent differential temperature is a function of background flux, target flux, and atmospheric transmission, where each is expressed as a spectral quantity. The following calculations are approximations of apparent temperature. Note that the quantity τ_{atm} is a band-averaged atmospheric transmission quantity equal to

$$\tau_{atm} = \frac{1}{\Delta\lambda} \int_{\lambda_1}^{\lambda_2} \tau_{atm}(\lambda)d\lambda \quad \text{[unitless]} \quad (5.25)$$

This quantity is used in some of the band-averaged approximations below. Each of these approximations is a function of range, however, the range dependence is addressed in each description.

Technique 1: Temperature-Broadband Beer's Law Product

The first technique is that of an apparent temperature determined by the product of the target-to-background temperature and the atmospheric broadband Beer's law transmission. That is:

$$\Delta T_{app} = \Delta T_{tgt}\tau_{1Km}^{R} \quad \text{[K]} \quad (5.26)$$

The broadband transmission shown is determined for a 1-km path length and R is the target-to-sensor range in km. The 1-km path length transmission can be found by averaging the spectral transmission for 1-km. Beer's Law, which we discuss in Chapter 6, is not generally accurate for the broadband transmission of light. This technique is one of the more common approximations for calculating apparent temperature (especially in the longwave).

Technique 2: Temperature-Broadband Transmission as a Function of Range

The second technique is similar to the first technique in that the apparent temperature is determined by a target temperature-broadband transmission product. The difference here is that a broadband Beer's law is not assumed, and the broadband transmission is determined using an atmospheric transmission program as a function of range. That is, an atmospheric program, such as LOWTRAN, is run for a number of desired ranges, and the spectral transmission is averaged for each range to give a broadband transmission as a function of range. From the LOWTRAN output, a table is formed with range and its corresponding broadband transmission. If the transmission for some range is needed that is not listed in the table, the transmission is interpolated from the tabular data. The apparent temperature is then determined by

$$\Delta T_{app} = \Delta T_{tgt}\tau(R) \quad [\text{K}] \qquad (5.27)$$

This technique is the method presently used in the acquisition program ACQUIRE, the most common sensor/scenario engagement calculation. Note that this technique eliminates the errors associated with a broadband Beer's law assumption, however; the errors associated with a nonspectral flux calculation are still present.

Technique 3: Flux-Broadband Beer's Law Product

Another technique is that of broadband radiance multiplied by the Beer's Law broadband transmission approximation to give the apparent radiance. This is a flux-based calculation, but still a gross approximation because of the broadband radiance and Beer's law associated errors.

$$\Delta L_{app} = \Delta L_{tgt}\tau_{1Km}^{R} \quad [\text{W/cm}^2\text{-sr}] \qquad (5.28)$$

The procedure for this calculation is described by the following. The broadband differential target-to-background radiance is calculated for some target radiance and background radiance. Once the differential radiance is computed, this target-to-background differential radiance is multiplied by the Beer's law broadband transmission to obtain an apparent differential radiance. Using this differential radiance, a blackbody source temperature and a blackbody background temperature (ambient background) are estimated that would provide a band-integrated differential radiance equal to the apparent radiance. This is a trial-and-error or lookup table procedure. This technique can also be extended with a broadband transmission that is calculated for a number of ranges (as in technique 2).

Technique 4: Flux-Temperature Differential

Lloyd [9] derives an apparent differential temperature based on the differential radiance with respect to the background temperature. The target-to-background signal is propagated through the atmosphere to give an equivalent differential temperature:

$$\Delta T_{app} = \frac{\Delta V}{\partial V/\partial T} = \frac{\int_0^\infty [L_{tgt}(\lambda)-L_{bg}(\lambda)]\tau_{atm}(\lambda)\tau_{optics}(\lambda)R(\lambda)d\lambda}{\int_0^\infty \frac{\partial L_{bb}(T_{bg},\lambda)}{\partial T_{bg}}\tau_{atm}(\lambda)\tau_{optics}(\lambda)R(\lambda)d\lambda} \quad [K] \tag{5.29}$$

This expression requires the responsivity of the detector $R(\lambda)$ and the transmission of the optical system $\tau_{optics}(\lambda)$. ΔV is the differential voltage on the output of the detector caused by the target-to-background differential flux.

Technique 5: Exact Transcendental Solution

The exact solution can be written in a manner that equates the differential voltage on the output of the detector corresponding to the target-to-background differential flux to that of close (atmospheric degradation is negligible) blackbody sources:

$$\int_0^\infty [L_{tgt}(\lambda) - L_{bg}(\lambda)]\tau_{atm}(\lambda)\tau_{optics}(\lambda)R(\lambda)d\lambda$$
$$= \int_0^\infty [L_{bb}(\Delta T_{app} + T_{bg},\lambda) - L_{bb}(T_{bg},\lambda)]\tau_{optics}(\lambda)R(\lambda)d\lambda \tag{5.30}$$

The left side corresponds to the differential voltage on the output of the detector from the target and background signals. The right side is the differential voltage on the output of the detector from an equivalent blackbody signal that is close. The background temperatures are assumed to be identical in many cases, so the unknown quantity is the apparent temperature. Because (5.30) is transcendental, the solution is found using a table, trial-and-error, or some other numerical technique (i.e., there is no-closed form solution for exact apparent temperature).

5.3 ELECTRO-OPTICAL TARGETS AND BACKGROUNDS

The majority of target radiation whose wavelength is less than 3 to 4 μm is attributed to external radiation, or radiation from some other source. In the natural world of terrestrial objects, this radiation is reflected by targets and backgrounds. The external radiation is the flux provided by the sun, moon, stars, skylight, and artificial sources. We assume that most objects are relatively opaque and diffuse.

Under these assumptions, the primary target light flux that is viewed by an electro-optical sensor comes from target reflections. The exception to these conditions is where the objects themselves provide visible light either by extremely hot blackbody emissions or by artificial means. Examples are rocket exhausts, fluorescent lamps, and laser emissions. With electro-optical systems, the target-to-background signal is described primarily as a contrast. We first provide some background in sources and reflectivities and then describe the method for calculating contrast.

External Sources

The primary source for EO systems is the sun which can be modeled outside Earth's atmosphere by a large 5,900 deg K blackbody source. Figure 5.13 shows the irradiance of the sun both inside and outside Earth's atmosphere. Note the modification by the atmospheric transmission (given by the sea-level irradiance). The graph shown corresponds to the sun located directly overhead. For the sun located at other angles, the flux traverses a longer atmospheric path, reducing the irradiance even further. The sun's irradiance just outside Earth's atmosphere, for the mean Earth-sun distance, over all wavelengths is 1,390 W/m^2. Also, measurements of illuminance at sea level with the sun at its zenith (directly overhead) gives 1.24 x 10^5 lux. Illuminance for solar angles from the Earth's surface of 90, 45, 10, and 0 deg (sunset or sunrise) correspond to 12.4 x 10^4, 7.59x10^4, 1.09 x 10^4, and 732 lux, respectively.

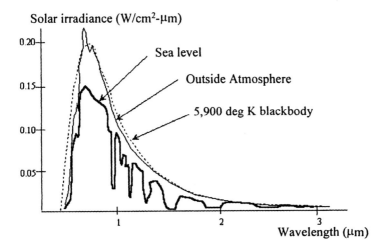

Figure 5.13 Solar irradiance at the Earth's surface.

An air mass *m*, corresponding to the secant of the angle from the zenith, can give a rough approximation of a corresponding irradiance reduction. This factor is the reduction factor for the solar irradiance across all wavelengths. More detailed atmospheric transmission is addressed in Chapter 6. Skylight, the light scattering from the atmosphere, also contributes to the target-and-background irradiance. Skylight becomes significant for objects in the shade and for large air masses. Skylight accounts for around one-fifth of the total illuminance at Earth's surface on a clear day. The treatment of skylight and cloud coverage can be found in Waldman and Wootton [10].

The irradiance and illuminance provided by moonlight, or rather sunlight reflected by the moon, are related to a number of factors. The angular distance between the moon and the sun, the variation in Earth-to-moon distance (26% variation), the differences in the reflectance of the moon's surface (20% variation), and the angle of the moon above Earth's horizon all contribute to variations in moonlight. Moonlight illuminance ranges from 3.12×10^{-5} lx at worst conditions to 0.267 lx at its brightest.

Star brightness [11] is specified with a stellar magnitude that represents the visual brightness of a star at a point just outside Earth's atmosphere. A zero-magnitude star corresponds to an illuminance of 2.65×10^{-6} lx. The true illuminance of a star referenced (divided) by the zero-magnitude illuminance is given by 2.512^{-sm} where *sm* is the stellar magnitude. Stars contribute 2.2×10^{-4} lx to the clear night sky. The illuminance provided by stars accounts for one-fourth of the light in the night sky with no moon. The rest of the light is provided by emissions from various atoms and molecules in the atmosphere. The spectral irradiance provided by the stars can be approximated with blackbody sources outside Earth's atmosphere. The *Electro-Optics Handbook* provides peak wavelengths for the generation of blackbody sources corresponding to various stars.

There is a large number of human-made illuminators, including tungsten lamps (2,700-3,300 deg K), phosphors, sodium lamps, and mercury lamps. While some of these sources can be modeled with blackbody curves, they all produce a significant amount of light at electro-optical wavelengths. The spectral emission of these illuminators can be found in a number of the handbooks and described in vendor references. The military spectral bandpass of choice for military electro-optical (not infrared) systems is 0.65 to 0.90 μm. The human eye has little response within this band region.

For the typical solar, skylight, moonlight, starlight, and artificial illumination, reflectivity is the primary target parameter. The human eye is, in some ways, very similar to an electro-optical sensor in that the variations in reflectivity drive the eye response. Different colors seen by humans correspond to the spectral reflectivity characteristics of objects. We use these characteristics to help us recognize objects. The exitance of light from an object is equal to the irradiance impinging on the object from some source, multiplied by the target reflectivity as a function of wavelength. An object that appears red has an impinging irradiance with red (around 0.6 μm) light content and the object reflectivity is higher at the red wavelength than at other wavelengths. Keep in mind that reflectivity can peak at a number of different wavelengths, where the wavelengths do not have to be within our visible response band of 0.4 to 0.7 μm. Therefore, objects can have peak reflectivities at wavelengths, or "colors," that humans cannot sense. Figure 5.14 shows the reflectivities for a number of backgrounds.

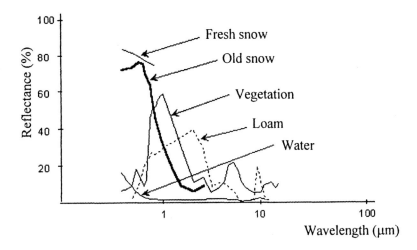

Figure 5.14 Reflectivity as a function of wavelength [10].

Three important spectral quantities affect the radiation leaving an object. The first is the source spectral irradiance $E_v(\lambda)$ of the object given a vacuum path (i.e., no atmospheric effects). The second is the atmospheric transmission between the source and the object $\tau_1(\lambda)$ and the third is the reflectivity of the object $\rho(\lambda)$. The exitance of the object is then

$$M(\lambda) = E_v(\lambda)\tau_1(\lambda)\rho(\lambda) \quad [\text{W/cm}^2\text{-μm}] \qquad (5.31)$$

This exitance is a function of space over the object, especially because the reflectivity usually varies dramatically across object space. To determine the voltage from a detector within a given optical system from the object exitance described in (5.31), a few other parameters are required (Figure 5.15). These are the atmospheric transmission between the object and the sensor $\tau_2(\lambda)$, the sensor transmission $\tau_{optics}(\lambda)$, and the detector responsivity $R(\lambda)$, in V/W. If the target surface is Lambertian, the radiance is calculated as $M(\lambda)/\pi$ W/cm²-sr-μm. The radiance can be multiplied by the source area seen by the detector abR^2/f^2 to obtain an intensity in W/sr-μm. a and b are the detector dimensions, f is the lens focal length, and R is the range from the target to the electro-optical sensor. Finally, the intensity can be multiplied by the sensor solid angle $\Omega = \pi D^2/4R^2$ to obtain the flux on the detector. This combination of parameters over a given spectral bandwidth $[\lambda_1, \lambda_2]$ gives a detector voltage:

$$V = \frac{abD^2}{4f^2} \int_{\lambda_1}^{\lambda_2} E_v(\lambda)\tau_1(\lambda)\rho(\lambda)\tau_2(\lambda)\tau_{optics}(\lambda)R(\lambda)d\lambda \ [V] \qquad (5.32)$$

(5.32) illustrates the complexity of EO systems. Unlike infrared systems, where the target is the source, a dual-path calculation is required. The dual paths are the source-to-target path and the target-to-sensor path.

All spectral modifications must be included to determine the correct voltage. An interesting phenomenon occurs when either (1) a target and background have completely different reflectivities (as a function of wavelength), but a common source spectrum or (2) detector responsivity varies in a manner that causes identical voltage responses for the target and background. The multiplication and integration of (5.32) is identical for both the target and the background, but the reflectivities are different. In this case, the sensor cannot discern the target from the background. This phenomenon occurs occasionally with EO systems, but rarely with infrared systems.

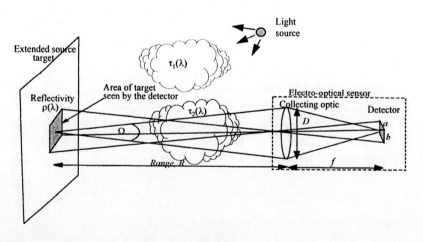

Figure 5.15 Electro-optical system light path.

For an exact response of a system, all source, transmission, reflectance, and sensitivity quantities should be developed as a function of wavelength and the final response would be the collective responses (integrated) across all wavelengths. However, source irradiance, atmospheric transmission, reflection, and detector sensitivity is frequently specified as a band-integrated quantity [12]. For example, a silicon detector may have a sensitivity of 1,654 μA/lx between the wavelengths of 0.55 and 0.70 μm. While this quantity may not make sense, it is the ratio of the band-integrated source irradiance weighted by the spectral response of the silicon detector to the band-integrated source irradiance weighted by the response (efficacy) of the human eye:

$$R_{band} = \frac{\int_{0.55}^{0.70} S(\lambda)E(\lambda)d\lambda}{\int_{0.38}^{0.78} K(\lambda)E(\lambda)d\lambda} \qquad [\text{A/lx}] \qquad (5.33)$$

Note that the integration bands are not identical, causing some discrepancy in the notion of a reference. This type of band-averaging and illuminance-referencing is used widely and contributes to sensor response errors and limited accuracy. The errors can be reduced with a reduction in spectral bandwidth and a shift of the detector response to the visual response band. A high-fidelity analysis requires analytical terms to be band-integrated after all responses are included. For a quick-and-dirty analysis, band quantities are useful with reasonable results if the source irradiance, reflectivities, and atmospheric transmission do not vary significantly over the band.

Contrast

While all sensor systems respond to changes in radiation, EO systems have been modeled as responding to target-to-background contrast. This input parameter must be determined using the characteristics of illumination, target reflectivity, and background reflectivity. Contrast [13] is defined as the target-to-background luminance divided by the background luminance

$$C = \frac{L_T - L_B}{L_B} \qquad (5.34)$$

The luminance quantities are in photometric units and are proportional to the detector output voltages. The weighting function that corresponds to the appropriate light level of the human eye (i.e., photopic response), however, can be modified to the spectral response of the EO sensor. L_T becomes

$$L_T = \frac{abD^2}{4f^2} \int_{\lambda_1}^{\lambda_2} E(\lambda)\rho_T(\lambda)\tau_{atm}(\lambda)R_s(\lambda)d\lambda \qquad (5.35)$$

where $E(\lambda)$ is the source irradiance on the target, $\rho_T(\lambda)$ is the reflectivity of the target surface, $\tau_{atm}(\lambda)$ is the atmospheric transmission between the target and the sensor, and $R_s(\lambda)$ is the spectral response of the sensor. The background luminance is calculated in the same manner.

The contrast perceived by the sensor is reduced from the value in (5.34) by *path radiance*, or stray light caused by the source illumination of particles in the atmospheric path. This modification results in the perceived contrast being

$$C = \frac{L_T - L_B}{L_B + L_{atm}} \tag{5.36}$$

where L_{atm} is the path radiance in the band of the sensor. This value is typically calculated with LOWTRAN or MODTRAN and can significantly affect the contrast.

Similar to the analysis of I^2R systems, there are various levels of accuracy in analytical techniques. It is rare that (5.35) and (5.36) are calculated in practice. More gross analysis is usually performed with a target-to-background contrast calculated at the target position as

$$C = \frac{\int_{\lambda_1}^{\lambda_2} E(\lambda)\rho_T(\lambda)R_s(\lambda)d\lambda - \int_{\lambda_1}^{\lambda_2} E(\lambda)\rho_B(\lambda)R_s(\lambda)d\lambda}{\int_{\lambda_1}^{\lambda_2} E(\lambda)\rho_B(\lambda)R_s(\lambda)d\lambda} \tag{5.37}$$

The source irradiance on the target has been measured for the sun, moon, and stars at Earth's surface for different seasons, climates, and times. Note the number of variables that are present in the analysis. These measurements allow consideration of the illumination geometry and atmospheric path between the illumination source and the target. The missing link between the contrast at the target position and the perceived contrast at the sensor is the path radiance. The contrast at the target position must be degraded by the atmosphere to obtain the perceived, or apparent, contrast.

Contrast at the target location can be calculated using various models. The U.S. Army Night Vision and Electronic Sensors Directorate (NVESD) has a contrast model that includes libraries of source irradiance, target and background reflectivities, and sensor-responsivity curves. These libraries show that a target and background can have dramatically different reflectivities but still produce a small contrast from the spectral characteristics of the source and sensor response.

Holst [13] approximates the perceived target-to-background contrast:

$$C_R = C\tau_{atm} \tag{5.38}$$

where τ_{atm} is the band-averaged atmospheric transmission approximated by

$$\tau_{atm} = e^{-\sigma_{atm}R} \tag{5.39}$$

R is the range in kilometers, and σ_{atm} is the atmospheric scattering coefficient. The atmospheric scattering coefficient is given for a number of conditions in Table 5.4.

Table 5.4
Scattering coefficients (from Holst [13])

Condition	Scattering coefficient [km⁻¹]
Dense fog	78.2
Moderate fog	7.82-19.6
Thin fog	1.96-3.92
Haze	0.98-1.96
Clear	0.19-0.39
Very clear	0.078-0.19

Example

An Armored Personnel Carrier (APC) travels along an Alabama clay road during a sunny day. Determine the target-to-background contrast of the vehicle using the human eye as the sensor. The normalized solar irradiance, the eye's normalized photopic response, the reflectance of the APC, and the reflectance of Alabama clay are given in Figure 5.16.

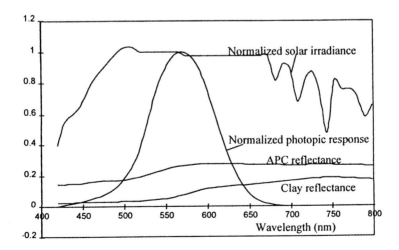

Figure 5.16 Contrast example.

The eye's luminous response to the target is determined by the product of the solar irradiance, the APC reflectance, and the photopic response. The total luminous response is determined by integrating this product. The integral for the curves shown is 23.8 (normalized luminance). The eye's response to the background is determined by the integral of the product of the solar irradiance, the clay reflectance, and the photopic response. The normalized background luminance is 7.65. The contrast is determined using (5.37) to be 2.11 or 211%. Normalized values for the solar irradiance and the photopic response are acceptable as long as the target and the background are both evaluated as normalized quantities.

5.4 OTHER SENSITIVITY CONSIDERATIONS

We have shown methods for calculating the power on detectors in the infrared and electro-optical cases. The methods for determining a delta T for the infrared and a contrast for electro-optical systems have been presented. Be careful, however, when using these quantities, as they are first-order approximations of target-to-background signals. Many assumptions accompany these calculations, and care should be taken not to apply these signal descriptions when the assumptions are not satisfied.

Bidirectional Reflectance Distribution Function

While we have provided generalizations in order to obtain first-order characterizations of targets and backgrounds, an exact model of targets and backgrounds must address the reflectivity, emissivity, and transmissivity of every surface in the scenario. This is rarely performed by I²R and EO sensor developers; however, it is a common practice for target coating researchers. The Coatings Engineering Evaluation Program (CREEP) is an example of a model that was developed for the purposes of evaluating paints and coatings.

Programs such as CREEP derive directional parameters for infrared (and other bands) emissivity and reflectivity [14]. The directional emissivity is given by

$$\varepsilon(\lambda) = \frac{L(\theta,\phi)}{L_{BB}} \tag{5.40}$$

where θ and ϕ define emissivity direction and L_{BB} is the radiance of a blackbody at the same temperature as the coating. The bidirectional reflectance distribution function or BRDF (Figure 5.17) is defined as

$$\rho_{BRDF} = \frac{L_r(\theta_r,\phi_r)}{E_i(\theta_i,\phi_i)} \tag{5.41}$$

where $L_r(\theta_r, \phi_r)$ is the reflected radiance and $E_i(\theta_i, \phi_i)$ is the incident irradiance. Note that with reflectivity, there are both incident angles and reflected angles. The units of ρ_{BRDF} are reciprocal steradians. For a Lambertian surface:

$$\rho_{BRDF} = \frac{\rho_o}{\pi} \tag{5.42}$$

where ρ_o is the reflectivity. If the surface is specular, the reflectance is only nonzero when $\theta_r = \theta_i$

$$\rho_{BRDF} = R(\theta_i) \frac{\delta(\theta_r - \theta_i)\delta(\phi_r - \phi_i + \pi)}{\cos\theta_r \sin\theta_r} \tag{5.43}$$

where $R(\theta_i)$ is the Fresnel reflectance. Recall that $\varepsilon = 1 - \rho_{BRDF}$ for a surface that does not transmit light. There are many models of BRDF for surfaces that are not Lambertian or specular. They can be thought of as surfaces between Lambertian and specular. Scientists attempt to optimize these surface coatings for particular applications. These applications include low observable (LO) technology, laser damage susceptibility, and radiation management.

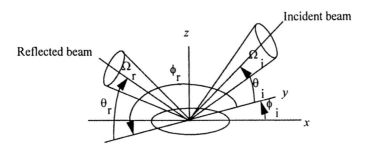

Figure 5.17 BRDF nomenclature.

Color Considerations

Many commercial EO sensors have separate detectors that correspond to red, green, and blue wavelength bands to obtain color information. These three bands have been shown, when used together, to give appropriate representation of the human visual response. Once detected, the three bands are combined and displayed using the color representation of images. Humans perceive the three colors to represent the entire visual spectrum. For most military systems, all of the light within a given band (not necessarily in the visual band) is integrated on a single detector response to give gray-level images. Highly reflective objects within a given band are represented by white (i.e., higher gray levels), where low-reflective objects are represented with dark gray levels. A single picture element (pixel) is typically represented by anywhere from 16 (four bits) to 1,024 (10 bits) shades of gray.

Some new approaches in the use of reflectivity as a function of wavelength to detect, recognize, and identify targets are currently under investigation. For sensors that can detect flux as a function of wavelength (imaging spectrometers), neural networks are being used to discriminate targets based on their spectral signatures. In another approach, electro-optical, midwave infrared, and longwave infrared bands are pseudocolored with red, green, and blue colors for display to humans. The human training and human responses to these pseudo colored images are yielding high probability levels of recognition and identification. One of the associated problems with this approach is the pixel registering of the three images (electro-optical, midwave infrared, and longwave infrared). That is, each picture element must be aligned in the three images before the color coding and subsequent image display. As imaging systems become more sophisticated, spectral capabilities will be used frequently in tactical sensors. Currently there are few platforms that include extensive spectral segregation. Usually, a single-band electro-optical sensor for day viewing and a single imaging infrared (midwave or longwave) sensor band, present for night viewing are fielded on a weapons platform.

5.5 TARGET AND BACKGROUND SPATIAL CHARACTERISTICS

We have previously discussed the radiometric characteristics of targets and backgrounds. In the infrared, the important target and background parameters are object temperatures and emissivities, where in the electro-optical wavelengths, they are the reflectivities and external source irradiances. While the resultant object radiometry quantity is exitance as a function of wavelength, the exitance is also a function of space. In fact, an exact analysis of a sensor's response to a particular target and background requires an exact expression for the target and background exitance as a function of space, $M_\lambda(x,y)$.

Spatial exitance describes the plane of the target, but exitance can be represented in many ways. Three methods are common. The first is the exitance as a function of space in the plane of the target (normal to the sensor line-of-sight), where x and y are the horizontal- and vertical-independent variables, in meters. The second is in angular space where x and y are horizontal and vertical angular variables, in milliradians, that describe the azimuth and elevation points in the target plane as seen by the sensor. These angular variables are found simply by the horizontal and vertical positions in the target plane divided by the range from the sensor to the target. This angular method for describing targets is very useful in the linear systems approach to sensor analysis, as spatial frequencies are typically specified in cycles per milliradian. Finally, another useful method of representing a target image is to write the irradiance pattern provided by the target and background on the sensor detector plane. The scaling of the $M_\lambda(x,y)$ function from the object plane to the image plane is performed simply by reducing the object size by the ratio of the effective sensor focal length to the target range

$M_\lambda(\frac{xR}{f}, \frac{yR}{f})$. Note that this scaling typically reduces the function by orders of magnitude in size and that the object exitance function must be multiplied by the appropriate radiometry parameters to convert the scene image to an irradiance in the detector plane.

The spatial frequency content, or spectrum, of a scene (target and background) can be found by taking the two-dimensional Fourier transform of the scene exitance

$$M_\lambda(\xi, \eta) = \mathcal{J}\mathcal{J} \{M_\lambda(x,y)\} \qquad (5.44)$$

where ξ and η are in cycles per meter. Note that the wavelength dependence is shown. The spectrum must be integrated over wavelength from the target exitance, through the atmosphere, through the sensors' optics, and onto the detector. With this in mind, the wavelength dependence is dropped and assumed to be given for some wave band of interest.

In a typical scene, a large number of frequency components are present. In practice, a Fast-Fourier Transform (FFT) can be applied to the image to determine the spectrum of the image. Small objects have high-frequency components and large objects have lower frequency components. A common exercise for electro-optical students involves a tank hiding within the leaves of a tree. An optical system is designed such that components of the tree leaves do not pass the optical system, but the significant tank frequency components are allowed to pass through the system. This reduction in resolution allows the viewer to quickly find the tank.

Angular space is used when an object position is specified in azimuth radians x and elevation radians y within an optical system's FOV. Spatial frequencies of the scene are then given in terms of cycles per milliradian. These are the typical quantities that are used in sensor and target analysis. A 3-m by 4-m truck located 1 km from a sensor would subtend 3 mrads by 4 mrads in angular space. Given that the truck is modeled as a two-dimensional rectangle function $M(x,y) = rect(\frac{x}{3}, \frac{y}{4})$, the frequency components associated with the target are

$$M(\xi, \eta) = \mathcal{J}\mathcal{J} \{rect(\frac{x}{3}, \frac{y}{4})\} = 12 \, sinc(3\xi, 4\eta) \qquad (5.45)$$

where ξ and η are in cycles per milliradian. Oversimplification can occur by gross modeling of a truck with a large rectangle function. That is, the details of wheels, mirrors, headlights, doors, and so forth may not be resolvable given gross modeling. Sums of many different rectangles or other functions can give reasonable estimates. FFTs of real images taken with high-resolution imagers can give sufficient frequency component information to model targets and backgrounds. Other modeling includes facets of various shapes and sizes to construct a high-resolution target and background. The target spatial frequency spectrum is then the sum of the individual facet component spectra.

Bar Target Representation of Targets

   An exact analysis of whether a human can recognize a given object with a sensor requires a spatial frequency analysis of the object and the sensor system. However, a technique that has been shown to provide reasonable results is that of *bar target representation of targets* by John Johnson [15]. It is common practice to represent objects with bar targets for the purpose of sensor evaluation, analysis, and design. Johnson conducted a number of experiments at the U.S. Army's Night Vision and Electronic Sensor's Directorate (NVESD) to develop requirements for detection, recognition, and identification of objects (in particular, tactical ground targets). Consider the targets in Figure 5.18 along with their bar target equivalents. Johnson determined the number of bar pairs, or cycles, necessary across an object to perform a discrimination task. Further NVESD experimentation yielded similar results. The requirements for detection, recognition, and identification of targets are described in Table 5.5.

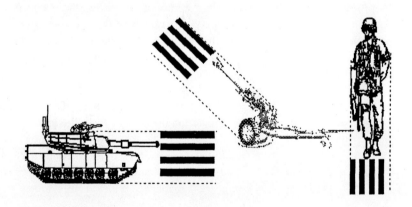

Figure 5.18 Objects and corresponding bar targets.

Table 5.5
Cycle criteria

Task	Description	Cycles across object minimum dimension N_{50}	Cycles across two-dimensional object N_{50}
Detection	Reasonable probability that blob is the object being sought	1.0	0.75
Recognition	Class discrimination (human, truck, tank, etc.)	4.0	3.0
Identification	Object discrimination (M1A, T-62, or T-72 tank)	6.4	6.0

The one-dimensional description corresponds to the number of cycles across the minimum dimension of the object. A two-dimensional cycle requirement is given for the critical target dimension (a function of target width and height as seen by the sensor):

$$h_c = \sqrt{W_{tgt}H_{tgt}} \qquad \text{[meters]} \qquad (5.46)$$

These criteria are valid for tactical targets that have a width-to-height aspect ratio of less than 3 or 4. They do not apply to long, thin targets. The cycle criteria in Table 5.5 correspond to a probability of 50% for the discrimination task given (thus, the N_{50} nomenclature). If other probabilities are desired, Holst [16] describes the target transfer probability function (TTPF) as a multiple of the number of cycles given in Table 5.5 to achieve a particular probability of discrimination. The TTPF is given in Table 5.6.

Table 5.6
Target transfer probability function (TTPF)

Probability	Multiplier
1.00	3.00
0.95	2.00
0.80	1.50
0.50	1.00
0.30	0.75
0.10	0.50
0.02	0.25
0	0

For example, recognition requires three cycles across a two-dimensional target to assess the probability of recognition at 50%. To provide a recognition probability of 95%, three cycles times the 2.0 TTPF factor yields a requirement of 6 cycles across the target.

While these resolution tasks are necessary for the discrimination of targets, sufficient sensitivity is assumed. Do not forget that both sensitivity and resolution are the performance requirements necessary to address any sensor task (given that basics such as size, weight, power, etc., have been met). Questions that should be discussed before any sensor design are: What are the flux characteristics of all objects that could be in the scene, of the target, and of the background? What are the possible target sizes and shapes? What are the resulting resolution requirements (sensitivity and spatial resolution) necessary to discriminate these targets? The target and background issues must be defined to proceed with a sensor design and/or analysis for any given scenario.

Clutter

As discussed in the introduction, clutter [17, 18] describes the background components that resemble the targets in size and shape. Clutter has been modeled by lowering the effective contrast of the target and the background and by edge contrast modification in a scene. A common model that is used frequently is one where the clutter is defined as

$$CL = \sqrt{\frac{1}{N} \sum_{i=1}^{N} \sigma_i^2} \qquad (5.47)$$

where the scene is divided into N blocks. The blocks are selected to be twice the size of the target (in pixels). The variance of the pixel intensities within block i is given as σ_i^2. The clutter is taken as the square root of the normalized variance as shown in (5.47). Finally, the signal-to-clutter ratio (SCR) is defined as the target to background contrast divided by the clutter.

The effect of clutter on human target acquisition capability is frequently modeled by three categories: low, moderate, and high. The TTPF is modified for these clutter levels to decrease the acquisition probability. Instead of modifying the TTPF, Holst suggests that the changes in TTPF can be approximated simply by multiplying the cycle criteria of Table 5.5 by the values given in Table 5.7. Note that the previous acquisition model was developed for the case of moderate-clutter (i.e., a multiplier of 1). Most natural scenes fall into the moderate-clutter region; however, some urban scenes correspond to the high-clutter region. Some desert and calm ocean scenes place clutter levels in the low region.

Table 5.7
Clutter modifications to N_{50}

Clutter	SCR	N_{50} *Multiplier*
Low	>10	0.5
Moderate	1 < SCR < 10	1.0
High	<1	2.5

Simulation of Target Characteristics

Modeling and simulation have been, and still are, a major thrust for the late 1990s. Particularly for the military industry, in which shrinking defense budgets require more modeling and simulation efforts than ever before. Live testing is being reduced and augmented with simulations. Not only are target engagements using particular sensors being modeled, but entire battles that include surveillance and fire control sensors are under development. Questions for the sensor designers are "how well and how quickly can I detect and classify what I am seeking?" and "can I hide from what is seeking me?" Additional questions that are asked by military leaders are "can this sensor significantly improve my chances of winning the battle?" and "can I use the technology to save human lives?" Modeling and simulation, if performed correctly, can provide answers to many of these questions.

Target simulations must provide realistic conditions such that sensor system performance can be evaluated when engaging the target. The conditions include both geometric and exitance fidelity of the target. For I²R systems, the exitance characteristics include the target temperature and the wavelength dependency in the appropriate wavebands. In some cases, solar reflections must be addressed. EO systems require characterization of target reflectance and illumination parameters. The geometric fidelity requirement can be derived from the sensor resolution and the apparent temperature difference between resolution elements on the target.

There are a number of different methods for modeling targets, including modeling only the target exterior surface (boundary representation) or modeling entire target volumes (solids modeling). The temperature and emissivity modeling or reflection and illumination modeling can be implemented from actual target measurements or from first principle calculations. Advantages of first principle calculations are that one can apply greater flexibility to operating conditions, whereas the disadvantage is that they result in greater inaccuracies than measured data. Not only are models on hardbodies required, but rocket plumes, jet engine exhausts, and combustion engine exhausts are also needed.

A large number of programs are currently available for target modeling. They are more popular in the I²R systems because infrared testing is much more expensive than EO testing. A partial list of target models includes the following:

AEMAT	AvLab Electro-Optical Model for Aerial Targeting
EMAT	Electro-Optical Model for Aerial Targeting
GTSIG	Georgia Tech Thermal Contrast Model
IRMA	Infrared Modeling and Analysis
PCNirATAM	NATO Infrared Air Target Model
PRISM	Physically Reasonable Infrared Signature Model
SIRIM	Simulated Infrared Image Model
SPIRITS	Spectral and In-Band Radiometric Imaging of Targets and Sensors Model

Many of these models are owned by the U.S. Government and can be obtained with Government agreement. See *Infrared Signature Simulation of Military Targets* [19] for further information.

EXERCISES

5.1 A light source delivers 3 W of power uniformly over an entire sphere. What is the source intensity?

5.2 The power of sunlight is measured in a 1 m² area on Earth's surface and is 1,353 W. Find the intensity of the sun if the distance from Earth to the sun is 150,000,000 km.

5.3 A laser delivers 5 W of power in a beam with a 1 mrad divergence angle. Determine the laser intensity.

5.4 A spherical ball with a 1-cm radius emits 2 W of radiation. Determine the average exitance of the sphere.

5.5 A neutral density filter is placed in front of a square light source as shown in Figure 5.19 such that the exitance of the source/filter combination is

$$M = 5x \qquad [\text{W/m}^2]$$

Determine the total power emitted by the combination.

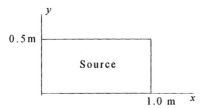

Figure 5.19

5.6 A Lambertian blackbody source is heated to 500 deg K as shown. An aperture is placed 1 m away from the source, first on axis and then 30 deg off-axis. Determine the radiance of the source, the power through the on-axis aperture, and the power through the off-axis aperture.

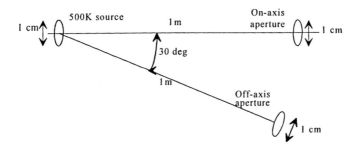

Figure 5.20

5.7 Determine the exitance and radiance of a 773 deg K blackbody source:
   (1) over all wavelengths.
   (2) for the 3- to 5-μm wavelength band.
   (3) for the 8- to 12-μm wavelength band.
   (4) determine the peak emission wavelength.
   (5) repeat (1) through (4) for a 300 deg K source.

5.8 Calculate the difference in radiance for a 275 deg K background and a 300 deg K target. Repeat for a 300 deg K background and a 325 deg K target. Provide these calculations first for all wavelengths, then for the midwave and longwave bands. Does a 25 deg K difference in temperature always give the same difference in radiance?

5.9 Provide the cycle criteria necessary to recognize a target with a 90% probability of recognition. Provided the target is 4 m by 6 m in size, what is the required angular spatial frequency that must be resolved by the sensor?

REFERENCES

[1]   *The Photonics Dictionary,* Pittsfield, MA: Lauren Publishing Company, p. D-97, 1996.

[2]   Pinson, L., *Electro-Optics,* New York: Wiley, p. 18, 1985.

[3]   Jacobs, P., *Thermal Infrared Characterization of Ground Targets and Backgrounds,* Bellingham, WA: SPIE Press, p. 22, 1996.

[4]   Wolf, W., and G. Zissis, *The Infrared Handbook,* Environmental Research Institute of Michigan, Office of Naval Research, Washington, DC, pp.1 - 18, 1993.

[5]   Pinson, L., *Electro-Optics,* New York: Wiley, p.15., 1985.

[6]   Waldman, G., and J. Wootton, *Electro-Optical Imaging System Performance,* Boston: Artech House, p.184, 1993.

[7]   Driscoll, W., and W. Vaughn, *Handbook of Optics,* New York: McGraw-Hill, pp.1 - 6, 1978.

[8]   Wolfe, W., and G. Zissis, *The Infrared Handbook,* Environmental Research Institute of Michigan, 3rd Printing, p. 2 - 77, 1987.

[9]   Acetta, J., and D. Schumaker, *The Infrared and Electro-Optical Handbook,* Vol. 4, ERIM and SPIE, p. 31, 1993.

[10]   Waldman, G., and J. Wootton, *Electro-Optical Imaging System Performance,* Boston, MA: Artech House, p. 70, 1993.

[11]   *Electro-Optical Handbook,* Burle Industries, Lancaster, PA, p. 65, 1989.

[12]   *TV Performance Modeling,* Army Communication Command, Ft. Monmouth, NJ, 1991.

[13]   Holst, G., *Electro-Optical Imaging System Performance,* Winter Park, FL: JCD Publishing, p. 337, 1995.

[14]   Ellis, K., *Reflectance Phenomenology and Modeling Tutorial,* at www.erim.com.

[15]   Johnson, J., "Analysis of Image Forming Systems," in the *Proceedings of the Image Intensifier Symposium,* pp. 249 - 273, Warfare Electrical Engineering Department, U.S. Army Research and Development Laboratory, Ft. Belvoir, VA, 1958.

[16]   Holst, G., *Electro-Optical Imaging System Performance,* Winter Park, FL: JCD Publishing, p. 421, 1995.

[17]   Rotman, R., and M. Kowalcyzk, "Clutter Analysis for Modeling and Improving Human and Automatic Target Acquisition," *Proceedings of SPIE, Infrared Technology, XIX,* San Diego, CA, 1993.

[18]   Schmieder, D., and M. Weathersby, "Detection Performance in Clutter with Variable Resolution," *IEEE Transactions and Electronic Systems,* Vol. 19, No. 4, July 1983.

[19]   Morey, B., K. Ellis, D. Perry, and K. Gleichman, *Infrared Signature Simulation of Military Targets,* Infrared Information Analysis Center, Environmental Research Institute of Michigan, 1994.

Chapter 6

Atmospherics

It is a common experience, especially for those living near a large city, to notice that one's view of the city skyline can vary dramatically from day to day depending on the weather (rain, sleet, fog, or pollution). The same factors that affect your ability to view distant objects also affect electro-optical and infrared sensors. The factors that affect the viewing of distant objects are the result of two primary phenomena: absorption and scattering. Absorption occurs when certain types of particles interact with the radiation from the object being viewed. Some key absorbers include water vapor, carbon dioxide, ozone, nitrous oxide, and carbon monoxide. Scattering is the redirection of the object's radiation by particles in the air. Examples of these particles are water droplets, snowflakes, smoke, airborne dust, pollution, and other human-made and natural aerosols, to name a few.

Both absorption and scattering are strong functions of wavelength. For sensors that operate in the infrared, both absorption and scattering are important. For sensors operating in the visible waveband, scattering is the dominant phenomenon. Besides being a function of wavelength, many other variables have an influence on atmospheric transmission. These variables include temperature, altitude of sensor and target, humidity, barometric pressure, and turbulence. A pictorial representation of the atmosphere in the sensor system is shown in Figure 6.1.

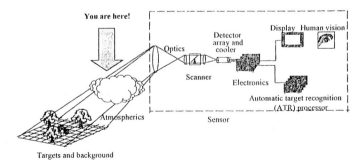

Figure 6.1 Atmospherics is the second component in the system.

With the exception of atmospheric (sometimes called "path") radiance, these atmospheric factors can reduce the amount of object radiation that is received by the sensor and produce a blurring of the image. This is especially apparent in long atmospheric paths. The extent of the impact depends on radiation wavelength. A graph of a typical atmospheric transmission is shown in Figure 6.2, depicting "windows" through the atmosphere in several spectral bands. This is one of the main reasons why the 3- to 5-μm and 8- to 12-μm spectral bands are commonly used for imaging in military applications. The transmission shown is a typical transmission, where the actual transmission changes with climate, temperature, humidity, and the like.

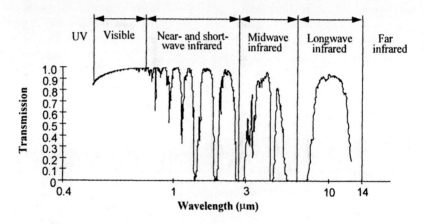

Figure 6.2 Typical atmospheric transmission for a 1-km path length.

While the detailed theory of analyzing atmospheric transmission is quite complex, this chapter presents the basic theory along with methods for calculating transmission and its overall effect on sensor performance.

6.1 ATMOSPHERIC COMPONENTS AND STRUCTURE

The atmosphere is a gaseous envelope that surrounds Earth's surface. It extends for several hundred kilometers above Earth and eventually transitions into the rarefied medium of the solar system. The gas that constitutes the atmosphere, air, comprises elements (of which there are 112) and compounds. The exact composition varies with geographic location and altitude. This is because both the atmospheric pressure and temperature change with the vertical structure of the atmosphere.

On a typical day, the morning air temperature starts out cool, then gradually warms until it reaches a peak in the afternoon and finally cools down in the evening. Everyone knows that the weather (e.g., the atmospheric condition) is very unpredictable. There are warm fronts, cold fronts, isolated storms, temperature variations, and many other weather phenomena. Two separate geographic locations within the same general area can have significantly different atmospheric conditions (temperature, pressure, and composition) at the same time. This difference in atmospheric makeup affects the atmospheric transmission differently in each region. Despite all these uncertainties, there are certain assumptions that can be made allowing a reasonable prediction of the transmission of radiation through the atmosphere.

The atmosphere consists of elements and compounds. The most common elements in the atmosphere are nitrogen and oxygen that constitute over 98% percent of the atmosphere by volume. Water vapor, carbon dioxide, nitrous oxide, carbon monoxide, and ozone are the major radiation absorbers. Water vapor has a significant affect on absorption of infrared radiation. It is also the most variable because of evaporation of water from bodies of water, damp grounds, and condensation into clouds or dew. Carbon dioxide does not vary as dramatically as water vapor but does tend to be concentrated around large cities and heavy vegetation areas. Carbon dioxide is a strong absorber in the midwave infrared (MWIR), but the midwave band is superior for sensor applications in high humidity compared with longwave infrared (LWIR) band.

Earth's atmosphere is generally divided into four layers, based primarily on temperature variations within each layer. These are the troposphere, stratosphere, mesosphere, and thermosphere. The temperature in the troposphere decreases with altitude at a rate of approximately 6.5 deg K/km. Also, note that between 80 to 85% of Earth's atmospheric mass resides in the troposphere. The next atmospheric division above the troposphere is the stratosphere, where the temperature is at first a constant, then increases until approximately 50 km. The temperature increases in altitude for both the stratosphere and thermosphere. In the mesosphere, the temperature behaves in a manner similar to that of the stratosphere by decreasing in altitude to about 85 km and then strongly rising in the thermosphere. A graph of the temperature versus altitude function is shown in Figure 6.3 [1].

In the same manner as temperature, both atmospheric pressure and density vary with altitude. A tabular representation of the relationships among altitude, pressure, temperature, and density based on the U.S. Standard Atmosphere (1976) is shown in Table 6.1. These three variables (atmospheric temperature, pressure, and density) must all be taken into account when calculating atmospheric transmission. The number and behavior of the variables involved in the accurate modeling of the atmospheric effects on the flux leaving the objects of a scene can be extremely complex. However, reasonable estimates can be determined with upper and lower error bounds within assumed conditions as is shown in the following sections.

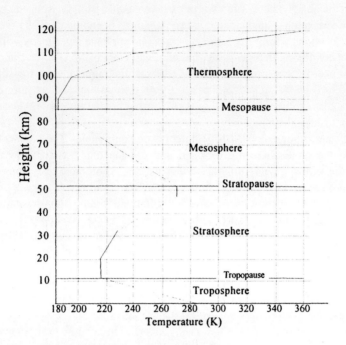

Figure 6.3 Temperature as a function of altitude.

Table 6.1
Parameters as a function of height

Height (km)	Pressure (hPa)	Temperature (K)	Density (g/m⁻³)
0	1.013E+3	288	1.225E+3
2	7.950E+2	275	1.007E+3
4	6.166E+2	262	8.194E+2
6	4.722E+2	249	6.601E02
8	3.565E+2	236	5.258E+2
10	2.650+2	223	4.135E+2
12	1.940E+2	217	3.119E+2
14	1.417E+2	217	2.279E+2
16	1.035+2	217	1.665E+2
18	7.565E+1	217	1.217E+2
20	5.529E+2	217	8.891E+1

6.2 ATMOSPHERIC TRANSMISSION

In calculating the optical transmission from an object to a sensor, there are three primary processes that affect the radiation: absorption, scattering, and refractive index fluctuations (turbulence). The atmospheric components (elements and compounds) discussed earlier are related to absorption and scattering, while the atmosphere's structural variations of temperature, pressure, and density contribute to turbulence. The effect of these three factors is both a reduction in the signal amplitude that reaches the sensor from the target and an atmospheric blurring of the image.

The first two processes, absorption and scattering, are usually grouped together under the topic of *extinction*. Extinction is defined as the reduction or attenuation in the amount of radiation passing through the atmosphere. Absorption is when a photon of radiation is absorbed by a gaseous molecule of the atmosphere that converts the photon into kinetic energy, thereby changing the energy level of the molecule or its component atoms and electrons. This energy change of the gaseous molecule manifests itself as a temperature change. When radiation is scattered, the direction of the incident radiation is changed by collision (and reflection) of a photon with an atmospheric molecule or particle. This process can be thought of as the atmospheric molecule momentarily capturing the incident radiation and then sending it out unchanged, but in all directions. The amount of radiation dispersed in a particular direction depends on the properties of the air particle interacting with the incident radiation.

To understand how the extinction affects the transmission of radiation through the atmosphere, visualize a single wavelength of incident radiation passing through an infinitesimal distance dx. The change in flux is

$$d\Phi = -\sigma \Phi dx \qquad \text{[W]} \qquad (6.1)$$

where the incident radiation is represented by Φ and σ is the extinction coefficient as shown in Figure 6.4. The negative sign indicates the reduction of power, or radiation, from the absorption and scattering processes. In general, the extinction coefficient is made up of two components:

$$\sigma = a + \gamma \qquad \text{[km}^{-1}\text{]} \qquad (6.2)$$

where a is the absorption coefficient and γ is the scattering coefficient. Both the absorption and scattering coefficients depend on the incident wavelength. Because of the interaction of the incident radiation with molecules comprising the medium, the radiation at the output is changed to $\Phi + d\Phi$. Equation (6.1) can be integrated to give the attenuation for a finite distance through a *homogeneous medium:*

$$\Phi = \Phi_o e^{-\sigma x} = \Phi_o \tau \qquad \text{[W]} \qquad (6.3)$$

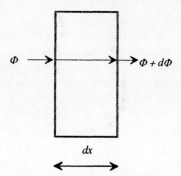

Figure 6.4 Transmission through an infinitesimal distance of atmosphere.

where $\tau = e^{-\sigma x}$ is the transmittance of the atmosphere over a distance x. This principle is known as Beer-Lambert law (sometimes shortened to Beer's law). As mentioned above, the extinction coefficient is highly dependent on wavelength, so Beer's law is usually written as

$$\tau(\lambda) = e^{-\sigma(\lambda)x} \qquad \text{[unitless]} \qquad (6.4)$$

Example

The transmittance of air $\tau_{atm}(\lambda)$ is the product of the molecular extinction transmittance and the aerosol extinction transmittance:

$$\tau_{atm}(\lambda) = \tau_m(\lambda)\tau_a(\lambda) \qquad (6.5)$$

A CO_2 laser (10.6-μm wavelength) is propagated through a 2-km horizontal path length. Determine the molecular transmittance given that the molecular extinction is 0.385 per kilometer (defined for the given wavelength and relative humidity). The solution gives the transmittance at

$$\tau_m(10.6\,\mu m) = e^{-(0.383)(2km)} = 0.465 \qquad \text{[unitless]} \qquad (6.6)$$

If the aerosol extinction is negligible (i.e., its transmittance is unity), a 10W laser provides 4.65W at a distance of 2 km.

6.3 ABSORPTION

Absorption is fundamentally a quantum process where an atmospheric molecule absorbs the energy from some incident photon. Absorption by an atmospheric molecule changes its internal state, increasing its energy, and resulting in a temperature change. When discussing absorption, it is best to consider the quantum nature of the atmospheric molecule. From introductory physics, the energy structure of a molecule is illustrated in Figure 6.5. The energy gap E_g required for absorption is given in Einstein's equation, $E = h\nu$. E is the energy of the photon, h is Planck's constant (6.626×10^{-14} J-sec), and ν is the frequency of the incident light.

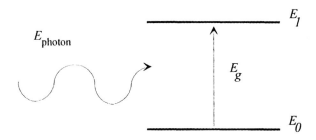

Figure 6.5 Absorption of a photon.

E_g is the energy gap that must be exceeded by a photon for an electron to change energy states within a molecule. There are a large number of "allowed" energy state changes within a molecular energy structure, so its absorption properties contain a spectral dependence. For a photon to be absorbed by a molecule, it must be at a sufficient wavelength such that $E_{photon} \geq E_g$ holds true. This energy difference is related to the different rotational and vibrational states of the particular atmospheric molecules. If the appropriate molecular energy band does not exist, the corresponding photons at that particular wavelength will not interact (to the first order) with that particular atmospheric molecule. Because of the quantum mechanical makeup of atmospheric gases, there is no significant absorption or radiation in the visible wavelengths (except for H_2O absorption between 0.65 and 0.85 µm). While in the infrared region of the spectrum, a number of molecules present are highly absorptive.

Specific atmospheric components that are absorptive in the infrared include the diatomic molecules nitrogen and oxygen; water; and carbon dioxide. Plots of the absorption characteristics for the primary components versus wavelength are shown in Figure 6.6.

Example

A molecule is sensitive [2] to photons with energies equal to, or slightly greater than, its molecular bandgaps. Lower energy photons pass and are not absorbed. Determine the wavelength with the most sensitivity (absorption) for a molecule with a gap at 0.18 eV. Planck's constant comes in two forms: 6.63×10^{-34}

J-sec or 4.14×10^{-15} eV. The speed of light is 3.00×10^8 m/s. The solution is determined by Einstein's relationship

$$E_g = h\nu \qquad [\text{eV}] \qquad (6.7)$$

With E at 0.18 eV, the frequency is 4.35×10^{-13} /s, or Hertz. The wavelength can then be determined from

$$\lambda = \frac{c}{\nu} \qquad\qquad [\text{meters}] \qquad (6.8)$$

yielding a wavelength of 6.9 μm.

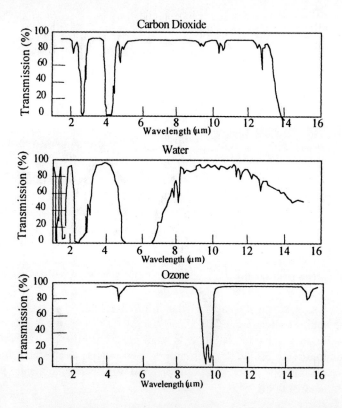

Figure 6.6 Transmission of atmospheric gasses for a 1-km path length.

The spectral graphs shown in Figure 6.6 are low-spectral-resolution graphs, where individual absorption lines cannot be seen (i.e., transmission has been averaged over some small wavebands). High-resolution-transmission graphs (1/16 wavenumber) are shown in Figure 6.7 for a 1-km horizontal path at sea level.

Frequently, transmission is plotted as a function of wavenumber, where the wavenumber is the inverse wavelength $1/\lambda$ and wavelength is given in centimeters. The graphs are produced by FASCODE, a high-resolution atmospheric spectral analysis program by Ontar.

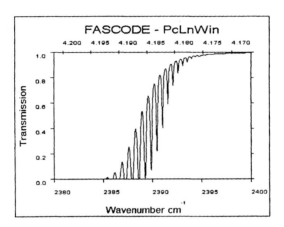

1-km horizontal path at sea level, no aerosols, U.S. standard atmosphere

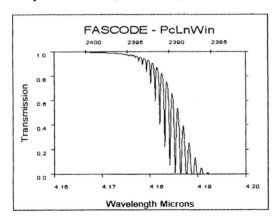

1-km horizontal path at sea level, no aerosols, U.S. standard atmosphere

Figure 6.7 High-resolution atmospheric transmission (courtesy of J. Schroeder, Ontar).

6.4 SCATTERING

The process of scattering is the resultant of photons colliding with atmospheric particles whereby the photon energy is reradiated in all directions. The fraction of the photon's energy extracted and the angular pattern that it is reradiated is a function of the relative atmospheric particle size to that of the incident photon wavelength. Scattering differs from absorption because the radiant energy scattered remains in the form of radiation, but is redistributed from the change in the direction of propagation of the incident radiation. Typical angular scattering patterns are shown in Figure 6.8 (adapted from Waldman and Wootton [3]).

In general, the scattering models are divided into three categories. These categories are based on the relationship between the particle size and the wavelength of the incident photon. These models are the Rayleigh scattering, Mie scattering, and Geometric optics models which will be discussed below. Typical examples of some atmospheric particles are shown in Table 6.2.

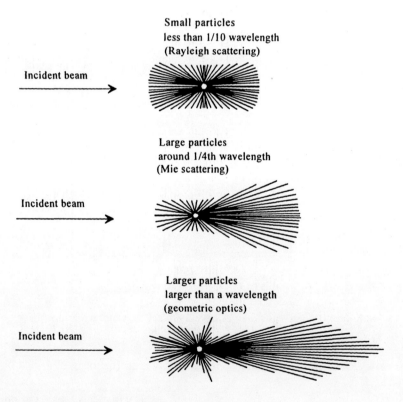

Figure 6.8 Scattering by particles.

The first type of scattering is Raleigh scattering. It is used when the particle radius is approximately less than one-tenth of a wavelength. The scattering coefficient is proportional to λ^{-4}. As shown in Figure 6.8, the angular distribution is symmetrical. It is Rayleigh scattering that leads to the blue color of the sky. The blue wavelengths have a strong scattering interaction with the atmosphere. The blue is scattered in all directions so that the sky appears blue, where the red end of the visible spectrum provides little scattering. The attenuation of light for Rayleigh can be represented by the first order approximation, given by simplification of (6.3)

$$\Phi(x) = \Phi_o e^{-\gamma x} \qquad [W] \qquad (6.9)$$

where only the scattering coefficient γ is considered. The Rayleigh scattering coefficient is given by

$$\gamma = \gamma_r N \qquad [km^{-1}] \qquad (6.10)$$

where γ_r is the Rayleigh scattering cross-section and N is the molecular number density. Examples of the molecular number density are shown in Table 6.2. The Raleigh scattering cross section is given by

$$\gamma_r = \frac{8\pi^3(n^2-1)^2}{3N^2\lambda^4} \qquad [km^2] \qquad (6.11)$$

where n is the index of refraction. Rayleigh scattering dominates more in the ultraviolet and electro-optical wavelengths since the Rayleigh cross section is proportional to λ^{-4}. For a 0.5-μm wavelength and good weather, the Rayleigh scattering coefficient is about 0.0172 km^{-1} [4].

Table 6.2
Atmospheric particles

Particle type	Radius (*µm*)	Density (per *cm³*)
Air molecules (Rayleigh)	10^{-4}	10^{19}
Haze particles (Rayleigh)	10^{-2}-1	10-10^3
Fog droplet (Mie)	1-10	10-100
Raindrops (Geometric)	10^2-10^4	10^{-5}-10^{-2}

The second type of scattering to be discussed is Mie scattering or aerosol scattering. This occurs when the wavelength is approximately the same size as the particle. Detailed Mie theory is based on classical electromagnetic equations with continuity conditions of the boundary between the particles and its surroundings. Most atmospheric models make certain assumptions to simplify the theory. One such assumption is that the atmospheric particles can be represented by simple shapes such as cylinders, ellipsoids, and spheres. It is beyond the scope of this book to derive the details of Mie theory. Instead, a first-order approximation is provided. This type of scattering is concentrated in the forward direction as shown in Figure 6.8. The attenuation given by Mie scattering is of the same form as Raleigh scattering and is expressed by

$$\Phi(x) = \Phi_o e^{-\gamma_m x} \qquad [W] \qquad (6.12)$$

where γ_m is the aerosol attenuation coefficient. The aerosol attenuation coefficient is a function of the aerosol density and is related by

$$\gamma_m(h) = \frac{M(h)}{M(0)} \gamma_m(0) \qquad [km^{-1}] \qquad (6.13)$$

where $M(h)$ denotes the aerosol density at a height h, and $\gamma_m(0)$ is the aerosol coefficient at sea level (density at sea level ~200 cm^{-3}). The aerosol coefficient also varies with wavelength. Several examples of the aerosol attenuation coefficient are given in Table 6.3 [5].

The third type of scattering occurs when the particles are much larger than the wavelength. An example of this scattering type is that of raindrops. For this case, the light is primarily scattered in the forward direction. This case can be approximated with geometrical optics.

Table 6.3
Aerosol attenuation coefficients

Wavelength (μm)	*Aerosol coefficient at sea level*
0.3	0.26
0.4	0.20
0.5	0.167
0.6	0.150
0.7	0.135
0.8	0.127
0.9	0.120

6.5 PATH RADIANCE

Path radiance is the natural emission of radiation by atmospheric particles within a sensor field-of-view. Given a path length between a source and a sensor, the atmospheric particles in this path contribute radiation to the total flux on the detector. To fully describe the flux on the detector, the path radiance must be taken into consideration.

Path radiance can be described in a number of different ways, but the simplest method is to model the particles as blackbodies. If the atmospheric particles are considered a blackbody at a particular temperature $L_{BB}(T_a)$, then the amount of path radiance seen by the sensor is

$$L_{path}(\lambda) = [1 - t_{path}(\lambda)]L_{BB}(T_a) \qquad \text{[W/cm}^2\text{-sr-}\mu\text{m]} \qquad (6.14)$$

where $t_{path}(\lambda)$ is the atmospheric transmission of the path. Given any sensor viewing geometry where the source fills the detector (i.e., the image of the object is larger than the detector), the total flux on the detector can be calculated using an effective total radiance:

$$L_{total}(\lambda) = L_{source}(\lambda)t_{path}(\lambda) + L_{path}(\lambda) \qquad \text{[W/cm}^2\text{-sr-}\mu\text{m]} \qquad (6.15)$$

If the source does not fill the detector and the background contributes flux on the detector, then background radiance must also be added to the total radiance.

There are many arguments on when to include path radiance and when to ignore path radiance. From (6.14), the path radiance becomes small when the path transmission is high. With a large transmission and cold-air particles (compared with the source), the path radiance may be negligible. However, a small path transmission, high air temperature (with respect to source), or both can provide significant path radiance. An additional note is that large path transmission corresponds to small paths, so path radiance may be negligible for short ranges.

6.6 TURBULENCE

Turbulence is a term used to describe time-varying temperature inhomogeneities of the atmosphere. The temperature (and pressure) variations result in index of refraction inhomogeneities. The index of refraction variations cause the direction of light propagation to "bend" in various directions. These directional changes vary with time. Turbulence is responsible for a variety of effects, such as temporal intensity fluctuations (i.e., scintillations). An example of scintillations is the twinkling of the stars (a small source through a large atmospheric path length). Turbulence affects imaging not only by visible sensors but also by infrared sensors. An example of infrared turbulence can be considered when viewing a distant object across a parking lot in the middle of the summer. The sun heats the pavement, causing the air above it to become heated. This heated air is unstable and radiation passing through it deviates from its original path. This phenomenon causes image motion and blurs the image. It is especially noticeable when viewing small, distant objects. It differs from extinction since motion or blurring is not uniform across the image. Overall, extinction affects the entire image in a uniform manner.

As with other sections of this chapter, a complete development of turbulence is out of scope, hence the focus here is on several key parameters. These parameters are defined along the optical path for small-scale atmosphere turbulence. Large-scale atmosphere effects are not generally considered in atmospheric modeling for imaging sensors.

Turbulence consists of time-varying fluctuations that change the localized index of refraction. The fluctuations of the refractive index in the atmosphere can be described by the index structure function:

$$D_n(r) = <(n_1 - n_2)^2> \tag{6.16}$$

where n_1 and n_2 are the indices of refraction at two points separated by a distance r. The notation $< >$ describes the ensemble average. In a similar manner, a temperature structure function is defined by

$$D_T(r) = <(T_1 - T_2)^2> \tag{6.17}$$

where T_1 and T_2 are the temperatures at two points separated by distance r. The Kolmogorov-Obukhov law states that differences in indices and temperatures are proportional to the distance to the two-thirds power:

$$D_n(r) = C_n^2 r^{2/3} \tag{6.18}$$

and

$$D_T(r) = C_T^2 r^{2/3} \tag{6.19}$$

where C_n^2 and C_T^2 are constants called the *index structure parameter* and the *temperature structure parameter*, respectively.

Solving for the temperature structure parameter using (6.17) and (6.19) shows that the temperature structure parameter can be measured directly:

$$C_T^2(r) = \frac{<(T_1-T_2)^2>}{r^{2/3}} \tag{6.20}$$

The two-thirds power rule holds for many cases. It describes the heat transfer between the surface and the atmosphere. The two-thirds power functions are valid for stable conditions (night), neutral conditions (sunrise and sunset), and for some daytime conditions where there is warm air over cold ground (e.g., snow or ice on the ground). For unstable conditions (free convection over hot surfaces during the day), a four-thirds power is more appropriate.

The index structure parameter C_n^2 is related to the temperature structure parameter by

$$C_n^2 = |\frac{\partial n(\lambda)}{\partial T}|^2 C_T^2 \qquad [m^{-2/3}] \qquad (6.21)$$

For dry air and optical wavelengths, (6.21) can be approximated by [6]

$$C_n^2 \approx \left[79x10^{-6}\frac{P}{T}\right]^2 C_T^2 \quad [m^{-2/3}] \qquad (6.22)$$

where P is the atmospheric pressure in millibars and T is the temperature in Kelvin. The index structure parameter ranges from 1×10^{-15} $m^{-2/3}$ for weak turbulence to 5×10^{-14} $m^{-2/3}$ for strong turbulence. Factors that increase the index structure parameter are strong solar heating, very dry grounds, clear nights with little wind, low altitudes, and surface roughness. Factors that provide reductions in the index structure parameter are heavy overcast, wet surfaces, high winds, and high altitudes.

It is useful to estimate C_n^2 as a function of weather conditions. Computer programs such as IMTURB and PROTURB have been developed by the U.S. Army Atmospheric Sciences Lab for these types of estimations. Also, a simple model [7, 8] has been developed using data taken by the U.S. Army Night Vision and Electronic Sensors Directorate. It is based on meteorological parameters and the Talmudic concept of temporal hours.

Talmudic hours are not 60 minutes, but are 1/12th of the time between sunrise and sunset. In the winter, temporal hours are shorter than 60 minutes and in the summer they are longer than 60 minutes. An example is that 3 temporal hours corresponds to 1/4th of the daylight time.

A weighting factor is used in the estimate of C_n^2 and is related to the temporal hour. The weighting factor is given in Table 6.4. A regression model was performed on C_n^2 as a function of this weighting factor, the temperature, relative humidity, and wind speed. Based on the temporal hour and this meteorological data, the index structure parameter in $m^{-2/3}$ can be estimated by

$$\begin{aligned} C_n^2 = {} & 3.8x10^{-14}W + 2.0x10^{-15}T - 2.8x10^{-15}RH + 2.9x10^{-17}RH^2 \\ & -1.1x10^{-19}RH^3 - 2.5x10^{-15}WS + 1.2x10^{-15}WS^2 \\ & -8.5x10^{-17}WS^3 - 5.3x10^{-13} \end{aligned} \qquad (6.23)$$

W is the weight given for the temporal hour in Table 6.4, T is the air temperature in Kelvin, RH is the relative humidity in percent, and WS is the wind speed in meters per second.

Table 6.4
Temporal hour and index structure parameter weight

Event	Temporal hour interval	Relative weight (W)
Night	... until -4	0.11
Night	-4 to -3	0.11
Night	-3 to -2	0.07
Night	-2 to -1	0.08
Night	-1 to 0	0.06
Sunrise	0 to 1	0.05
Day	1 to 2	0.1
Day	2 to 3	0.51
Day	3 to 4	0.75
Day	4 to 5	0.95
Day	5 to 6	1.00
Day	6 to 7	0.9
Day	7 o 8	0.8
Day	8 to 9	0.59
Day	9 to10	0.32
Day	10 to11	0.22
Sunset	11 to 12	0.1
Night	12 to 13	0.08
Night	over 13	0.13

This model has been validated over desert sand as well as vegetation surfaces. It is valid for temperatures of 9 to 23 deg C, relative humidities of 14 to 92%, and wind speeds of up to 10 m/s. The model applies to index structure parameters at heights of up to 15m. For heights that are not near Earth's surface (beyond 15m), C_n^2 can be scaled according to the Tatarski [9] model

$$C_n^2(h) = C_n^2(0)h^{-4/3} \tag{6.24}$$

where h is the height in meters and $C_n^2(0)$ is the ground-based index structure parameter. A modification to this model is provided by Sadot, et al. [8] for cases that include significant aerosol effects.

The affect of turbulence on EO systems is most pronounced for coherent systems (lasers), where the propagation of the optical wavefront is most critical. Strong turbulence also affects incoherent imaging systems by image blurring and smearing with the loss of high-frequency information. The affects of turbulence on imaging through the atmosphere can be characterized by atmospheric modulation transfer functions (MTF). While good progress has been seen in the modeling of atmospheric turbulence, there are no accepted standard turbulence models.

Example

Determine the index structure parameter for mid-day at a temperature of 27 deg C, relative humidity of 40%, and a wind speed of 2 m/s. The solution is determined by using the following parameters in (6.23).

$$W = 1.0$$
$$T = 300 \text{ deg K (27 deg C)}$$
$$RH = 40\%$$
$$WS = 2 \text{ m/s}$$

These parameters give an index structure parameter of 3.5×10^{-14} m$^{-2/3}$.

Example

Determine the index structure parameter for a height of 50m given that the ground-based index structure parameter is 2×10^{-14} m$^{-2/3}$. The solution is determined using the Tatarski model of (6.24)

$$C_n^2(50) = 2 x 10^{-14}(50)^{-4/3} = 1.09 x 10^{-16} m^{-2/3}.$$

Note that the index structure parameter decreases significantly for a height of only 50m.

6.7 ATMOSPHERIC MODULATION TRANSFER FUNCTION

In the previous sections, various atmospheric phenomena have been reviewed that affect the optical radiation. Absorption and scattering can be viewed as a reduction in the amount of radiation that reaches a sensor while scattering and turbulence result in image blurring and loss of detail. The blurring is quantified to describe its overall degradation effect on sensor performance. This degradation is characterized in terms of an atmospheric MTF. Atmospheric MTF can roughly be described as a reduction in contrast as a function of spatial frequency. The atmospheric MTF can be divided into two MTFs: an aerosol MTF and a turbulence MTF. This approach is not exact for atmospheric modeling but provides a first-order approximation. A limitation to this approach exists because MTF theory is based on linear invariant processes. Turbulence is not necessarily uniform across an image but is often assumed so for modeling purposes.

The atmospheric turbulence MTF has two forms depending on the exposure time. For the long-exposure-time case, the MTF is given by

$$MTF_{le}(\xi) = \exp[-57.53\xi^{5/3}C_n^2\lambda^{-1/3}R] \qquad (6.25)$$

where ξ is the spatial frequency in cycles per radian, R is the path length in meters, and λ is the wavelength in meters. If R is given in kilometers, the ξ can be plotted in milliradians. The term short-exposure time is defined by Goodman [10] as the "time required to freeze the atmospheric degradation and thus eliminate the time-averaging effects." This depends on wind velocity but is generally less than 0.01 to 0.001 sec. Short exposure turbulence MTF is given by

$$MTF_{se}(\xi) = \exp\{-57.53\xi^{5/3}C_n^2\lambda^{-1/3}R[1 - \mu(\frac{\lambda\xi}{D})^{1/3}] \qquad (6.26)$$

where μ is 1 for the nearfield and 0.5 for the farfield. D is the sensor's entrance pupil diameter. The nearfield is defined when $D \gg (\lambda R)^{1/2}$ and the farfield when $D \ll (\lambda R)^{1/2}$.

Example

Determine the MTF for a long-exposure-time sensor that operates in the longwave over a horizontal ground path length of 8 km. The atmospheric conditions are such that the index structure parameter is 5×10^{-14} m$^{-2/3}$. The solution is given by the long-exposure MTF of (6.25). Because the sensor is a longwave sensor, a 10-μm wavelength is assumed. The MTF is shown in Figure 6.9. Note that while (6.25) was developed for units of cycles per radian, the MTF of Figure 6.9 has been plotted against cycles per milliradian.

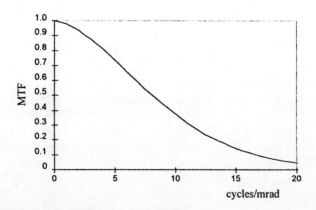

Figure 6.9 Turbulence MTF.

The aerosol MTF is a strong function of sensor FOV, sensitivity, and limiting bandwidth. The aerosol MTF comprises two components: a low spatial frequency function and a high spatial frequency function. The aerosol MTF is approximated [11] by

$$MTF_a(\xi) = \exp[-A_aR - S_aR(\frac{\xi}{\xi_c})^2] \qquad \xi \le \xi_c \qquad (6.27)$$

$$MTF_a(\xi) = \exp[-(A_a + S_a)R] \qquad \xi > \xi_c$$

where ξ_c is the cutoff spatial frequency that is approximately a/λ and a is the particulate radius. A_a is the atmospheric absorption coefficient and S_a is the atmospheric scattering coefficient. These quantities are usually measured, but Sadot and Kopeika [11] have outlined a detailed method for calculating these parameters. Holst [12] states that aerosol contributions to atmospheric MTF are significant when the target radiance scattering approaches the radiance scattering attributed to the background. For small signal targets such as tanks in tactical background scenarios in the infrared, the target scattered signal is small compared with the background scattered signal, and aerosol MTF can be neglected. For significant target scattering such as rocket plume signals against sky backgrounds in electro-optical wavelengths, aerosols must be considered.

6.8 MODELS

An accurate atmospheric transmission calculation requires that all molecular, aerosol, and precipitation effects be taken into account. When exact results are required, such as the design and manufacturing of a sensor system, a detailed model must be used. Three such models are LOWTRAN, FASCODE, and MODTRAN. These models are widely used in both government and private industry. The intent here is to make the reader aware of these models and their basic functionality.

Until recently, LOWTRAN was the most widely used and accepted model for atmospheric transmittance. The original computer code was developed at the Air Force Geophysics Laboratory in Cambridge, Massachusetts. The commercial software was developed by Ontar Corporation. This model was broken down into two components: absorption and scattering. The resolution of the LOWTRAN model in wave numbers ($1/\lambda$) is 20 cm^{-1}. The code calculates transmittance from 0.25 to 28.5 μm. Four example curves generated with LOWTRAN are shown in Figure 6.10. The curves shown are the transmission of a 1-km horizontal atmospheric path length for the climates given. It is readily apparent that water plays a large part in the decrease in longwave infrared transmission. In the cooler climates, the absolute humidity is much lower, so the water absorption is less. In the warmer climates, the air can hold more gaseous water, so the transmission is less. The water does not affect the visible or midwave as much as it does the longwave. This can be verified in LOWTRAN with the water absorption values.

Also, note that the three sensor bands addressed in this text (electro-optical, midwave, and longwave) have atmospheric windows where the transmission is good. Also, longer path lengths (e.g., 10 km) produce a much more severe transmission curve.

MODTRAN is currently the most widely used and accepted model for atmospheric transmittance. It evolved from LOWTRAN and computes both transmission and radiance at 2-cm^{-1} wavenumber resolution. An example of MODTRAN transmission is shown in Figure 6.11. The transmission shown is for a 1-km horizontal path at sea level. FASCODE is a line-by-line model that computes the transmission of each absorption line using the spectroscopic parameters in the HITRAN database. MODTRAN uses a two-parameter band model, derived from HITRAN, as its database of absorption parameters. Both models have the capability to handle arbitrary geometries and view conditions, and allow the user to select from several model atmospheres, aerosol profiles, and other weather conditions.

The commercial versions of MODTRAN and FASCODE are available from the Ontar Corporation (www.Ontar.com). More information about the HITRAN database can be obtained from their web site www.HITRAN.com.

6.9 DISCUSSION

To determine an exact amount of radiation originating from an object and propagating to the sensor detector (i.e., less path radiance and background radiance), one must consider the atmospheric transmission as a function of wavelength. The radiation received by the detector within a sensor can be expressed by

$$P_{sensor} = \int_{\lambda_1}^{\lambda_2} \frac{M_{source}(\lambda)}{\pi} A_{source} \Omega_{sensor} \tau_{atm}(\lambda) \tau_{sensor}(\lambda) d\lambda \qquad (6.28)$$

where

$\frac{M_{source}(\lambda)}{\pi}$ = the source (Lambertian) radiance in W/cm^2-sr-um,

A_{source} = the source area seen within the sensor field-of-view in cm^2,

Ω_{sensor} = the solid angle of the sensor entrance pupil as seen by the source in sr,

$\tau_{atm}(\lambda)$ = the transmission of the atmosphere between the source and the sensor, and

$\tau_{sensor}(\lambda)$ = the transmission of the sensor optical path (transmission is unitless).

Once the wavelength integration of the object radiance, atmospheric transmission, and sensor transmission is performed, there is no method to separate source distribution and atmospheric transmission. There are two exceptions: (1) the source exitance is constant within the spectral band, or (2) the atmospheric transmission is constant over the spectral band.

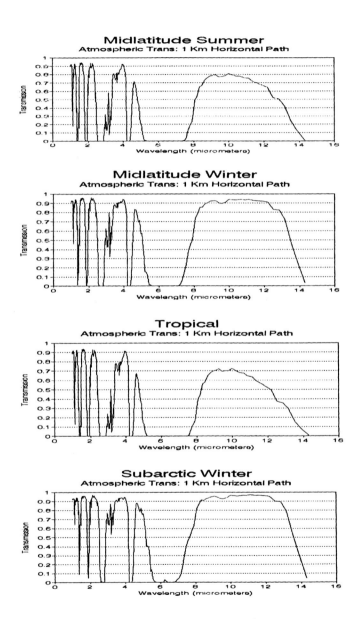

Figure 6.10 LOWTRAN transmission curves.

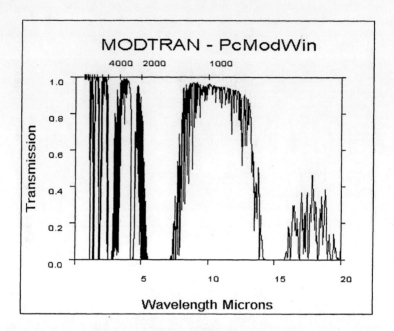

Figure 6.11 MODTRAN results (Courtesy of J. Schroeder, Ontar Corp.).

A common, but incorrect, practice is to perform a band transmission measurement of the atmosphere by viewing a near-blackbody source and then to view a distant blackbody source with a broadband sensor that matches the band of interest. The blackbodies are both at the same temperature to provide a similar signal and the collection geometries are accounted for. The ratio of the near power to the distant power is considered the average atmospheric band transmission. Even assuming the sensor transmission is constant and taking the constants outside the (6.28) integral, this approximation gives

$$\tau_{band} = \frac{c_1 \int_{\lambda_1}^{\lambda_2} M(\lambda) t_{atm}(\lambda) d\lambda}{c_2 \int_{\lambda_1}^{\lambda_2} M(\lambda) d\lambda} \tag{6.29}$$

This measurement gives a weighted transmission that is source dependent. An average transmission that is independent of source distribution cannot be taken from (6.29). However, the assumption that source distribution is relatively constant for low-temperature blackbody sources over the 8- to 12-μm spectral band has been known to give some reasonable error bounds. This is not the case for EO sources and 3- to 5-μm sensor bands.

A second method for determining average band transmission has become popular with the spectral radiometer. The spectral radiometer measures the power on the detector (i.e., equation 6.28) in fine spectral slices such that the ratio of the near- and far-detector responses can be normalized over wavelength to give $\tau_{atm}(\lambda)$. The average band transmission is then computed

$$\tau_{band} = \frac{1}{\lambda_2 - \lambda_1} \int_{\lambda_1}^{\lambda_2} \tau_{atm}(\lambda) d\lambda \qquad (6.30)$$

While this technique gives a non-source-weighted atmospheric transmission over a band of interest, it still does not describe the detector response through the atmosphere for a given source. Again, (6.28) describes the detector response that is a function of a spectral atmospheric transmission and source-radiance product. This response is not equal to the average source radiance and average atmospheric transmission product.

Now that average atmospheric band transmission quantities have been presented in a negative light, it is time to realize that we do not live in a perfect world. One does not always have the luxury of working with spectral quantities and instruments for spectral measurements are not always available. It is a good idea when it is necessary to work with average values to quantify the errors associated with particular assumptions. While the above approximations may provide acceptable errors in the longwave infrared band, they may not in the electro-optical and midwave infrared bands. Either way, quantification of error bounds is always a good sanity check.

Atmospheric transmission is the subject of many research projects and our knowledge is continually becoming more refined. MODTRAN, LOWTRAN, and other models are being updated frequently to account for more atmospheric phenomena. The data presented in this chapter are only a brief introduction to the issues of atmospheric transmission applied to I^2R and EO systems. While simple models are useful for back-of-the-envelope analyses, more exact system responses can be accomplished with sophisticated computer models.

EXERCISES

6.1 A CO_2 laser (10.6 μm) provides a peak intensity of 10 W/sr and is directed towards a detector 1 km away. Provide a rough estimate of the laser irradiance on the detector on a typical day (use Figure 6.2).

6.2 A particular atmospheric extinction coefficient for a given wavelength is 3.2 per kilometer. Calculate the transmission for a 4-km path length.

6.3 Determine the dominant absorption component of light with a (i) 4.2-μm wavelength, 6-μm wavelength, and 9-μm wavelength.

6.4 Determine the most sensitive wavelength of light for a material with a strong bandgap energy of 0.1 eV.

6.5 Describe the type of scattering pattern caused by fog droplets for (i) a He-Ne laser at 0.6328 μm, (ii) an Nd:YAG laser at 1.06 μm, and (iii) a CO_2 laser at 10.6 μm.

6.6 Calculate the temperature structure parameter for a 10 deg K differential temperature between a 2m vertical path length.

6.7 Calculate the index structure parameter for a typical desert day using the temperature structure parameter found in Exercise 6.6.

6.8 Determine the index structure parameter for a cool midnight with a temperature of 15 deg C, a relative humidity of 30%, and calm (negligible) winds.

6.9 Determine the ground-based index structure parameter given that the index structure parameter at a 25m height above the ground is 4.0×10^{-16} $m^{-2/3}$

6.10 A longwave infrared system (10-μm average wavelength) is operating in a farfield, long-exposure scenario. The ground-based index structure parameter is estimated to be 1×10^{-15}. The sensor is at an altitude of 25m and is viewing a target that is 5 km away in a horizontal direction. Determine the long-exposure turbulence MTF of the system. Determine the MTF for EO and midwave I^2R systems in the same conditions.

REFERENCES

[1] Neilburger, Edinger, and Bonner, *Understanding Our Atmospheric Environment,* W.H. Freedman, pp. 36-41, 1982.

[2] Streetman, B., *Solid State Electronic Devices,* New York, NY: Prentice-Hall, 1980.

[3] Waldman, G., and J. Wootton, *Electro-Optical Systems Performance Modeling,* Norwood, MA: Artech House, 1993.

[4] Seyrafi, K., and S. Hovanessian, *Introduction to Electro-Optical Imaging and Tracking Systems,* Norwood, MA: Artech House, p. 79, 1993.

[5] Seyrafi, K., and S. Hovanessian, *Introduction to Electro-Optical Imaging and Tracking Systems,* Norwood, MA: Artech House, p. 80, 1993.

[6] Military Handbook, *Quantitative Description of Obscuration Factors for Electro-Optical and Millimeter Wave Systems Metric,* DOD-HDBK-178(ER), pp. 2-11, 1986.

[7] Sadot, D., S. Shamriz, I. Dror, and N. Kopeika, "Prediction of Overall Atmospheric Modulation Transfer Function With Standard Weather Parameters: Comparison With Measurements With Two Imaging Systems," *Optical Engineering*, Vol. 34, No. 11, Nov. 1995.

[8] Sadot, D., and N. Kopeika, "Forecasting Optical Turbulence Strength on the Basis of Macroscale Meteorology and Aerosols: Models and Validation," *Optical Engineering*, Vol 31, No. 2, p. 200, Feb. 1992.

[9] Tatarski, V., *Wave Propagation in Turbulent Medium*, New York: McGraw-Hill, 1961.

[10] Goodman, J., *Statistical Optics*, New York: Wiley, 1985.

[11] Sadot, D., and N. Kopeika, "Imaging Through the Atmosphere: Practical Instrumentation-Based Theory and Verification of Aerosol Modulation Transfer Function," *Journal of the Optical Society of America A*, Vol. 10, No. 1, p. 1017, Jan. 1993.

[12] Holst, G., *Electro-Optical Imaging System Performance*, Orlando, FL: JCD Publishing, 1996.

[13] Lenoble, J., *Atmospheric Radiative Transfer*, Deepak Publications, 1993.

[14] *LOWTRAN Manual*, Ontar Corp, North Andover, MA.

Chapter 7

Optics

The optics of an I²R or EO system collect radiation from a scene and project an image of the scene onto the system detector array. In the design of the optics, it is important to understand the limitations that optical components introduce in the overall system parameters. Among the parameters that the optics define are spatial and spectral properties of the sensor system, resolution, and field of view (FOV). While the optics play a key role in defining these variables, other sensor system components, such as detector array characteristics, also have a strong system influence.

There are four basic goals in the design of an optical system. The first goal is to maximize overall system performance. The second is to maximize the resolving power for the desired task while maintaining good area coverage. The third goal is to maximize the amount of image flux that is collected, and the fourth goal is to minimize system complexity and weight. We focus here on the first two goals.

The effects of the optics (Figure 7.1) on overall system performance can be described by (1) the diffraction effects associated with the optics, (2) the geometric blur caused by imperfect imaging lenses, and (3) the amount of signal collected by the optical system. Before discussing these effects, we provide some background material on the interaction of light and glass.

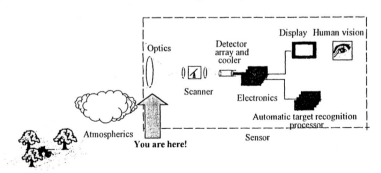

Figure 7.1 Optics in the sensor system.

7.1 LIGHT REPRESENTATION AND THE OPTICAL PATH LENGTH

In the analysis of optical systems, one must consider how to represent light at each stage of the analysis process. There are three primary methods, each with its own attributes. The first concept of light is that it is made up of a stream of photons. Each photon has an energy [1]:

$$E = h\nu \qquad (7.1)$$

where E is the energy in Joules of the photon, h is Planck's constant of 6.6252×10^{-34} Joule-seconds, and ν is the frequency of the light in Hertz. This representation is convenient in discussions where light interacts with a material such at the detector material.

The second representation of light is that of an electromagnetic wave that is written as

$$E = E_o \sin(\omega t - kz) \qquad (7.2)$$

where E_o is the wave amplitude, ω is the angular frequency, t is time, k is the propagation constant of $2\pi/\lambda$, and z is distance. Here, the light is referred to as a traveling wave because it is a function of both time and space. The wave nature of light is very different from the particle or photon nature of light, just as the molecular properties of water are different from the wave characteristics of ocean water at the beach. In fact, we can calculate the approximate number of water molecules in a beach wave, and it has been argued how many photons actually make up a wave of light.

The third representation of light is through the use of rays, as shown in Figure 7.2.

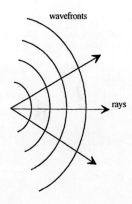

Figure 7.2 Light rays.

Rays are defined as lines in the direction of propagation that are everywhere perpendicular to the wavefronts. Rays depict light as traveling in straight lines and allow optical systems to be analyzed with simple techniques in a field called geometric optics. These three treatments of light have been summed up by Saleh and Teich [2] as "The theory of quantum optics provides an explanation of virtually all optical phenomenon. The electromagnetic theory of light provides the complete treatment within the confines of classical optics.... Ray optics is the limit of wave optics when the wavelength is short."

One of the laws that govern the propagation of light is known as Fermat's principle. Fermat's principle, or the Principle of Least Time, states that "a light ray extending from one point to another will, after any number of reflections and refractions follow the path requiring the least transit time [3]." Consider the ray in Figure 7.3.

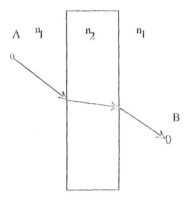

Figure 7.3   Optical path.

The path of the ray is not the path of least distance if more than one medium is involved. The speed of light in a material is c/n, where c is the speed of light in a vacuum and n is the material's index-of-refraction (or refractive index). Fermat's principle can be restated in terms of an *optical path length* (OPL)

$$OPL = \int_A^B n(x)dx \qquad (7.3)$$

The refractive index is given as a function of position along the path. It can be shown that Fermat's principle corresponds to the path with the smallest OPL.

7.2 REFLECTION AND SNELL'S LAW OF REFRACTION

When a ray of light strikes a boundary of two dissimilar, transparent surfaces, it is divided into two components. One component is transmitted into the second medium, and the other is reflected from the boundary surface. A diagram of this is shown in Figure 7.4.

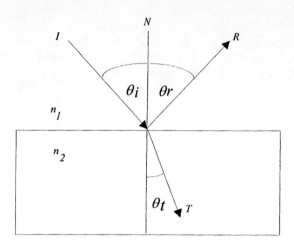

Figure 7.4 Reflection and refraction at an interface.

I is the incident light ray, R is the reflected light ray, and T is the transmitted light ray. N is the normal to the boundary surface, n_1 is the index of refraction of medium 1, and n_2 is the index of refraction in medium 2. θ_i is the angle of incidence light, θ_r is the angle of reflected light, and θ_t is the angle of transmitted light. These angles are defined as the angle between each ray and the normal to the surface. In the case shown, $n_2 > n_1$. The law of reflection is stated as follows [4]: The reflected ray lies in the plane of incidence, and the angle of reflection equals the angle of incidence. From the variables defined in the figure above, the law of reflection states

$$\theta_r = \theta_i \qquad (7.4)$$

The law of refraction, also known as Snell's law, is defined [5] as: The refracted ray lies in the plane of incidence, and the sine of the angle of refraction bears a constant ratio to the sine of the angle of incidence. This means that when light passes from one medium to another, the speed of the light as well as the propagation direction changes. The change is the ratio of the speed of light in one medium to the speed of light in the other medium. This ratio is defined as the index of refraction. That is:

$$n_1 \sin \theta_i = n_2 \sin \theta_t \qquad (7.5)$$

The index of refraction of a vacuum is 1 and ordinary air has an index of refraction of approximately 1.0003. Refractive indices given in glass catalogs are usually with respect to air, so vacuum calculations in lens design codes use 1/1.0003 as the refractive index of the vacuum. The index of refraction of a material is also a function of wavelength, but correction can be applied in the design of an imaging system to minimize spectral variation over a wavelength band of interest. Typical window glass has a refractive index of 1.5, whereas water has a refractive index of around 1.33.

7.3 GAUSS'S EQUATION

Ray analysis and *geometrical optics* are analogous. They are first-order analyses based on the geometric refraction of light with glass. The analyses often contain the thin-lens approximation where lenses are simplified to perfect imaging devices. This simplification is performed by ignoring the aberrations and diffraction. One of the more common first-order analysis tools is Gauss's [6] thin-lens equation.

$$\frac{1}{o} + \frac{1}{f} = \frac{1}{i} \qquad (7.6)$$

The sign convention for this equation is as follows. o is the distance from the lens to the object, i is the distance from the lens to the image, and f is the lens focal length that can be positive or negative. o or i to the left of the lens is negative and o or i to the right of the lens is positive. Remember the convention that light waves move from left to right across the analysis page.

The lenses may be represented in many ways as illustrated in Figure 7.5. The positive and negative lens types are given along with their representations. The single focal-length actions of the lenses are also shown. For the cases shown, the light is assumed to traverse from left to right. Parallel rays, or collimated light, entering a positive lens from the left will focus to a point at one focal length to the right of the lens. A point source located one focal length to the left of a positive lens will produce collimated light to the right of the lens. For negative lenses, collimated light entering the lens from the left will diverge as if the light had originated from a point located one focal length to the left of the lens. Light coming to a focus one focal length to the right of the lens, results in collimated light in the space to the right of the negative lens.

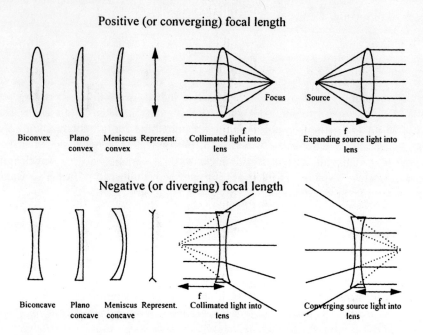

Figure 7.5 Lens nomenclature and representations.

Example

Gauss's equation can be demonstrated in the example of Figure 7.6. An object is placed 10 cm to the left of a 5 cm focal-length lens. From (7.6), the image location is determined to be 10 cm.

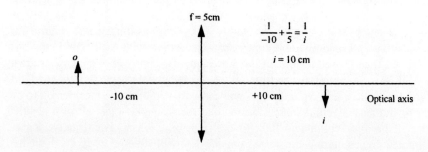

Figure 7.6 Example of Gauss's equation.

This configuration is known as a 2f-2f, unity magnification system. If an object is placed two focal lengths to the left of a positive thin lens, the image is located at two focal lengths to the right of the lens.

The transverse, or lateral, magnification of a lens system is defined as the image distance over the object distance

$$M_T = \frac{i}{o} \qquad (7.7)$$

In the previous example, $M_T = \frac{10}{-10} = -1$. The image is the same size as the object, but the image is inverted and reverted (i.e., top is down and left is right). Note that the arrow representing the image is pointing downward to show the inversion.

Example

Another example is given in Figure 7.7. An object is placed 30 cm from a thin lens of focal length 20 cm. Determine the transverse magnification.

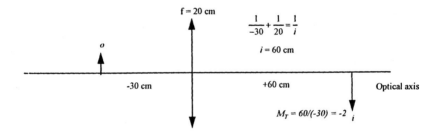

Figure 7.7 Magnification example.

Again, Gauss's equation is used to determine that the image is located 60 cm to the right of the lens. The transverse magnification gives an inverted image that is twice as large as the object.

Example

A virtual image occurs when the object is inside the first focal length of a lens. Consider Figure 7.8. An object 4 cm in height is placed in front of a 20-cm focal length lens by 16.7 cm. Determine the size and location of the image.

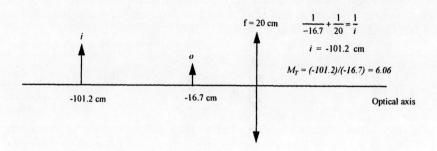

Figure 7.8 Virtual image example.

The size of the virtual image is 6.06 x 4 cm, or 24.2 cm high. Virtual images cannot provide image flux onto film or a detector without other imaging optics. However, one may view a virtual image through the right side of the lens. For the right side of the lens shown in Figure 7.8, the image would appear at the given image position and 24.2 cm in size.

　　　　Finally, we discuss negative lenses (lenses that are generally thinner in the center than on the periphery). Negative lenses alone cannot provide a real image (images that can be formed on a physical surface) of an object, only a virtual image. However, real images can be formed with a combination of positive and negative lenses (if the composite is considered and the object distance is greater than the total focal length).

Example

Consider Figure 7.9. An object 5 cm in height is placed 33.3 cm from a diverging lens of focal length -12.5 centimeters. Calculate the position and size of the image.

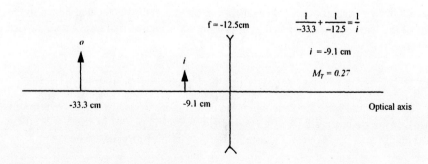

Figure 7.9 Negative lens example.

Sometimes lenses are specified by optical power rather than by their focal length. The power of a lens is simply $1/f$. If the focal length is given in meters, the power of a lens is specified in diopters, which is the same as 1/meters. This specification is common for eyeglass lenses. The use of diopters is limited in other applications.

7.4 VERGENCE

Recall that the convention for the direction of light propagation (on paper) is from left to right. Consider the three cases shown in Figure 7.10 where this convention holds true. The first case is an expanding beam that is diverging from a point source of light. The second case is light that is neither converging nor diverging, but propagates as *collimated* light. The third case is a beam that is coming to a focus at a point. All these cases can be described with the analytical technique known as *vergence* [7].

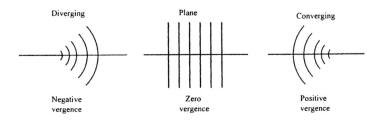

Figure 7.10 Examples of vergence.

The curvature of the light wavefront is inversely proportional to the length of the wavefront radius:

$$C \propto \frac{1}{R} \qquad (7.8)$$

Vergence can be thought of as wavefront curvature, with a modification for the medium refractive index:

$$V \equiv \frac{n}{R} \qquad (7.9)$$

Usually, units of vergence are in 1/meters or diopters. Some simple rules govern the vergence sign convention:

1. Light travels from left to right.
2. All distances are measured from a reference surface (where vergence is calculated).
3. Distances to the left of the reference surface are negative and distances to the right are positive.
4. The radius of curvature is measured from a wavefront to the center of curvature:
   (i) Radii to the left are negative.
   (ii) Radii to the right are positive.
   (iii) Plane waves give zero vergence.

Example

An example here is appropriate, so consider the point source shown in Figure 7.11. Determine the vergence of light 2m from a point source. The reference is the location at which vergence is calculated (shown by the dotted line). The radius is to the left of the wavefront, so it is negative.

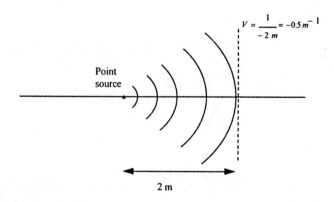

$$V = \frac{1}{-2\,m} = -0.5\,m^{-1}$$

Point source

2 m

Figure 7.11 Vergence example.

Example

A second vergence example shows (in Figure 7.12) the positive vergence that results in a focus. Determine the vergence of light 8 cm before the light comes to a focus in air. The vergence is high for high curvature. That is, the vergence becomes higher as the position nears the point source or focus position. Vergence is a function of location, and not a parameter of the system.

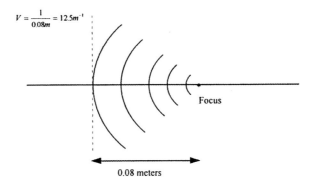

Figure 7.12 Converging example.

To determine the change in vergence from one plane to another without the requirement of a point source or focus position, we derive a vergence propagation relationship. Consider the vergence positions shown in Figure 7.13.

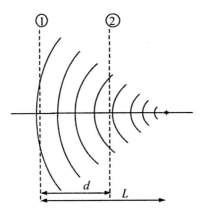

Figure 7.13 Vergence propagation.

We know that V_1 (the vergence at plane 1) corresponds to a focus at a distance, L.

$$V_1 = \frac{n}{L} \tag{7.10}$$

The same type of relationship can be written for the vergence at plane 2, where the focus is d closer to the wavefront at plane 2 than the wavefront at plane 1.

$$V_2 = \frac{n}{L-d} \tag{7.11}$$

With the substitution of (7.11) into (7.10)

$$V_2 = \frac{n}{(\frac{n}{V_1})-d} = \frac{V_1}{1-V_1(\frac{d}{n})} \tag{7.12}$$

(7.12) is known as the *vergence propagation* equation. Consider the example of an expanding wavefront propagating through water ($n = 1.33$). The known wavefront has a vergence of -0.5 diopters. We are interested in the vergence of the light 10m away from the known wavefront. Using (7.12), we can compute the new position vergence to be -0.0105 diopters.

The next property associated with vergence is one of surface or lens interaction. The power of a surface or lens is simply added to the input vergence to obtain an output vergence:

$$V' = V + \beta \tag{7.13}$$

where V is the input vergence, V' is the output vergence, and β is the surface or lens power. The power of the curved surface shown in Figure 7.14 is $(n_2 - n_1)/R$.

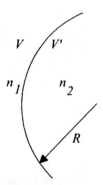

Figure 7.14 Vergence and surface power.

Recall that the power of a thin lens is the inverse of the lens focal length. The Lensmakers formula [8] allows one to find the focal length and power of a lens using the lens curvatures and indices:

$$\beta = \frac{1}{f} = (n_l - n_m)(\frac{1}{R_1} - \frac{1}{R_2}) \tag{7.14}$$

where n_l is the refractive index of the lens, n_m is the refractive index of the medium surrounding the lens, and R_1 and R_2 are the curvatures of the lens surfaces (center of curvature to the right is positive and to the left is negative). For a biconvex lens surrounded by air, $R=R_1=- R_2$ and if $n_m=1$, then

$$\beta = (n_l - 1)\frac{2}{R} \qquad (7.15)$$

Consider the case of the single 2f-2f example given in Figure 7.6. The vergence corresponding to the object light just to the left of the lens is $V_1 = \frac{1}{-0.10} = -10$ diopeters. The lens has a power of $\beta = 1/f = \frac{1}{0.05} = 20$ diopters. The vergence to the right of the lens is the vergence to the left added to the lens power or $V_1' = -10 + 20 = 10$ diopters. The image length is located where the vergence is zero (center of curvature) at $i = \frac{1}{V_1'} = 0.1$ m or 10 cm.

The transverse magnification can be derived for vergence using (7.7). Simply using the image distance over the object distance, it can be shown that

$$M_t = \frac{V}{V'} \qquad (7.16)$$

Again, the size of the image is given by the transverse magnification times the size of the object.

7.5 MULTIPLE-LENS SYSTEMS

For multiple-lens systems, each lens is considered separately, and the system is worked from left to right (again, assuming that the light path is from left to right). The principles are the same as those presented in the previous sections. To illustrate the concepts, we will work a multiple-lens system first using vergence and then using Gauss's equation. Consider the multiple-lens system shown in Figure 7.15, where the system is imaging a scene very far away (i.e., the object distance is infinity).

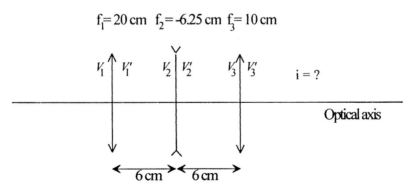

Figure 7.15 Multiple-lens system.

We are interested in the position of the system image. First, we know that the vergence to the left of the first lens, V_1, is $\frac{1}{-\infty} = 0$. In other words, the scene lies far enough away from the input aperture of the optical system that the input wavefronts can be considered plane waves. Next, we can compute the vergence to the right of the first lens:

$$V_1' = V_1 + \beta_1 = 0 + \frac{1}{0.20m} = 5 \text{ diopters} \tag{7.17}$$

The vergence to the right side of the first lens is then propagated to the left side of the second lens

$$V_2 = \frac{V_1'}{1 - V_1'(\frac{d}{n})} = \frac{5}{1 - 5(\frac{0.06}{1})} = 7.14 \text{ diopters} \tag{7.18}$$

Again, the power of the second lens is added to V_2 to yield a vergence to the right of the second lens, $V_2' = V_2 + \beta_2 = 7.14 + \frac{1}{-0.0625m} = -8.86$ diopters. In the same manner, V_3 is found to be -5.78 diopters by using the propagation equation for the 6 centimeter distance. V_3' is found to be 4.22 diopters by adding the power of the third lens to V_3. Finally, the image distance (from the right of the third lens) is found

$$i = \frac{1}{V_3'} = \frac{1}{4.22m^{-1}} = 0.237m = 23.7cm \tag{7.19}$$

Note that the light to the right side of the first lens is converging and corresponds to a positive vergence. Once the light passes the second lens, the light diverges until it passes the third lens. The light is then refocused to a converging beam.

The same problem can be worked using Gauss's equation. Each lens is considered a separate imaging system. We take the first lens as the first imaging system with an object distance of $o_1 = -\infty$. We can now find the location of the image from the first lens

$$\frac{1}{-\infty} + \frac{1}{20} = \frac{1}{i_1} \tag{7.20}$$

where the units are consistent in centimeters. The image distance of the first lens is found to be 20 cm to the right of the first lens, $i_1 = 20$ cm. If all other optical lenses were removed, a single real image would occur at this position. Because it is a real image, it can be viewed on a screen or detector array.

The image of the first lens now becomes the object of the second lens: $o_2 = i_1$. Be careful here because the second lens is not located at the same position as that of the first lens. The second lens is 6 cm to the right of the first lens, so i_1 is really 14 cm to the right of the second lens. That is, $o_2 = 20 - 6 = 14$ cm. The image of the second lens can now be found:

$$\frac{1}{14} + \frac{1}{-6.25} = \frac{1}{i_2} \tag{7.21}$$

The second image distance is found to be -11.29 cm, or 11.29 cm to the left of the second lens. Note that this image is virtual and can only be viewed through the second lens. The second image is also the object of the third lens (shifted, of course). Because the second image distance is 11.29 cm to the left of the second lens, and the third lens is 6 cm to the right of the second lens, $o_3 = -11.29 - 6.0 = -17.29$. The third and final image can now be found:

$$\frac{1}{-17.29} + \frac{1}{10} = \frac{1}{i_3} \tag{7.22}$$

where i_3 is 23.7 cm. This is the same result that was found using the vergence technique.

For multiple-lens systems, there is a corresponding transverse magnification that describes the effect of all lenses. The overall transverse magnification is simply the product of the individual lens magnifications:

$$M_{total} = M_1 M_2 M_3 \ldots \tag{7.23}$$

This quantity does not provide a useful value for the system in the above example, because the first object distance is infinite. However, it does apply to the second and third lenses. That is, the product of the two magnifications can describe the ratio of the first image size to the last image size. For systems like the one given, it is often described by the FOV. Also, for collimated (infinite object distance) input to the lens, these systems have an "effective" focal length, or single lens equivalent.

7.6 FIELD-OF-VIEW

The FOV of an I²R or EO system is one of the most important design parameters. It is the parameter that describes the angular space in which the system accepts light. The system FOV is specified because many systems image objects at great distances, so the transverse magnification would be extremely small. The system FOV and the distance, or *range*, from the sensor to the object determine the area that a system will image. Consider the optical system in Figure 7.16.

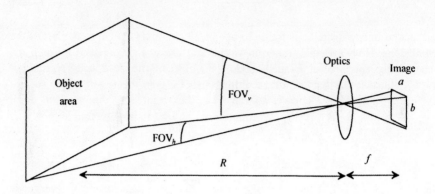

Figure 7.16 Field-of-view.

For the system shown, FOV_h and FOV_v are the horizontal and vertical FOVs, respectively. For systems that view objects at a range R much larger than the focal length f, the FOVs are the arctangents of the image size divided by the focal length:

$$FOV_h = 2\tan^{-1}\frac{a}{2f} \quad \text{and} \quad FOV_v = 2\tan^{-1}\frac{b}{2f} \tag{7.24}$$

For small angles, the FOVs can be estimated as a/f and b/f. Then, the side lengths of the object area are simply FOV_hR and FOV_vR.

The image size is bounded by a *field stop*. The field stop is located in an image plane (or an intermediate image plane) and is specified by a and b. The light-sensitive material is limited to the area inside the field stop, so the field stop can be merely like a frame (like a picture frame). This is usually the case for film-based sensors. Sometimes the field stop is placed in an intermediate (not the final) image plane. However, I²R and EO systems exploit light with detectors. The detectors take the form of a two-dimensional array of individual detectors called a *staring array* or a single detector or rows of detectors that are scanned across the image space. In these cases, the size of the image plane is defined by the light-sensitive area of the array and the possible light-sensitive positions of the scanned systems. A field stop larger than the detector array size would not limit the FOV and hence would not be required.

The optics of a system usually comprises of a number of lenses with a single *effective focal length* (sometimes shortened to just *focal length*). This is the equivalent focal length of the system that, given the true field stop or detector array size, yields the correct FOV. For example, a system has a 35 mrad (horizontal) by 35 mrad (vertical) FOV and uses a 512 by 512 detector array where each side of the detector array is 1 cm long. The optical system may have five lenses in the optical train, but the effective focal length is 28.6 cm.

To calculate the effective focal length for a multiple-lens system, one needs the field stop size (or detector specifics) and the FOV. The FOV can be computed by using the field stop (or detector) as an object and working its images back through the optical system (the reverse of the technique given in Section 7.6). This process is employed to the point of the last lens (just before leaving the sensor). The angle created by the image size of the field stop before the last lens and the last lens focal length gives the FOV. Consider the two-lens example given in Figure 7.17.

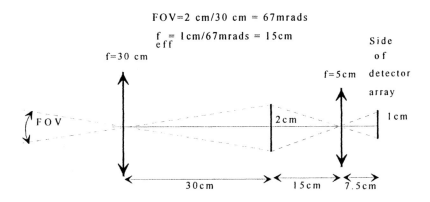

Figure 7.17 Effective focal length example.

The system has two lenses: a 30-cm objective lens and a 5-cm demagnifier (relay lens). The FOV is computed only for one direction to illustrate the concept. We are interested in the effective focal length of the entire system. First, we find the image of the detector array to be located 15 cm from the lens using the material presented earlier. The magnification of the detector array by the 5-cm focal length lens is *15 cm/7.5 cm = 2*. So now the detector image is 2 cm in height. The FOV of the system is this detector image divided by the 30-cm focal length of the objective lens, which is equal to 0.067 rad, or 67 mrads. Finally, the actual detector array size divided by the FOV gives the effective focal length of 15 cm. The effective focal length is used frequently because a detector can be replaced with a different-size detector and the new FOV can be quickly computed.

Now we discuss the design nature of the FOV. A large, or wide, FOV allows the sensor to view a larger area, but the detector elements are spread over this larger area yielding lower resolution (i.e., image fidelity). A narrow FOV gives better resolution, but it is difficult to find objects of interest over a large area. Many military applications require the sensor to have two FOVs. The first is a medium FOV for finding, or detecting, objects of interest, and the second is a narrow FOV that can be used to interrogate potential targets. For tactical systems, large FOVs are about 10 deg and up, medium FOVs are around 5 deg, and narrow FOVs are less than 3 deg.

The tradeoffs for system FOV include sensor resolution, sensitivity, and area coverage. The optics and detectors are designed to provide sufficient resolution and sensitivity for a given task. Overall sensor performance is evaluated to accomplish discrimination of a particular target, and finally the largest possible FOV is selected that still allows the required target discrimination. Chapters 11, 12, and 13 cover the procedure for accomplishing both discrimination performance and FOV selection.

7.7 RESOLUTION

The concept of diffraction was presented in Chapter 4, so we know that a lens cannot provide a perfect image of point source. Even for perfect lenses with no aberrations (imaging imperfections caused by refraction or reflection), the images of point objects are not points but are optical psf. With or without aberrations, there is an ultimate resolving limitation for a lens or optical system. The resolution of a lens or optical system can be specified by either Raleigh's criterion or Sparrow's criterion [9].

If we consider the geometrical optics representation, the light is characterized as traveling in straight lines. The ray representation of light from an ideal point source at infinity and imaged by a lens is shown in Figure 7.18.

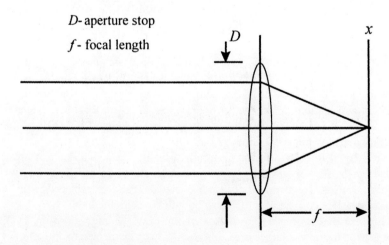

Figure 7.18 Perfect point imaging system.

From the approach of a perfect imaging system, the point source would be focused to an ideal point and hence would produce infinite resolution. For real world systems, however, this is not the case. The actual size of the imaged point source is determined by three contributions: (1) diffraction, (2) aberrations, and (3) manufacturing defects and assembly tolerances. The actual image of a point source by a real system is often referred to as a *blur circle*. For many optical systems, diffraction produces the primary constraint on resolution because aberrations and manufacturing defects can be minimized by good optical design and tight manufacturing tolerances or alignment procedures. Figure 7.19 shows an illustration of the relative intensity across the space of an imaged point.

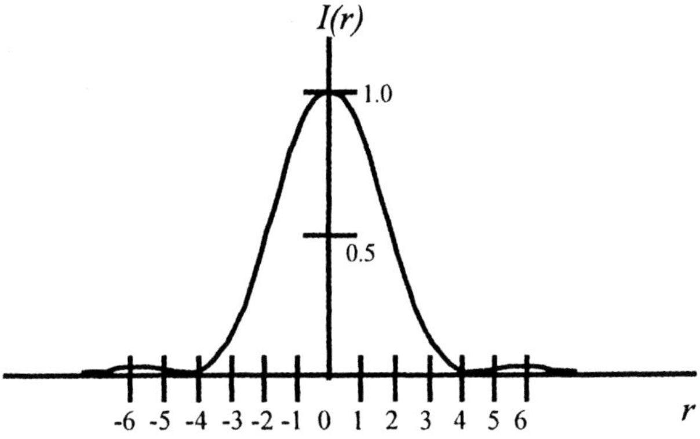

Figure 7.19 Cross-section of imaged point intensity.

The normalized intensity profile of a point source image for a diffraction-limited optical system is given by [10]

$$I(r) = somb^2(\frac{Dr}{f\lambda}) \qquad (7.25)$$

where r is the axial distance from the peak, D is the lens diameter, f is the focal length of the lens, and λ is the wavelength. This function is the psf of the optics where the *somb* function is defined in Chapter 2.

Given that a point source is not imaged as a perfect point but is spread out in the image plane, we want to be able to define just how well an optical system can resolve objects that are placed very close together. In other words, what is the spatial resolution of the sensor system? Consider two separate, adjacent, equal-intensity point sources that are imaged very close together, as shown in the Figure 7.20.

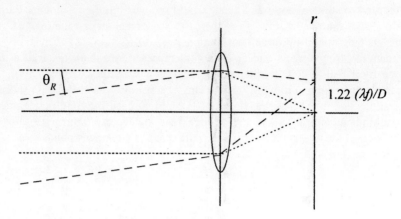

Figure 7.20 System imaging two point sources.

We know that each point source is not focused to a perfect point, but spread out. A sample profile of two closely spaced point sources in the image plane is shown in Figure 7.21.

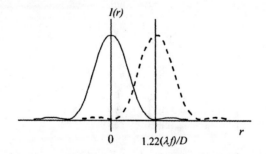

Figure 7.21 Intensity of two point images just resolved by Rayleigh limit.

The Rayleigh resolution limit defines two point sources as just resolved when the peak of one point source image coincides with the first zero of the second point source image. This distance is defined mathematically by

$$r_R = 1.22\frac{\lambda f}{D}$$ (7.26)

where r_R is the distance in meters at the image plane. The Rayleigh criterion is given by

$$\theta_R = \frac{1.22\lambda}{D}$$ (7.27)

where θ_R is the angular distance between perfect point sources at an infinite distance from the lens. Note that the Rayleigh criterion is not a mathematical law but a rule of thumb, though it is very commonly used to define the diffraction-limited resolution of an optical sensor.

Another common technique for defining optical resolution is the Sparrow's criterion that states that "two image points A' and B' in the image plane can be just resolved if the intensity is a constant as we move from the image point A' to point B' in the image plane." The Sparrow angular resolution is given by

$$\theta_S = \frac{\lambda}{D} \qquad (7.28)$$

The angular separation is less than that of the Rayleigh criterion. Both these criteria, Rayleigh and Sparrow, were derived assuming incoherent sources.

Another common term for defining resolution is the *blur circle*, or the *airy disk*. This definition uses the same Bessel-based *sombrero* intensity equation defined above but defines the central blur as containing 84% of the energy. The angular size of the blur is given by

$$\theta_A = \frac{2.44\lambda}{D} \qquad (7.29)$$

The diameter of the blur in the image plane is given by

$$d_{blur} = \frac{2.44\lambda f}{D} \qquad (7.30)$$

Because the F/# (f-number) is approximately f/D, the spot size is not a function of optics diameter or focal length alone, but only a function of the wavelength and F/#. The overall goal in high-resolution sensor design is to minimize the separation distance of the two imaged point sources, which equates to minimizing the diameter of the blur. In I^2R and EO systems, the blur spot is designed with the detector and sensor performance characteristics in mind. As seen in (7.30), the separation parameter (e.g., blur diameter) depends on the optical parameters of focal length and aperture size.

7.8 MODULATION TRANSFER FUNCTION

In the previous section, we discussed the resolution of an optical system using the spatial separation of the point-source image blur. This blur spot has been identified by two other names: the incoherent impulse response and the psf. These are equivalent quantities that are used in different contexts. This spatial function can be converted to the spatial frequency domain. Consider the optical system shown in Figure 7.22.

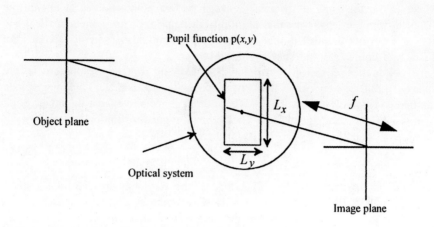

Figure 7.22 Optical system with pupil function.

The lens system shown [11] provides an image one focal length from the entrance pupil given that the object plane is sufficiently far away. In typical imaging systems, the collection aperture is located at the limiting pupil function, *p(x,y)*. We know from Chapter 4 that the system shown has both a coherent transfer function and an incoherent transfer function (or optical transfer function (OTF)). While we are not usually interested in the coherent transfer function, it is easier to start with it to develop the incoherent transfer function. For the rectangular aperture shown, the coherent transfer function is

$$H(\xi, \eta) = rect(\frac{x}{L_x}, \frac{y}{L_y})|_{x=\xi\lambda f, \, y=\eta\lambda f} \qquad (7.31)$$

Recall that the Fourier transform of this coherent transfer function gives the coherent impulse response (i.e., a two-dimensional *sinc* function). A large aperture here corresponds to a small impulse response and consequently higher spatial resolution in the image plane. Also, from Chapter 2, the *rect* function transitions from 1 to 0 at arguments of 1/2. This transition occurs when $\xi = L_x/2\lambda f$ and $\eta = L_y/2\lambda f$. These are the cutoff spatial frequencies in the image plane. Note that the units are cycles per meter or cycles per millimeter depending on the units of length used for aperture size, wavelength, and focal length.

To determine the optical transfer function of the system shown in Figure 7.22, the normalized autocorrelation of the coherent transfer function must be found:

$$OTF(\xi, \eta) = \mathcal{H}(\xi, \eta) = \frac{\gamma_H(\xi,\eta)}{|\gamma_H(0,0)|} \qquad (7.32)$$

While (7.32) appears complicated, the OTF is simply the autocorrelation of the coherent optical transfer function with the peak value (at the function origin) set to 1. With the substitutions given in (7.31), the system OTF is

$$OTF(\xi, \eta) = tri(\frac{\xi \lambda f}{L_x}, \frac{\eta \lambda f}{L_y}) \tag{7.33}$$

The cutoff spatial frequencies for the OTF occur at $\xi = L_x/\lambda f$ and $\eta = L_y/\lambda f$, which are twice as large as the coherent case.

Three very important characteristics of the transfer functions must be discussed here. First, the functions describe the transfer of spatial frequencies onto the image plane where they are there defined in cycles per distance. It is not always convenient to represent spatial frequencies in these units and they can be converted to angular spatial frequencies simply by dropping the f in (7.31) through (7.33). While the cycles per distance unit is convenient for image plane calculations, many times we are interested in the angular spatial frequency response of the system. For example, many sensor performance specifications are given in units of cycles per milliradian.

The second characteristic is the segmentation of the OTF into the modulation transfer function (MTF) and the phase transfer function (PTF). The MTF is the magnitude or modulus of the OTF and the PTF is the phase of the OTF. In some cases, the OTF actually gives a negative value for some range of spatial frequencies. When this occurs, the PTF provides the phase shift necessary to change bright regions in the image to dark, and dark regions to bright (i.e., phase reversal). This occurs for the spatial frequencies where the PTF is negative. This is not a desirable design characteristic, so it is not the intent of sensor designers to have their systems operate in this mode. Severe defocus is one of the primary causes of phase reversal.

Finally, the third important characteristic is that of signal transfer. Consider a slice through the OTF in the horizontal direction for both the coherent and optical transfer functions (Figure 7.23). For the coherent transfer function, input spatial frequencies higher than dc light but less than the cutoff frequency transfer through undegraded. This is not the case for the OTF, where the amplitude of the higher spatial frequencies is reduced. The amplitude of an output signal with a frequency half the cutoff will be reduced by one-half. This transfer is with respect to the dc (zero frequency) signal because there is some transmission loss of even the dc signal through the optical system. In summary, the resolution of the coherent system is less than that of the incoherent system, but signals of all frequencies less than the cutoff transfer through the system in the same manner. The resolution of the incoherent system is twice that of the coherent system, but higher spatial frequency signals suffer more degradation as they pass through the system. In either system, no signals higher than the cutoff frequencies are seen in the output image.

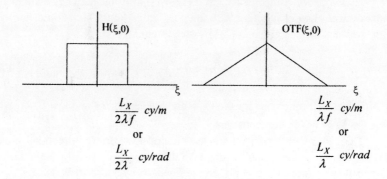

Figure 7.23 Coherent and optical transfer functions.

While the rectangular aperture was selected to illustrate OTF and MTF concepts for simplicity, most apertures are circular. An unobstructed circular aperture placed in the system of Figure 7.22 yields a coherent transfer function:

$$H(\rho) = cyl(\tfrac{r}{D})|_{r=\rho\lambda f} \qquad (7.34)$$

where ρ is the circularly symmetric spatial frequency. The OTF is the normalized autocorrelation of this function:

$$OTF(\rho) = \frac{\gamma_H(\rho)}{|\gamma_H(0)|} \qquad (7.35)$$

and the MTF is the magnitude of this function. While a closed-form solution for the autocorrelation of the cylinder function is a straightforward geometry problem, the results are cumbersome. We know that the function is twice the width of the original *cylinder* function, so the cutoff frequency is twice that of the coherent system. Also, we know that the correlation degrades the higher frequencies because of the smoothing operation. The solution this autocorrelation function is provided by Gaskill [12] as

$$MTF(\rho) = \tfrac{2}{\pi}[\cos^{-1}(\tfrac{\rho}{\rho_c}) - \tfrac{\rho}{\rho_c}\sqrt{1 - (\tfrac{\rho}{\rho_c})^2}\,] \qquad (7.36)$$

where $\rho_c = D/\lambda f$ in cycles per unit length (usually, millimeters or meters) or $\rho_c = D/\lambda$ in cycles per radian. D is the diameter of the circular pupil function. (7.36) is valid only for spatial frequencies less than the cutoff frequency, and the MTF is zero at spatial frequencies above the cutoff frequency. A comparison of this function with the MTF of a rectangular aperture of the same size is shown in Figure 7.24.

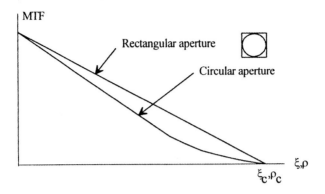

Figure 7.24 MTFs for rectangular and circular apertures.

The Fourier transform of either function shown yields the psf, or blur spots, of the diffraction-limited optical systems. The transfer functions for optics with aberrations must be treated separately.

Example

Determine the MTF, plotted with units of cycles per milliradian and cycles per millimeter, for a diffraction-limited optical system in the longwave. Assume that the entrance pupil has a diameter of 20 cm and a focal length of 60 cm. Also, plot the psf in milliradians and in millimeters. We obtain a solution with an assumed wavelength of 10 μm which gives an angular spatial cutoff frequency of 20 cycles per milliradian and the focal plane spatial frequency is 33.3 cycles per millimeter. We use (7.36) for the MTF approximation of a sensor with a circular entrance pupil and (7.25) for the psf. The MTF is first plotted in angular spatial frequency and then in distance spatial frequency (Figure 7.25). The corresponding psfs are also shown. Recall that they are the Fourier transform of the transfer functions. All plots shown are circularly symmetrical.

7.9 ABERRATIONS AND VIGNETTING

The first-order imaging system analytical techniques given in the earlier sections were only approximations of actual optical system behavior. The differences in the actual behavior and the first-order estimates are known as *aberrations* [13]. Hecht and Zajac provide two main classifications of aberrations: chromatic aberrations and monochromatic aberrations.

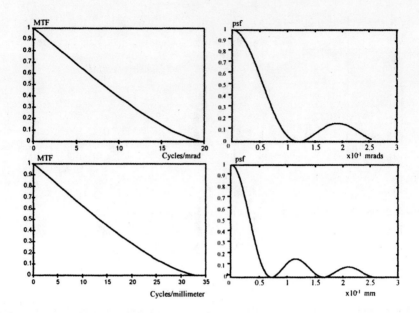

Figure 7.25 MTF and psf results.

Chromatic aberrations occur because the index of refraction for a particular material is a function of frequency (color in the visible spectrum). It can be shown using the lensmakers formula, given in (7.14), that the focal length of a lens and its corresponding image plane location changes with a change in the lens index of refraction. The effect of chromatic aberration within a lens system can be determined by performing a number of imaging calculations over a band of refractive indices across to the waveband. A number of computer ray tracing programs can easily perform this task.

Aberrations can occur even when the light is monochromatic. They can degrade the image in clarity and can even deform the image. Spherical aberration, coma, astigmatism, Petzval field curvature, and distortion are all monochromatic aberrations.

Spherical aberrations evolve from the first-order approximation that we made of surface power. In reality, the refractive action at a spherical surface has higher order terms:

$$\frac{1}{f} = \frac{n_2 - n_1}{R} + h^2 \left[\frac{n_1}{2o} \left(\frac{1}{o} + \frac{1}{R} \right)^2 + \frac{n_2}{2i} \left(\frac{1}{R} - \frac{1}{i} \right)^2 \right] + \dots \qquad (7.37)$$

The higher order term shown here would give a third-order approximation. Note that the additional term is a function of ray height above the optical axis. That is, the error between the first-order and third-order approximations is a function of the ray height. A large h causes the light to focus at a shorter distance from the surface, as shown in Figure 7.26.

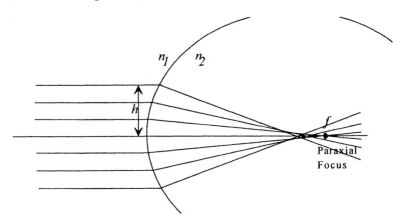

Figure 7.26 Spherical aberration.

The paraxial focus position is valid for those rays that enter the surface near the optical axis. For a given application that uses spherical lenses, h is limited and a "circle of least confusion" is found where the image plane is set between the marginal focus and the paraxial focus. This position provides an image with a minimum diameter. In some cases, where large relative apertures are required (relative aperture is the aperture diameter over the focal length), surfaces and lenses are constructed with aspheric surfaces that correct for spherical and other aberrations. In lens systems, the resultant spherical aberration is a summation of each surface contributor, so the overall spherical aberration can sometimes be corrected with a series of spherical surfaces. Also, optical designers can minimize spherical and other aberrations by adding more lenses of lower power to the system.

Spherical aberrations occur on the optical axis, or on-axis. An off-axis aberration is *coma* that occurs for off-axis image points. Coma comes from a Greek word meaning "tail of a comet." The imaging planes, or principle planes, within a lens are actually curved, giving a transverse magnification that differs for rays traversing off-axis. In short, coma is the result of an error in off-axis magnification. The resulting image of a point appears to be a comet-like image (a round spot with a trailing tail).

Astigmatism is another image degrading aberration. It occurs when an image point lies an appreciable distance from the optical axis such that rays strike the lens in an asymmetric manner. The plane defined by the center ray, or chief ray, of the bundle and the optical axis is called the *meridional plane*. The plane defined by the chief ray but normal to the meridional plane is called the *sagittal plane.* Astigmatism occurs when the image location in the meridional plane does not occur in the same position as that of the sagittal plane. For example, if the image of a point in the sagittal plane is a vertical line, the image at the meridional focus will be a horizontal line. The best image is between these two line images. Astigmatism also occurs when the curvature of the lens is different in one direction versus another. Lens astigmatism is purposely used to correct vision from a distorted eye in prescription lenses.

Two other aberrations are *field curvature* and *distortion.* Field curvature, or Petzval field curvature, results from too many positive lenses. The image surface is actually curved or spherical in shape, so images projected onto flat surfaces appear sharp near the optical axis and blurred on the edges. Field curvature can be flattened by balancing the number and power of the positive and negative lenses in the system. Distortion occurs when the magnification varies as a function of radial image location. Therefore, the image size varies as a function of distance from the optical axis. The two types of distortion are *pincushion* and *barrel,* as shown in Figure 7.27.

Original   Pincushion   Barrel
object   distortion   distortion
                   image   image

Figure 7.27 Distortion.

Holst points out that it is convenient to represent aberrations as a single transfer function where the overall optical MTF can usually be represented:

$$MTF_{optics} = MTF_{diff}MTF_{aberr}. \tag{7.38}$$

MTF_{diff} is the diffraction-limited MTF of the optics. Aberrations can be approximated by a Gaussian function, where the MTF is given as

$$MTF_{aberrations}(\rho) = Gaus(\sqrt{2\pi}\,\sigma\rho). \tag{7.39}$$

The FLIR92 model, developed by the U.S. Army Night Vision and Electronic Systems Directorate (NVESD), uses this approach, but Holst [14] states that the scaling factor is not directly measurable because any optical measurement includes both the diffraction and the aberration characteristics. It can be determined given a measurement with the calculation of the diffraction effects. Also, the approximation of (7.37) does not yield good results if the aberration MTF and diffraction MTF are similar. Ray-tracing programs provide a means for determining an overall MTF that includes diffraction and vignetting.

Vignetting [15] occurs when there is a mismatch between elements of an optical system resulting in a partial obstruction of the aperture for some points in the image plane. It is not necessarily a design defect, as it is sometimes a calculated way to eliminate aberrated rays at the expense of flux throughput. Vignetting is much more common in the wide field of view systems as opposed to telescopes. An example of this is shown in Figure 7.28.

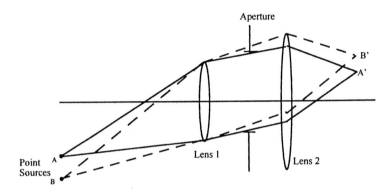

Figure 7.28 Vignetting in an optical system.

The bundle of rays from point source A pass through the two-lens system and are imaged at A'. The bundle of rays from point source B are partially blocked by the aperture. This vignetting effectively results in a different-size aperture that results in an object's being reduced in brightness.

7.10 OPTICAL MATERIALS

The selection of lens materials involves the consideration of many issues. A primary consideration is that of optical transmission. Many materials that transmit visible light are opaque in the infrared wavelengths. Examples here are normal window glass, Plexiglas, and quartz. Germanium is transmissive from 2 µm well past 15 µm, but it is opaque over EO wavelengths and over the visual spectrum. Zinc selenide is a broadband glass that transmits EO, midwave, and longwave light. There are families of glasses with a wide range of transmissions. An example is that of the IRTRAN glasses that are tailored for use in infrared systems. EO system lenses are constructed of fused silica, BK7, Zerodur, barium flouride, and many other types of glass.

The transmissions of system lenses are usually grouped into a single system optical transmission, $\tau_{optics}(\lambda)$. The transmission of an optical system affects the amount of flux that propagates through the system and falls on the detector. A large transmission in the band of interest is desired. Also, the transmission is usually a strong function of wavelength, so the spectral transmission must be known along with the source spectrum and atmospheric transmission to determine the flux on the detector. The detector response is also a function of wavelength. All these spectral quantities are integrated over wavelength in order to give accurate radiometric quantities.

Lens selection must also include index of refraction considerations. If the index varies as a strong function of wavelength, large chromatic aberrations occur. Sometimes a lens is constructed from two different materials with spectral index functions (dispersions) that cancel each other. Such lenses are called *achromats*. Typical index of refractions are around 1.5 for EO lens materials. Infrared lens materials usually have a higher index of refraction. Zinc selenide's index varies (depending on wavelength) from 2.4 to 2.7. Germanium has an index of refraction of around 4 in the midwave.

Other material considerations are thermal properties, elastic constants, hardness, and other mechanical properties. Lens design and material selection is an extremely complicated process. Usually, a system-level engineer or scientist does not perform this level of development, as there are optical professionals that spend their lives producing optical designs. These professionals are usually consulted during the development of an I^2R or EO system.

7.11 A TYPICAL OPTICAL SYSTEM

This chapter would not be complete without a description of a typical optical system. There are too many different types of optical systems to begin to address the characteristics of various optical systems. These include microscopes, telescopes, night sights, target acquisition sensors, navigation sensors, cameras, camcorders, and the like. Here, we describe one classical system as an example: the common module FLIR [16].

Consider the optical diagram shown in Figure 7.29. The common module FLIR was developed in the 1970s as an attempt to standardize the infrared technology across many military platforms. The FLIR comprises an infrared side and an electro-optical side. The infrared side includes three optical systems. The first system is the infrared afocal, which consists of the first two lenses in the optical train. Note that the collimated light into the first lens is also collimated on the output of the second lens (i.e., the light bundle is smaller). That is, there is not a focus for the two-lens system, thus afocal means "without a focal length." The second optical system is the scanner. The scanner is an infrared mirror (a mirror with a coating that is reflective at IR wavelengths) on one side and an electro-optical mirror on the other. The collimated light from the afocal is reflected from the scanner into the third optical system, an infrared imaging lens. The scanner causes the object scene in the field of view to be scanned across a line of 180 detectors (a 180-detector linear array). The result is 180-line output voltages that correspond to image scene irradiance on the image plane. The scanner then tilts in angle such that the space between the detectors is now filled with the other half of the scene and scans back across the detectors. This 2:1 interlacing provides an effective 360 lines of spatial information.

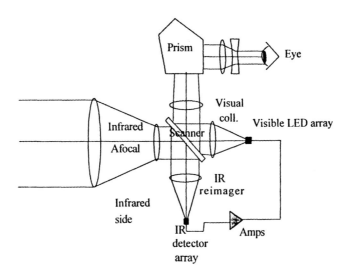

Figure 7.29 Common module FLIR.

The output voltage from the detector array and amplifier bank is input to a 180-element linear light emitting diode (LED) array that emits energy in the visible wavelengths. A higher drive voltage corresponds to a brighter LED output. The output light of the LED array is collimated by a visible collimator and reflected off the backside of the scan mirror in the same manner as the infrared light. The output of the scanner is reoriented with a prism and demagnified for human viewing. The overall system provides a 30-frame-per-second image scan that is presented to the human viewer in real time.

The technique of scanning the visible LED outputs in the same manner as the signal input to the infrared detectors is called an *electro-optical multiplexer* or an *EO MUX*. The linear detector array of 180 elements is indicative of the first-generation FLIR technology.

EXERCISES

7.1 Calculate the OPL from point A to point B in the system shown below.

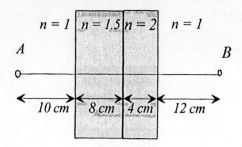

Figure 7.30

7.2 Calculate the angle of the refracted ray in the system shown below.

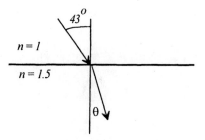

Figure 7.31

7.3 Determine the image position and size (assume an object size of 1 cm) corresponding to the object shown in Figure 7.32 when the object distance is

(a) $x = \infty$
(b) $x = 60\ cm$
(c) $x = 40\ cm$
(d) $x = 25\ cm$
(e) $x = 10\ cm$

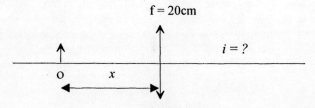

Figure 7.32

7.4 Determine the image position and size (assume an object size of 1 cm) corresponding to the object shown in Figure 7.32 when the object distance is

(a) $x = \infty$
(b) $x = 40$ cm
(c) $x = 20$ cm

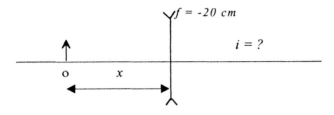

Figure 7.33

7.5 Calculate the vergence of a wavefront that is 10 cm away from a point source.

7.6 Calculate the vergence of a wavefront that is 30 cm before coming to a focus.

7.7 A lens is dropped upright into a fishtank and is lodged 5 cm from the tank glass in the sand. An object is placed 10 cm from the tank glass. Assuming the glass thickness to be negligible, find the image distance from the lens. The biconvex lens refractive index is 1.67, and the radius of curvature for both sides is 6.8 cm.

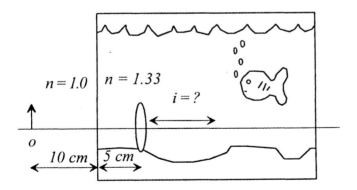

Figure 7.34

7.8 Determine the FOV for a system that has an effective focal length of 80 cm and a detector staring array size of 1.5 cm by 2.0 cm.

7.9 Three lenses with focal lengths 5 cm, -5 cm, and 5 cm, respectively are placed 1 cm apart from each other. Given that parallel light enters the first lens, how far behind the third lens does the light come to a focus?

7.10 Determine the diameter of a telescope aperture required to resolve two stars separated by 100 million km where the pair of stars are both 10 light years away from Earth. Assume a wavelength of 0.5 μm.

7.11 Determine the limit on angular resolution for diffraction-limited infrared sensors with apertures of 5 in, 10 in, and 15 in. Assume a wavelength of 10 μm.

7.12 Determine both the MTF and psf for a 3- to 5-μm midwave infrared sensor with a 5-in aperture and a 10 in focal length. Specify the MTF in both cycles per milliradian (angular spatial frequency) and cycles per millimeter (spatial frequency in the detector plane). Specify the psf in both angular space and detector plane size.

REFERENCES

[1]   Pinson, L. J., *Electro-Optics,* New York: Wiley, p. 3, 1985.
[2]   Saleh, B. H., and M. C. Teich, *Fundamentals of Photonics,* New York: Wiley, p. 2, 1991.
[3]   *The Photonics Dictionary,* Pittsfield, MA: Lauren Publishing, 1996.
[4]   Jenkins, F. A., *Fundamentals of Optics,* New York: McGraw-Hill, 1957.
[5]   Jenkins, F. A., *Fundamentals of Optics,* New York: McGraw-Hill, 1957.
[6]   Yu, F. T., and I. C. Khoo, *Principles of Optical Engineering,* New York: Wiley, p. 66, 1992.
[7]   Meyer-Arendt, J. R., *Introduction to Classical and Modern Optics,* New Jersey: Prentice-Hall, 1984.
[8]   Banerjee, P. P., and T. C. Poon, *Principles of Applied Optics,* Boston, MA: Aksen Associates (IRWIN), p. 34, 1991.
[9]   Guenther, R., *Modern Optics,* New York: Wiley, 1990.
[10]   Pinson, L. J., *Electro-Optics,* New York: Wiley, 1985.
[11]   Boreman, G. D., class notes from the SPIE course *Electro-Optical Systems for Engineers,* Orlando, FL: Personal Notes, 1988.
[12]   Gaskill, J., *Linear Systems, Fourier Transforms, and Optics,* New York: Wiley, pp. 305 - 307, 1978.
[13]   Hecht, E., and A. Zajac, *Optics,* Reading, MA: Addison-Wesley, p. 175, 1979.
[14]   Holst, G. C., *Electro-Optical Imaging System Performance,* Orlando, FL: JCD Publishing, 1995.

[15] Smith, W. J., *Modern Optical Engineering, The Design of Optical Systems,* New York: McGraw-Hill, 1966.

[16] *FLIR Common Module Design Manual,* Night Vision and Electronics Systems Directorate (NVESD), Ft. Belvoir, VA, 1978.

Chapter 8

Detectors and Scanners

The detector is the component of the system which transforms the optical signal into an electrical signal. This electrical output is proportional to the incident optical power. The detector component in the sensor plays a key role in determining system-level parameters including spectral operating band, sensitivity, and resolution. The spectral response is determined by the detector material characteristics and the operating temperature. A strong energy band for photon acceptance must be present for the energy conversion process to occur. The detector sensitivity is a function of material (i.e., energy gap), wavelength, detector size, bandwidth, and shielding. Finally, the resolution is set by the detector size and pitch (center-to-center spacing) and the optical focal length.

The detectors (Figure 8.1) must be distributed over the image plane in order to convert the image into a spatial signal. The spatial representation can be performed in terms of a continuous signal or in terms of a sampled signal. The detector distribution across the entire image is accomplished by scanning the image across single detectors or linear detector arrays. The spatial distribution is inherent with staring arrays. We focus on the spectral sensitivity and detector resolution in this chapter along with the necessary scanners required to perform the spatial image representation.

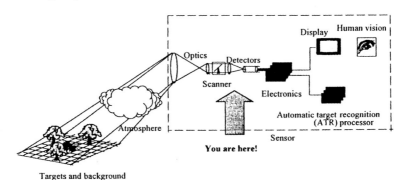

Figure 8.1 Detector and scanner components of the system.

8.1 TYPES OF DETECTORS

There are two general classes [1, 2] of detectors: *photon* (or quantum) and *thermal* detectors. Photon detectors convert absorbed photon energy into released electrons (from their bound states to conduction states). The material bandgap describes the energy necessary to transition a charge carrier from the valence band to the conduction band. The change in charge carrier state changes the electrical properties of the material. These electrical property variations are measured to determine the amount of incident optical power. Thermal detectors absorb energy over a broad band of wavelengths. The energy absorbed by a detector causes the temperature of the material to increase. Thermal detector materials have at least one inherent electrical property that changes with temperature. This temperature-related property is measured electrically to determine the power on the detector. Figure 8.2 shows the detectors described in this chapter.

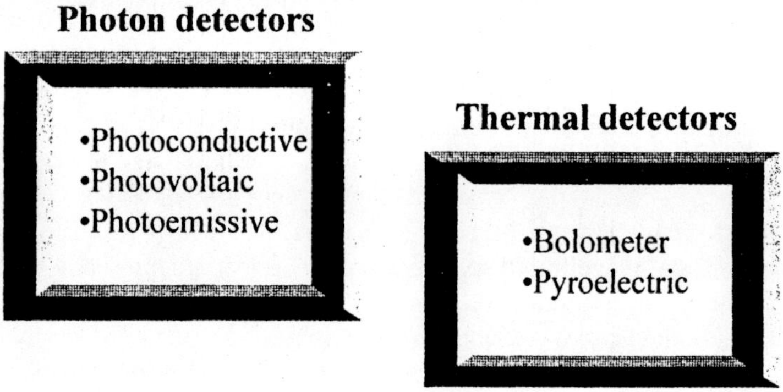

Photon detectors

•Photoconductive
•Photovoltaic
•Photoemissive

Thermal detectors

•Bolometer
•Pyroelectric

Figure 8.2 Types of detectors.

Photon detectors include photoconductors, photovoltaic (PV), and photoemissive detectors. The photoconductive detector is constructed of semiconductor material that converts absorbed photons into free-charge carriers. The change in free carriers varies the conductivity (and resistance) of the detector. A simple circuit provides a bias current that reflects the change in conductivity.

The photovoltaic detector absorbs photons at a P-N junction. Hole-electron pairs are generated that alter the junction voltage. The change in voltage describes the amount of optical power on the detector. The photovoltaic detector does not require any external bias voltage. The inherent voltage of the P-N junction changes without bias and can be read out directly. Like photoconductors, the photovoltaic detector has spectral characteristics that are derived from the material's molecular energy levels.

Photoemissive devices are different from photoconductors and photovoltaic detectors in that an electron physically leaves the detection material when a photon is absorbed. Usually placed in a vacuum tube with high voltage, a photocathode absorbs the photon and the energy absorbed is enough (higher than the electron work function) to release the electron in the vacuum chamber. The voltage potential moves it toward the anode. Once electrons reach the anode, they are measured as a current that reflects the optical flux on the photocathode.

Thermal detectors [3] include bolometers and pyroelectric detectors. Bolometers are sometimes called *thermistors*, because the material provides a resistance that changes with temperature. Semiconductors are used with high-temperature coefficients of resistance. The material is usually a long, narrow strip of material coated with highly absorbent coating. The electrical resistance of the strip is measured with a bias current to determine the amount of absorbed radiation.

Pyroelectric detectors are the most common thermal detectors. The pyroelectric detector is a ferroelectric material between two electrodes. The material exhibits a change in polarization with temperature. It can be thought of as a capacitor whose capacitance is temperature sensitive. As with any capacitor, measurement requires an ac signal, so most pyroelectric detectors are chopped to vary the incident flux.

In this chapter, we discuss each of the photon and thermal detectors mentioned above. The list is not exhaustive, but it does contain most of the commonly specified detectors.

8.2 PHOTON DETECTORS

Photon detectors generate free-charge carriers through the absorption of photons. The absorption occurs without any significant increase in the detector temperature [4]. Detection occurs by a direct interaction of the photon with the atomic lattice of the material. Material parameters that can be changed by the interaction are resistance, inductance, voltage, and current. The concepts presented here apply to detectors that sense wavelengths from 0.2 to 1,000 μm.

A variety of bandgaps (and corresponding wavelength sensitivities) can be achieved with the selection of materials. Recall that $E = h\nu$, where $\nu = c/\lambda$, h is Planck's constant, and c is the speed of light. The wavelength of a photon has to be short enough so that the photon energy exceeds a material's bandgap energy level for absorption. Intrinsic detectors are those that are constructed from semiconductor crystals with no introduced impurities or lattice defects [5]. Extrinsic detectors have impurities introduced to change the effective bandgap energy.

Cryogenic cooling (with closed-cycle coolers or liquid nitrogen) is typically required for infrared photon detectors to reduce dark-current generated electron noise. The reduction in temperature reduces the level of dark-current noise to below that of photon-generated signal. Photon-detector responsivity is sometimes characterized by a quantum efficiency that describes the number of electron transitions per absorbed photon. Intrinsic detectors have quantum efficiencies of around 60%. Typical quantum efficiencies for photoconductors range from 30 to 60%. Photovoltaic and photoemissive detectors have quantum efficiencies of around 60% and 10%, respectively.

The detection mechanisms for the three most common types of photon detectors are covered in this chapter. The following describes photoconductive, photovoltaic, and photoemissive detectors.

Photoconductors

Photoconductors sense optical power with a change in conductance (or inverse resistance). Longer wavelengths can be detected by *doping* a pure material with impurities, giving an extrinsic detector. The energy gap transition for the intrinsic detector is depicted in Figure 8.3(a). An extrinsic bandgap is shown in Figure 8.3(b). A p-type extrinsic detector decreases the conduction band energy level and an n-type extrinsic detector raises the valence band energy level. The result is a smaller bandgap material that can detect longer wavelengths. Quantum efficiencies are lower (around 30%) for extrinsic detectors because the dopant is less abundant than the host material.

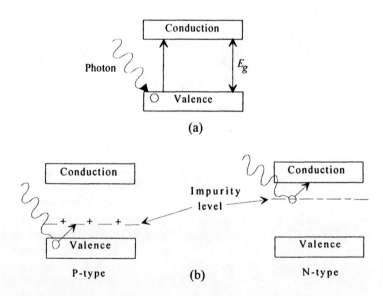

Figure 8.3 Intrinsic (a) and extrinsic (b) detection.

For photoconductors, an increase in the incident optical power increases the number of free-charge carriers, so the effective resistance of the detector decreases. The differential charge provided by the impinging photons is given by [1]

$$dq = E_p \eta_q wt_q el_d \qquad \text{[Coulombs]} \qquad (8.1)$$

where E_p is the incident irradiance in photons per second per square centimeter, w is the detector width in centimeters, l_d is the detector length in centimeters, η_q is the quantum efficiency, t_q is the charge carrier mean lifetime in seconds, and e is the charge on an electron (1.602×10^{-19} Coulombs). Figure 8.4 shows a typical photoconductor.

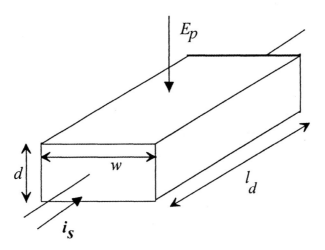

Figure 8.4 Photoconductive detector.

The photo-induced current is related to the transit time of the charge carrier across the detector length l_d, where the transit time is estimated to be $dt = l_d^2/(\mu V_{bias})$. V_{bias} is the bias voltage across the detector and μ is the carrier mobility in $cm^2/(Volt-s)$. Now the photo-induced current is

$$i_s = \frac{E_p \eta_q w t_q e \mu V_{bias}}{l_d} \quad [A] \quad (8.2)$$

The photo-induced change in resistance is the bias voltage divided by the photo-induced current

$$\Delta R_s = \frac{l_d}{E_p \eta_q w t_q e \mu} \quad [Ohms] \quad (8.3)$$

Finally, a photo-induced conductivity can be found using the conductivity-resistance relationship

$$\Delta R_s = \frac{l_d}{\Delta \sigma_s w d} \quad [Ohms] \quad (8.4)$$

where $\Delta \sigma_s$ is the photo-induced conductivity of the resistor.

Example

An indium antimonide photoconductor detector is 100 μm long and 50 μm wide. Its quantum efficiency is 0.45 and its mean carrier lifetime is 5×10^{-7} seconds. Its mobility is 3×10^4 cm²/(V-s). Determine the detector's change in resistance for an in-band incident irradiance of 3×10^{10} photons/(s-cm²). The solution is given by (8.3)

$$\Delta R_s = \frac{(0.01)}{(3x10^{17})(.45)(0.005)(5x10^{-7})(1.602x10^{-19})(3x10^4)} = 6.2 \text{ kohms}$$

The conductivity is found, using (8.4), to be 0.064 ohms/cm.

Photovoltaic

Photovoltaic detectors are constructed with the formation of a P-N type junction in a semiconductor. The P-N junction has an inherently generated voltage and does not require a bias voltage or current. A typical photovoltaic detector energy diagram is shown in Figure 8.5.

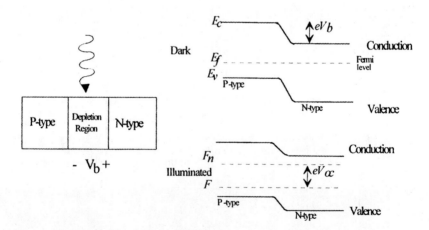

Figure 8.5 Photovoltaic energy diagram.

The photons are absorbed at the junction of the P- and N- type materials, an area called the *depletion region*. The junction is the same as a diode with the added effect that voltage is generated with illumination. The energy diagrams of Figure 8.4 show the diode in the dark and illuminated states. The voltage in the dark state is related to the differences in conduction (and corresponding valence) energy levels for the P- and N-type materials across the depletion region. Pinson [1] provides the following voltage description. The voltage is given by

$$V_b = \frac{kT}{e} \ln \frac{n_n}{n_p} \qquad [V] \qquad (8.5)$$

where k is Boltzmann's constant (1.38 x 10^{-23} J/deg K or 8.62 x 10^{-5} eV/deg K), T is the junction temperature in degrees Kelvin, e is the charge on an electron, and n_n and n_p are the free-electron densities in the N- and P- type materials, respectively. The fermi level shown describes the energy at which 50% of the energy levels are likely to be occupied by electrons. This energy level applies when there are no excess carriers generated by optical excitation. Quasifermi levels apply for the optically excited state, where these levels describe how far the electron and hole populations have deviated from the equilibrium values. The open-circuit voltage is proportional to the difference in these energy levels.

The voltage across the junction when excess electron-hole pairs are generated can be described by the changes in the electron and hole populations, δn_n and δn_p. The junction voltage becomes

$$V_b = \frac{kT}{e} \ln \frac{n_n + \delta n_n}{n_p + \delta n_p} \qquad [V] \qquad (8.6)$$

The changes in the number of excess electron-hole pairs can be approximated by

$$\delta n_n = \delta n_p = \frac{\eta q E_s}{d} t_n \qquad [electrons/m^3] \qquad (8.7)$$

where d is the detector depth and t_n is the carrier lifetime. A differential incident photon irradiance gives a differential voltage of

$$\frac{dV_b}{dE_s} = \frac{d}{dE_s} \left[\frac{kT}{e} \ln \frac{(n_n + \frac{\eta q E_s}{d} t_n)}{(n_p - \frac{\eta q E_s}{d} t_n)} \right] \approx \frac{kT}{e} \left[\frac{\frac{\eta q}{d} t_n (n_n + n_p)}{(n_n + \frac{\eta q E_s}{d} t_n)(n_p - \frac{\eta q E_s}{d} t_n)} \right] \qquad (8.8)$$

If the number of excess electron-hole pairs generated by the irradiance can be assumed to be small compared with n_n, then

$$\frac{dV_b}{dE_s} \approx \frac{kT\eta q t_n (n_n + n_p)}{e d n_n n_p} \qquad (8.9)$$

Pinson states that this differential quantity is a constant that relates the photo-induced voltage to the incident irradiance. The current-voltage characteristics of photovoltaic detectors are very similar to those of a diode. These characteristics are given in Chapter 9. Because of this similarity, photovoltaic detectors are sometimes referred to as photodiodes. Photovoltaic detectors offer several advantages over photoconductor detectors, including better responsivity, simpler biasing, and a better theoretical signal-to-noise ratio (SNR).

The photovoltaic detector is normally operated in the open-circuit mode, where the photo-induced voltage is measured directly. This mode has SNR advantages over a system that requires external amplification. However, the detector can be operated in the reverse-bias direction, known as the *photoconductive mode*. The electric field strength and the depletion region width are increased. Advantages are higher speed, lower capacitance, and better linearity. The disadvantage is that dark currents are greater.

The avalanche photodiode (APD) [6] is a specialized photovoltaic detector that is operated in the photoconductive mode. Large reverse-bias voltages are applied to the P-N junction. This causes some of the electrons passing through the large electric field to gain added energy so that additional electron-hole pairs are generated. This process is known as *impact ionization*. If the newly created electon-hole pairs attain sufficiently high energy levels, they create more electron-hole pairs. This process is known as *avalanche multiplication* and is the means for large internal gains. Typical internal gains are from 50 to 500.

Photoemissive

Photoemissive detectors release electrons from the photosensitive surface during the detection process. The incident photon of energy $h\nu$ provides the energy necessary to release an electron from the surface. The process is shown in Figure 8.6.

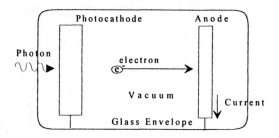

Figure 8.6 Photoemissive detection.

The photon enters a glass envelope that houses the photocathode and anode. Usually the envelope comprises a vacuum tube where conductive material deposited on the glass surface acts as the cathode. The photon energy is absorbed, producing a free electron that is accelerated to the anode through the vacuum. Only electrons that have sufficient energy to overcome the work function of the photocathode material result in released electrons. The electrons are collected at the anode and the corresponding current is measured to determine the amount of light on the photocathode. Photocathodes are designed with high optical absorption and small work functions.

The photomultiplier tube (PMT) is a special case of the photoemissive detector. The PMT is used when large gains are required to sense very low light levels. The PMT consists of a photocathode, electron multipliers (dynodes), a collection anode, and a evacuated glass or metal envelope. The photomultiplier is shown in Figure 8.7.

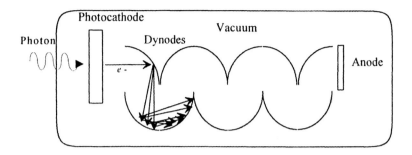

Figure 8.7 Photomultiplier.

An electron is released from the photocathode and is accelerated to the first dynode. The electron strikes the first dynode with enough energy to release a number of electrons that are accelerated to the next dynode. This multiplication occurs through a number of dynodes resulting in a large number of electrons collected on the anode. The gain of a PMT is estimated by

$$G = \chi^n \tag{8.10}$$

where G is the current gain, χ is the secondary emission ratio for dynodes, and n is the number of dynodes. A nine-stage PMT with a secondary emission ratio of 8 gives a gain of around 10^7. This large gain and low noise make the PMT an attractive detector for many applications.

8.3 THERMAL DETECTORS

For thermal detectors, the detector signal is related to the temperature of the detector material, which is altered because of incident radiation. These detectors typically operate at room (ambient) temperature and do not require cryogenic cooling. The change in temperature produces one of three electrical property changes in the detector material: resistance, voltage, or capacitance. Thermal detectors are grouped by the type of electrical property change.

In the past, thermal detectors have been characterized by their slow response time. Significant developments in recent years, however, have made these detectors viable candidates for many applications. Thermal detectors today exhibit many good characteristics, including quick response time, low noise, and linear operation. While the sensitivity of thermal detectors has improved dramatically in recent years, they are still behind the performance of photon detectors. In this section, we discuss two common types of thermal detectors for imaging sensors: the bolometer and pyroelectric detector.

Bolometers

Bolometer detection is derived from a change in the resistance of the detector material. A simple bolometer detector consists of a thin, blackened metal or semiconductor filament, as shown in Figure 8.8.

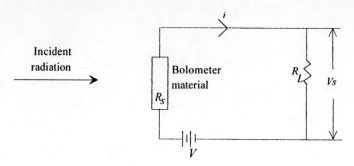

Figure 8.8 Bolometer configuration.

The change in the bolometer resistance due to incident radiation is given by [7]

$$\Delta R_b = R_o \, \alpha \, \Delta T \quad \text{[Ohms]} \quad (8.11)$$

where ΔT is the change in temperature of the filament, R_o is the strip resistance when $\Delta T = 0$, and α is the temperature coefficient of resistance. The temperature coefficient is positive for metals and negative for semiconductors. In the absence of incident radiation, there are changes in the detector from conduction from the surrounding environment. The changes are statistical in nature and contribute to detector noise. For this reason, the detector is isolated from the local environment to help ensure that signals are a result only of incident radiation. Isolation is achieved through special manufacturing techniques and by placing the bolometric detector in a vacuum.

The incremental temperature difference is defined by

$$\Delta T = \frac{\Delta \Phi}{\left[K^2 + (2 \pi f_c \, C_T)^2 \right]^{1/2}} \quad \text{[K]} \quad (8.12)$$

where $\Delta \Phi$ is the absorbed radiant power in W, K is the heat transfer coefficient in W per degree Kelvin, f_c is the chopping signal frequency in hertz (if the detector is chopped), and C_T is the heat capacity of strip in Joules per Kelvin.

The voltage responsivity is the ratio of the change in voltage with respect to the change in input radiation

$$R = \frac{\Delta V_s}{\varepsilon \, \Delta \Phi} = \frac{i \, R_o \, \alpha \, \varepsilon}{\left[K^2 + (2 \pi f_c C_T)^2 \right]^{1/}} \quad \text{[V/W]} \quad (8.13)$$

where ε is the detector material emissivity. At low frequencies, $f_c \ll 1/2\,\pi(C_T/K)$, (8.13) can be simplified to

$$R = \frac{i\,R_o\,\alpha\,\varepsilon}{K} \qquad \text{[V/W]} \qquad (8.14)$$

Example

Calculate the responsivity for a metal bolometer at low frequencies given the following parameters:

$i = 15$ mA
$K = 5*10^{-4}$ (W/deg K)
$R_o = 50\Omega$
$\alpha = 0.01$/deg K
$\varepsilon = 0.9$

Inserting the values into (8.14), R is determined to be:

$$R = \frac{(15x10^{-3}A)(50V/A)(0.01/K)(0.9)}{5x10^{-4}\,W/K} = 1.35\ \text{[V/W]} \qquad (8.15)$$

Pyroelectric Detectors

Pyroelectric detectors have a change in surface charge with a change in temperature. This pyroelectric effect, as it is called, produces a current that is proportional to the change in temperature:

$$i_p = p_T\,A_d\,\frac{dT}{dt} \qquad \text{[A]} \qquad (8.16)$$

where p_T $(C\ cm^{-2}\ K^{-1})$ is the pyroelectric coefficient at the temperature T Kelvin, A_d is the surface area of the detector in square centimeter, and $\frac{dT}{dt}$ is the time rate of temperature change. When a constant radiation is applied to the detector, no current can be sensed. A chopper must be used with the detector in order to provide changing temperatures that produce a current to sense a constant signal. Pyroelectric detectors are in essence capacitors. The responsivity for a pyroeletric detector is similar to that of the bolometer and is given by

$$R = \frac{\Delta v_s}{\varepsilon\,\Delta\Phi} = \frac{4\pi\varepsilon\,\rho\,A_d f_c}{\left[K^2 + (2\,\pi f_c\,C_T)^2\right]^{1/2}} \qquad \text{[V/W]} \qquad (8.17)$$

where ρ is the pyroelectric coefficient, A_d is the detector area, and f_c is the chopping frequency.

Pyroelectric materials are ferroelectric crystals that show spontaneous changes in polarization along one axis. Two example materials used for this kind of detector are PZT (doped lead zirconate titanate) and BST (barium strontium titanate) [8]. The polarization of these materials varies with the temperature and is characterized by the pyroelectric coefficient. This family of thermal detectors is characterized by fast response times across a broad spectrum.

8.4 CHARGE-COUPLED DEVICES

The charged-coupled device (CCD) [9-11] has become a very familiar term due to the popularity of hand-held video cameras operating in the visible band, although there are also infrared CCDs (IRCCD). The term CCD does not refer to a specific detector type but rather a detector readout architecture. The basic concept of charge-coupling is that once the photo-generated charge is collected in potential wells, they are selectively transferred or read out of each detector location in a serial process. CCDs are typically metal-oxide-structure (MOS) devices. The basic structure for these gates are shown in Figure 8.9.

When a positive voltage is applied, V_g, between the top metal electrode and the substrate, the majority carriers (holes) are moved from the oxide layer creating a depletion region at the interface. If a photon is absorbed into the region, then an electron-hole pair is produced. For the photon to be absorbed, its energy must be greater than that of the bandgap.

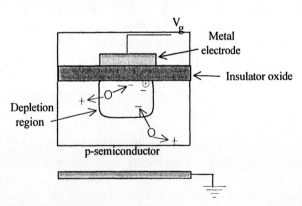

Figure 8.9 Metal oxide structure.

The CCD is an analog shift register in which an entire sequence of charge packets can be shifted simultaneously along the surface of the chip by applying clock voltages (V_g). The electric charge varies from one packet to the next. The sequence of charge packets are scanned as they move past an output electrode connected to an on-chip amplifier. To read out the charge packets, each component in the array is connected to sequential shift registers on the periphery.

The packets are then clocked out of the shift registers by a clock that controls the time delay.

As can be expected, the readout process is not perfect, and, hence, there is a small amount of charge lost with each transfer. This loss is quantified by the charge-transfer inefficiency η_{ct}. For a total of P charge transfers, the total fractional loss is given by $\alpha = 1 - (1 - \eta_{ct})^P \cong P \eta_{ct}$. The typical charge inefficiency is on the order of 10^{-4}, and typical array sizes (i.e., charge transfers) are 1,000 by 1,000 elements.

8.5 DETECTOR RESPONSIVITY

The fundamental purpose of a detector is to convert an optical signal into an electrical current or voltage. The term *responsivity* is used to describe the amplitude of the electrical signal with respect to the incident flux. Responsivity is a function of wavelength and temporal frequency and can be determined by

$$R(\lambda, f) = \frac{V_{out}}{\Phi_{incident}} = \frac{V_{out}}{E(\lambda, f) A_d} \quad [\text{V/W or V/L}] \tag{8.18}$$

where V_{out} is the detector output voltage, $\Phi_{incident}$ is the incident flux in Watts, $E(\lambda, f)$ is the incident irradiance in watts per square centimeter, and A_d is the detector area in square centimeters. Current responsivity would have units of Amperes per watt. A typical photon detector responsivity curve is shown in Figure 8.10.

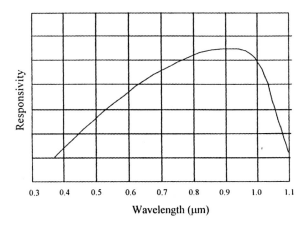

Figure 8.10 Responsivity curve.

The responsivity is typically measured by the detector manufacturer and provided as a specification or calibration document. The band-averaged responsivity over a spectral band $[\lambda_1, \lambda_2]$ is given by

$$R = \frac{\int_{\lambda_1}^{\lambda_2} \Phi(\lambda)R(\lambda)d\lambda}{\int_{\lambda_1}^{\lambda_2} \Phi(\lambda)d\lambda} \quad \text{[V/W or A/W]} \quad (8.19)$$

This value is used frequently in cases where the incident flux and the responsivity are not expected to vary significantly over the spectral band. For EO systems, the responsivity is given [10] frequently in terms of photometric units:

$$R_{photopic} = \frac{\int_{\lambda_1}^{\lambda_2} \Phi(\lambda)R(\lambda)d\lambda}{683 \int_{\lambda_1}^{\lambda_2} V(\lambda)\Phi(\lambda)d\lambda} \quad \text{[V/Lumen or A/Lumen]} \quad (8.20)$$

where $V(\lambda)$ is the human eye's photopic efficiency. From Chapter 5, there are 683 L/W at the peak visual efficiency. For EO systems that are closely matched to the human eye in spectral response, the use of photometric responsivity is reasonable. For systems with other-than-photopic spectral responses, however, large differences can be seen between actual voltages and those predicted by the photopic responsivity.

Example

The irradiance on a detector at a wavelength of 10.6 μm is 100 x 10^{-6} W/cm^2. The detector has a surface area of 5 cm^2 and the output voltage is 35 mV. Determine the detector's responsivity. The solution is determined by calculating the power on the detector. It is equal to $(100x10^{-6})(5) = 5x10^{-4}$ W. The responsivity is then $R = .035/5x10^{-4} = 70$ V/W.

In a manner similar to that of responsivity, the flux response of infrared systems is typically characterized by the system intensity transfer function (SITF). The SITF is measured with a large square target against a uniform background as shown in Figure 8.11(a).

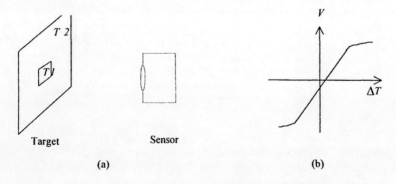

(a)   (b)

Figure 8.11 System intensity transfer function (a) measurement, (b) curve.

The temperature difference between the target and the background (ΔT) is varied, and the corresponding output voltage is recorded. A typical SITF curve is shown in Figure 8.11(b). The SITF value is the slope of the curve in the linear region. This voltage-temperature relationship is important to determine the noise equivalent temperature difference (NETD) of the sensor. Given an rms noise voltage at the output of the sensor, the NETD is

$$NETD = \frac{V_{Noise}}{SITF} \quad [\text{deg C or deg K}] \qquad (8.21)$$

The NETD is a sensitivity measure of infrared systems that describes noise in terms of source temperature variation. The definition and estimate of NETD are discussed in Chapter 11.

8.6 DETECTOR SENSITIVITY

The responsivity of a detector relates the signal level, in volts or amps, to the incident flux on the detector. A large responsivity does not mean that the detector can be used to easily discern small optical signals. An SNR is required to determine whether the signal can be differentiated from the noise. Because a large responsivity may not correspond to a large SNR, the term *sensitivity* was developed to describe a detector's SNR characteristics. The SNR at the output of a detector can be described [12] as

$$\frac{S}{N} = \frac{\Phi}{i_n} R \quad [\text{unitless}] \qquad (8.22)$$

where R is the responsivity of the detector in amps per watt, Φ is the flux on the detector in watts, and i_n is the noise current in amps. If the SNR is set to 1 to determine a noise equivalent incident power (NEP), we can rewrite (8.22) as

$$NEP = \Phi_{S/N=1} = i_n / R \qquad [\text{W}] \qquad (8.23)$$

If the responsivity is written in terms of volts per watt, then the NEP would be v_n / R. NEP is a function of wavelength and of the optical signal frequency (modulated or chopped light). That is, $R = R(\lambda, f)$ and $NEP = NEP(\lambda, f)$. NEP is also a useful quantity in that it provides a noise equivalent flux on the detector so that we can determine the overall system SNR. This is assuming that we know the noise current or the noise voltage on the output of the detector.

A better figure of merit is $D*$ ("dee star") or normalized detectivity. The $D*$ is also a function of wavelength and modulation frequency and can be written as

$$D*(\lambda, f) = \frac{\sqrt{A_d \Delta f}}{NEP} \qquad [\frac{cm - Hz^{1/2}}{Watts}] \qquad (8.24)$$

where A_d is the detector area in square centimeters and Δf is the noise equivalent bandwidth of the system that limits the detector output noise. When D^* is specified, it is normalized to a 1-cm² area and a 1-Hz noise equivalent bandwidth. With D^*, a larger value corresponds to a higher sensitivity. The units of $\frac{cm-Hz^{1/2}}{Watts}$ is also known as *Jones*. In addition, there is a blackbody D^*, where the radiant power on the detector is that of a blackbody, so the D^* is a broadband response that is a function of temperature and frequency $D^*(T,f)$.

For photon detectors, spectral D^* is an increasing function to a peak D^* near the cutoff frequency. Figure 8.12 shows the typical spectral D^*. The cutoff wavelength occurs when the incident wavelength does not exceed the material bandgap energy. The blackbody D^* is the equivalent sensitivity of the detector over all of the blackbody emitted wavelengths. The blackbody D^* is always less than the peak D^* because the detector does not respond to the blackbody wavelengths beyond the detector cutoff frequency.

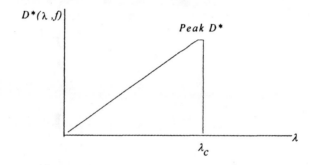

Figure 8.12 Spectral D^*.

One of the more common questions addressed by sensor designers and analysts involved with the use of detectors and SNR calculations is: "Does my SNR increase or decrease with a larger or smaller detector?" While this may seem like a simple question, the answer is, like many answers, "it depends." We consider the solution as an exercise in detection of resolved and unresolved sources.

Consider a simple sensor with a single lens and a single round detector as shown in Figure 8.13. The sensor is a large distance from the source, so that the image of the source is one focal length from the lens. Also, the atmospheric and optical transmissions are assumed to be 1 (i.e., there are no losses). Resolved sources (sometimes called extended sources) are those that more than fill the detector's instantaneous field-of-view (IFOV) as shown in Figure 8.13. Because the target is larger than the detector's FOV, not all of the targets emitted radiation that enters the sensor's input aperture falls on the detector. Any radiation leaving the source that is outside the sensor's FOV cannot fall on the detector.

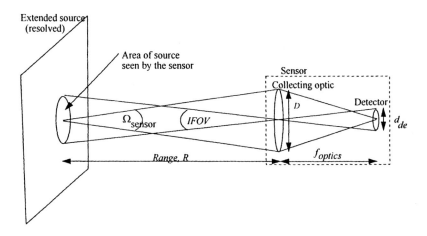

Figure 8.13 Resolved source.

The resolved-source example is one that is common in imaging systems because a large number of detectors (i.e., a detector array or scanned detector) are designed to image a single source. Therefore, the detectors may view only a small part of the entire target. The common problem seen in most applications for the resolved source is to determine the amount of the target flux impinging on the detector. We treat the sensor as a spectral instrument. The first source quantity considered, as usual, is the emittance of the source $M(T, \lambda)$. If the target is not a blackbody, then the emittance is given by $\varepsilon(\lambda)M(T, \lambda)$, where $M(T, \lambda)$ is the emittance of a blackbody at the temperature of the target. Assuming a Lambertian source, the radiance of the source is given by

$$L(T, \lambda) = \frac{\varepsilon(\lambda)M(T, \lambda)}{\pi} \quad [\text{W/cm}^2\text{-sr-}\mu\text{m}] \quad (8.25)$$

The radiance here applies to the entire source surface if the emissivity and temperature of the source are uniform over the source area. Only flux from within the source area corresponding to the sensor *IFOV* is seen by the detector. Therefore, an effective intensity (as seen by the sensor) can be given for the area viewed by the detector. The area of the source seen by the detector is

$$A_s = \frac{\pi R^2 [IFOV]^2}{4} \quad [\text{cm}^2] \quad (8.26)$$

where R is the range from the source to the sensor and is given in centimeters. Also, the small-angle approximation is used where the sine of the *IFOV* is equivalent to the angle itself when measured in radians. This is a reasonable approximation for angles less than 5 deg.

The equivalent intensity of the area seen by the sensor can now be calculated. The intensity is given by the source area multiplied by the radiance:

$$I(T,\lambda) = L(T,\lambda)A_s = \frac{\varepsilon(\lambda)\,M(T,\lambda)\,R^2\,[IFOV]^2}{4} \quad [\text{W/sr-}\mu\text{m}] \qquad (8.27)$$

This is only the intensity provided by the source area seen by the sensor. A sensor with a larger *IFOV* views a larger source area, and, hence sees a larger intensity. However, the intensity given radiates outward from the source over the entire hemisphere. Only the flux directed into the entrance aperture of the sensor is collected onto the detector. The intensity is converted into flux on the detector by multiplying the sensor's solid angle by the intensity. The sensor's solid angle (as seen by the source) is given by

$$\Omega_{sensor} = \frac{\pi D^2}{4R^2} \qquad [\text{sr}] \qquad (8.28)$$

The intensity for a flat source falls off with the cosine of the off-axis angle (see Chapter 5), so it is assumed that the diameter of the sensor's entrance pupil is small compared with the range. Now, the flux into the sensor's entrance pupil (and subsequently onto the detector) is

$$\Phi(T,\lambda) = I(T,\lambda)\Omega_{sensor} = \frac{\pi D^2 IFOV^2}{16}\varepsilon(\lambda)M(T,\lambda) \quad [\text{W/}\mu\text{m}] \qquad (8.29)$$

This is an important equation because the power on the detector is not a function of range. With the assumptions given in this section, the equation shows that no change in flux is observed by moving the sensor closer to or farther from the target. The only significant changes in flux from geometric considerations are due to the diameter of the sensor's entrance aperture and the instrument's IFOV. For a rectangular FOV, the process is the same with the exception that the source area is calculated for rectangular area. The rest of the above procedure applies.

Broadband instruments collect flux over some band of wavelengths. To compute this broadband flux, (8.29) is integrated over wavelength:

$$\Phi = \frac{\pi D^2 IFOV^2}{16}\int_{\lambda_1}^{\lambda_2}\varepsilon(\lambda)M(T,\lambda)d\lambda \quad [\text{W}] \qquad (8.30)$$

Because detector output voltage (or current) can ideally be considered directly proportional to flux on the detector, we can measure this quantity directly. The output voltage of a detector is determined by placing the detector responsivity inside the integral of (8.30).

The NEP for the detector is estimated by

$$NEP(\lambda) = \frac{\sqrt{A_d \Delta f}}{D*(\lambda)} \qquad [\text{W}] \qquad (8.31)$$

where the detector frequency is operating in a flat response region. The SNR can now be determined for a waveband:

$$\frac{\Phi}{NEP} = \frac{\pi D^2 IFOV^2}{16\sqrt{A_d \Delta f}} \int_{\lambda_1}^{\lambda_2} \varepsilon(\lambda) M(T, \lambda) D * (\lambda) d\lambda \quad \text{[unitless]} \quad (8.32)$$

Finally, we can simplify (8.32) by providing the detector area as $\pi d_{det}^2/4$ and setting $IFOV$ to d_{det}/f. In both cases, d_{det} is the linear diameter (in centimeters) of the detector. Now the SNR becomes

$$\frac{\Phi}{NEP} = \frac{\sqrt{\pi} \, D^2 d_{det}}{8 f^2 \sqrt{\Delta f}} \int_{\lambda_1}^{\lambda_2} \varepsilon(\lambda) M(T, \lambda) D * (\lambda) d\lambda \quad \text{[unitless]} \quad (8.33)$$

There are a number of qualitative relationships brought out by (8.33). Some general rules that describe the SNR of a detector viewing a resolved source are

- A small focal length and large optics diameter is desired (a small f-number). This relationship gives a squared (very strong) improvement in SNR.
- A larger detector diameter (or root of the area) gives a larger SNR, but poorer spatial resolution.
- A larger detectivity is desired (directly related).
- A smaller bandwidth is desired (related by the root).

Optimization of these parameters yields a system that can see very small changes in source exitance.

When the background photon flux is much larger than the signal flux and photon noise is the dominant noise source, we have the case of *background limited infrared photodetection (BLIP)*. This is the case where the background (nonsource) light on the detector is larger than the signal flux. For terrestrial infrared systems, this case is common. The background objects including ground, ocean, and sky path radiance is that of 300 deg K objects. These take up the majority of the FOV. The targets, or sources of interest, in the FOV are small and the temperatures (and corresponding emissions) are similar to that of the backgrounds such that the overall flux contributions are small. This situation corresponds to the unresolved source case.

We now consider the case where the source is unresolved (i.e., the source is smaller than the IFOV). For sources that do not fill the sensor's IFOV, the analysis is very similar to that of the previous analysis. The exception here is that the source emittance is only considered over the size of the source for the signal calculation. The $D*$ is given to be BLIP where the $D*$ is considered to be viewing objects that are around 300 deg K. Most ground-based sensors can be considered BLIP as terrestrial objects are close to the temperature at which most $D*$ are specified. This is the same $D*$ that was given in the resolved case, assuming that the resolved source was at a typical terrestrial temperature. Consider the geometry of the unresolved target case in Figure 8.14.

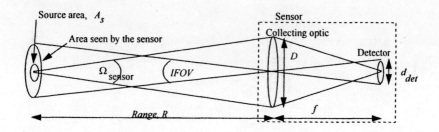

Figure 8.14 Unresolved source.

Small sources are typically specified by an intensity parameter. To obtain a better understanding of the radiometric configuration, however, we start with the exitance of the source. If the source is Lambertian, the source radiance is

$$L(T,\lambda) = \frac{\epsilon(\lambda)M(T,\lambda)}{\pi} \quad [\text{W/cm}^2\text{-sr-}\mu\text{m}] \tag{8.34}$$

The intensity of the source is the radiance integrated over the source area. For a uniform radiance source:

$$I(T,\lambda) = L(T,\lambda)A_s = \frac{\epsilon(\lambda)M(T,\lambda)A_s}{\pi} \quad [\text{W/sr-}\mu\text{m}] \tag{8.35}$$

To determine the amount of flux on the detector, the sensor's solid angle (as seen by the source) is required:

$$\Omega_{sensor} = \frac{\pi D^2}{4R^2} \quad [\text{sr}] \tag{8.36}$$

Again assume that the diameter of the sensor's entrance pupil is small compared with the range. The flux on the detector is now

$$\Phi(T,\lambda) = I(T,\lambda)\Omega_{sensor} = \frac{\epsilon(\lambda)M(T,\lambda)A_s D^2}{4R^2} \quad [\text{W/}\mu\text{m}] \tag{8.37}$$

Note the flux dependence on range. The broadband flux is calculated by integrating the previous equation over wavelength:

$$\Phi(T,\lambda) = \frac{A_s D^2}{4R^2} \int_{\lambda_1}^{\lambda_2} \epsilon(\lambda)M(T,\lambda)d\lambda \quad [\text{W}] \tag{8.38}$$

where, again, this value can be measured directly because the detector output voltage is proportional to input flux.

Using (8.31) for detector background-limited noise, the SNR becomes

$$\frac{\Phi}{NEP} = \frac{A_s D^2}{4R^2 \sqrt{A_d \Delta f}} \int_{\lambda_1}^{\lambda_2} \varepsilon(\lambda) M(T,\lambda) D * (\lambda) d\lambda \qquad (8.39)$$

Where the source is smaller than the sensor FOV, the guidelines for SNR are

- A decrease in range gives a squared improvement.
- A larger optics diameter is desired and gives a squared improvement.
- A larger detectivity is desired and is related directly.
- A smaller detector is desired and gives a root improvement.
- A small bandwidth is desired and gives a root improvement.

A BLIP scenario assumes that the target signal is small compared with the background signals. The background signal limits the detection of the signal through the specification of $D*$, where $D*$ is usually given for 300 deg K backgrounds. If the background is cooler, $D*$ becomes higher, and if the background is hotter, $D*$ becomes lower. In some space applications where a small signal is discerned from backgrounds that are extremely cold, the $D*$ can be extremely high. If a detector is viewing a small target inside a furnace, where the background is high in temperature, then the $D*$ can be very low. BLIP conditions are usually satisfied in most tactical scenarios and many strategic scenarios. Images with the ground, ocean, and horizontal atmospheric backgrounds provide a large majority of BLIP conditions. However, space and vertical atmospheric backgrounds are cold and are characterized by different BLIP conditions.

The resolved SNR and the unresolved SNR can be compared directly if BLIP conditions are met. This would mean that the source temperature for the resolved case would be around 300 deg K. For the unresolved case, the background is also near 300 deg K. We also assume that the target signal is not too far from 300 deg K, so that the $D*$ does not vary significantly. It is worthwhile to evaluate the SNR as a function of detector size to determine the optimal SNR configuration of a sensor. We provide this comparison through the following example.

Example

A round object at 310 deg K is positioned in front of a 300 deg K background. The source is 10m in diameter at a range of 100m. A round detector is operating in a 9- to 10-μm band, where the $D*$ is considered to be a constant $1 \times 10^{10} \frac{cm-Hz^{1/2}}{Watts}$ for BLIP conditions. The $D*$ can be considered constant over this band and is approximately the same for the 310 and 300 deg K conditions. The signal is chopped with blades at 300 deg K so that no differential signal is seen when the detector views the background. Assume that the emissivities of the blades, background, and signal are 1 (i.e., no losses). The noise equivalent bandwidth is 1,000 Hz. The optical system has a 10-cm entrance aperture diameter and a 20-cm focal length. Assume that the optical transmissions of the atmosphere and the sensor are 1. Determine the optimal round detector size for the largest SNR along with an estimation for the SNR.

The solution is provided by using (8.39) for the unresolved case with band-averaged values for D^*, emissivity, and differential emittance:

$$\frac{\Phi}{NEP} = \frac{A_s D^2}{4R^2 \sqrt{A_d \Delta f}} \varepsilon \Delta M D*$$

(8.33) is used for the resolved case with the same band-averaged assumptions:

$$\frac{\Phi}{NEP} = \frac{\sqrt{\pi}\, D^2 d_{det}}{8 f_{optics}^2 \sqrt{\Delta f}} \varepsilon \Delta M D*$$

The differential emittance can be found using the blackbody equation within the 9- to 10-μm band for a source of 300 deg K and a source of 310 deg K. The corresponding emittances are 3.119 mW/cm² and 3.672 mW/cm², respectively, giving a differential emittance of 0.553 mW/cm². If all of the above parameters are placed in the above equations and the detector size is varied, the resulting plot is shown in Figure 8.15.

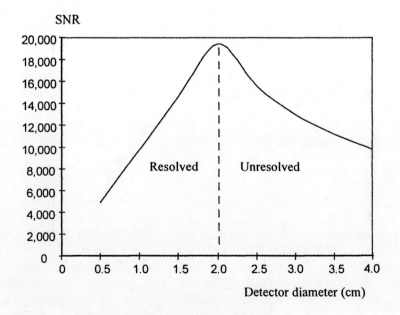

Figure 8.15 SNR as a function of detector diameter.

With a small detector size, the source is resolved so that the signal grows with an increase in detector diameter. Once the detector diameter reaches the angular subtense of the source, the SNR is at a peak. The source subtends an angle of 5.7 deg that is matched by a 2-cm detector diameter at a focal length of 20 cm. At this detector diameter, the SNR is just under 20,000. As the detector size becomes larger, the source becomes unresolved. The source power decreases with the source area where the noise decreases with the root of the source area, so the SNR decreases. An important SNR lesson in this example is that a detector's SNR is at a maximum when the detector is matched to view the source area.

8.7 DETECTOR ANGULAR SUBTENSE

While the SNR is maximum when a detector is matched to a source, a single detector sample of a source does not provide an image of the source. That is, a single radiometric sample of the source exitance cannot be mapped into a reasonable spatial depiction of a target. A large number of detector samples is desired across the source so that a high-resolution picture can be constructed of the source exitance. The detector angular subtense (DAS) was developed to described the resolution limitations of the detector size. For a square detector, there are two DASs: a horizontal DAS and a vertical DAS. Figure 8.16 shows that the DAS is the detector width or height divided by the focal length.

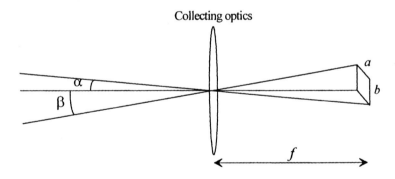

Figure 8.16 Detector angular subtenses.

For the horizontal DAS of a square detector, the DAS is the detector width divided by the effective focal length of the optics:

$$\alpha = \frac{a}{f} \qquad [\text{rad}] \qquad (8.40)$$

nd the vertical DAS is the detector height divided by the effective focal length:

$$\beta = \frac{h}{f}. \qquad [rad] \qquad (8.41)$$

The horizontal and vertical DASs are usually specified in milliradians; the quantities described in (8.40) and (8.41) must therefore be multiplied by 1,000. The DAS describes the very best resolution that can be achieved by an EO or I^{2}R system due to the detector size limitations. Two point sources of light separated by 0.1 mrad cannot be resolved as two sources if a system has a focal plane array with DASs of 0.25 by 0.25 mrad.

Example

Two stars are separated by 2 mrad and are imaged by an EO sensor with a CCD detector array. The CCD array has rectangular detectors that are 35 μm in width and 50 μm in height with 100% fill factor (this means that the detectors are placed side by side with no gaps between detectors). The sensor has a focal length of 20 cm. Given that the sensor resolution is detector limited (the optical blur diameter is smaller than the detector), determine whether the two stars can be discriminated. The solution is determined simply by taking the DAS and comparing it with the star separation. The horizontal DAS is $\alpha = (35x10^{-6}m/20x10^{-2}m)x1000 = 0.175$ mrad and the vertical DAS is $\beta = (50x10^{-6}m/20x10^{-2}m)x1000 = 0.250$ mrad. With a 100% fill factor, the images of the stars would be separated by around 11 detectors in the horizontal direction or around 8 detectors in the vertical direction. Note also that the DAS for a circular detector is described only by the detector diameter divided by the effective focal length.

The IFOV of a detector is sometimes confused with DAS, but Holst [10] describes the IFOV as the solid angle (in steradians) subtended by a detector. In the tradition of other solid angles, the IFOV would be defined as the detector area divided by the square of the effective focal length. It is quite common to see IFOV described in the same manner as the DAS, however, where the IFOV is given as both DASs in milliradians. Both conventions are used throughout this book.

8.8 SCANNING CONFIGURATIONS AND IMPLEMENTATIONS

A scan mechanism is required for sensor systems that have either a single element or a linear detector array in order to move the image formed by the optics across the detectors. In this way, the detectors are distributed evenly over the image so that the image can be spatially represented. A scanner is not required for sensor systems that have large two-dimensional arrays. When infrared sensors were first developed and built in the 1970s and 1980s, the detector semiconductor manufacturing technology was not mature enough to build large format arrays. Therefore, a variety of scanning approaches were derived to allow either single element or linear array detectors to be scanned to form an image. Since that time, the detector technology has matured significantly. Today, there are scientific EO CCD arrays that are 7,000 by 9,000 pixels on a single integrated wafer. The infrared community has developed 640 by 480 arrays in the midwave, while the technology is still somewhat behind in the LWIR. With respect to their detector array configurations, imaging sensor systems can be broadly grouped into two categories: *scanning* and *staring*. Scanning systems can be further subdivided into *serial* and *parallel* systems. Table 8.1 summarizes the array configurations and scanning types.

Table 8.1

Detector/scanning configurations

Configuration	Single element	Linear array	2-D array
Serial scanning	x	x	
Parallel scanning		x	x
Staring			x

Staring systems, as the name implies, are the system approach where the image plane area is filled with detectors that have been distributed onto a single substrate. With this approach, there is no scanning required, though there is usually some type of periodic shuttering for gain-and-level correction. Staring-array systems offer the potential of having a much higher sensitivity than scanning systems because they have much longer integration times. In the SNR calculation of (8.33), the temporal frequency is replaced with $1/(2\tau_{int})$ for these systems. The higher sensitivity does come at the price of lower resolution because the detector elements have spacing limitations in both the horizontal and vertical directions. Note that a relatively new technique known as microscanning helps to circumvent this problem. Microscanning is a technique, whereby the line-of-sight is stepped or dithered to increase the effective spatial sampling frequency.

For serial-scan systems, a scan mechanism is required to move the scene over a linear array of one or more fixed detector elements. The elements are aligned horizontally and scanned sequentially in a two-dimensional rectilinear raster pattern to form an image as shown in Figure 8.17. This type of system requires a two-axis scanner to produce an image. One variation of the scanning pattern shown is to have a number of adjacent detectors in the active or in-scan direction to help increase the SNR. The number of adjacent detectors is defined as the number of time-delay-integration (TDI) detector, N_{tdi}.

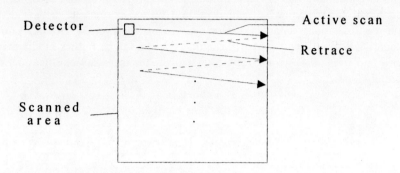

Figure 8.17 Two-dimensional serial (raster)-scan pattern.

One line corresponds to the detector output for a single active scan across the image (shown in Figure 8.17). The line direction, or in-scan direction, which is the direction of highest speed (15,750 lines per second for the U.S. RS170 standard 525-line format), is usually the horizontal direction. The cross or vertical-scan direction is slower (60 fields per second for U.S. RS170 standard 525-line format). Sometimes the detector-line rate and number of lines do not correspond to the RS170 television standard, so a special display or a reformatter is required to interpolate the line information.

The parallel-scan system consists of a linear array that is orthogonal to the cross-scan direction. This linear array has one or more columns of detectors, while the number of detectors in the vertical direction is sufficient to cover the desired FOV. Three primary types of parallel-scan configurations are shown in Figure 8.18.

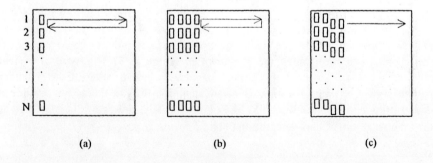

Figure 8.18 Parallel-scan configurations. (a) Bidirectional interlaced scan; (b) bidirectional interlaced scan with TDI; (c) unidirectional scan with TDI.

Figure 8.18(a) shows a linear array of N detector elements. The image formed by the optics is scanned horizontally across the linear array during which the detectors are sampled. At the end of the first scan, a slight tilt of the scanner in the vertical direction is applied and the image is scanned across the detector array in the opposite direction. This provides coverage in the region of the image plane, which was not covered with the first scan. Each scan forms a field and the two fields are combined to form a frame that represents a complete image. The field rate for these types of systems is typically 60 Hz, which produces a frame rate of 30 Hz. This scan configuration is used in the common module FLIR, which was developed by the military. The second figure, Figure 8.18(b), is similar to that of the first with the addition of serial (horizontal scan) TDI. TDI is when two or more detectors are sampled in the in-scan direction at the same positions and the output of the detectors are added together. The noise adds in rms fashion and the signal adds directly giving a $\sqrt{N_{tdi}}$ improvement in SNR. The last configuration, Figure 8.18(c), includes a staggered array of detector elements along with TDI to allow the entire image plane to be covered with a single scan. In the detector array configuration, the increased number of detector elements in the vertical field of view (VFOV) gives redundant sample points.

There are several associated parameters that are used to describe scanning-type sensor systems. The scanner efficiency, denoted by η_{sc}, is the ratio of the amount of time that the detectors actively sample the sensor's FOV during one frame time t_s for a given frame rate F_r:

$$\eta_{sc} = t_s F_r \tag{8.42}$$

where t_s is in seconds, and F_r is in frames per second. There are two primary reasons for the efficiencies being less than unity. The first is that the scanner traverses a distance larger than the horizontal field of view (i.e., dead space or radiometric reference scanning), and second, the turnaround time of the scanner is significant because of the mass of the mirror. Typically, scanner efficiencies vary from as low as 50% to greater than 90%.

Two other parameters are the number of samples per horizontal DAS and the number of samples per vertical DAS. The number of samples per horizontal DAS is sometimes called the *serial scan ratio*, N_{ss}, and the number of samples per vertical DAS is sometimes called the overscan ratio N_{os}. There are other definitions for the serial-scan ratio [13]; however, we use the nomenclature described above. These parameters have been called by other terms, such as the number of samples per horizontal IFOV and the number of samples per vertical IFOV. Consider the detectors shown in Figure 8.19.

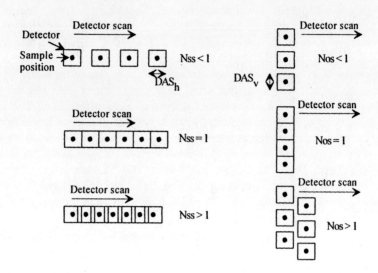

Figure 8.19 Serial-scan and overscan ratio.

N_{ss} of less than 1 shows that detector sample is taken at positions that are farther apart than the horizontal DAS (or in linear dimensions, the separation of the detector samples are farther apart than the horizontal detector dimension in meters). The distance between samples in meters is sometimes called the *pixel pitch*. The sample spacing for N_{ss} equal to 1 gives a sample distance in radians that is equal to the horizontal DAS. Finally, the N_{ss} greater than 1 case gives a sample spacing that is less than the horizontal DAS.

N_{os}, or the overscan ratio, of less than 1 means that the vertical sampling distance is farther apart than the vertical DAS. An N_{os} equal to one gives a vertical sample spacing equal to the vertical detector angular subtense, and an N_{ss} greater than 1 gives a vertical sample spacing smaller than the vertical DAS.

The angular distance between samples is related to the serial-scan ratio and the overscan ratio along with the horizontal and vertical DASs. The horizontal angle between samples is given by

$$\delta_h = \frac{\alpha}{N_{ss}} \quad [\text{rad}] \tag{8.43}$$

and in the vertical direction

$$\delta_v = \frac{\beta}{N_{os}}. \quad [\text{rad}] \tag{8.44}$$

For staring arrays, $\delta_h \le \alpha$ and $\delta_v \le \beta$, so that N_{ss} and N_{os} are both less than 1 unless microscanning is employed. Microscanning takes the staring array and jitters it in a small pattern as shown in Figure 8.20, so that N_{ss} and N_{os} are greater than 1.

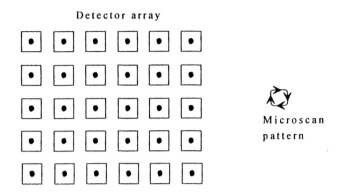

Figure 8.20 Microscanning.

The entire array traverses the microscan pattern shown to the right of the detector array in Figure 8.20. The detectors are sampled a number of times (typically four times) during this scan pattern which lowers the effective sampling distance.

Another important parameter is the detector dwell time t_d. This is defined as the time required for a detector to scan over a single point. The detector dwell time is given by

$$t_d = \frac{\alpha}{v_s} \quad \text{[sec]} \tag{8.45}$$

where α is the in-scan detector angular subtense in mrad and v_s is the angular scan velocity in mrad/sec. For staring arrays, the dwell time is sometimes approximated as $1/F_r$ if the scan efficiency is nearly 1 (the frame transition time is the only nondetection period). Also, the bandwidth of the SNR equations given in this chapter is typically matched to the detector dwell time, so that $\Delta f \approx 1/(2t_d)$.

A wide variety of methodologies (hardware) implement the scanning approaches discussed above. Scanning systems include mechanical, acousto-optical, and holographic scanning techniques. The most widely used are mechanical because they are the most efficient and well developed. There are two basic types of mechanical scanners: *parallel* and *converging beam* devices. These types differ by where the scanner is placed in the optical path. The parallel beam scanner is placed in front of the final image-forming lens and the converging beam scanner is placed between the final lens and the image. Of the mechanical scanners, the two most common are the rotating reflective drum and oscillating mirror or galvanometric scanner that are shown in Figure 8.21.

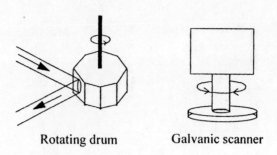

Rotating drum   Galvanic scanner

Figure 8.21 Common mechanical scanners.

The rotating-drum scanner is ideal for systems that require a high constant velocity with which it can operate with very little loss in distortion of the imagery. These scanners are used primarily with parallel-beam systems because with a converging system, the oscillatory motion changes the focal point and hence causes severe distortion. The disadvantages of this scanner are cost and the inability to start and stop the scanner at a particular time and position. The galvanometric mirror oscillates periodically between two stops and can work with either parallel or convergent beams. This type of scanner is less expensive and more flexible than the drum scanners, but the oscillation becomes unstable near the field edges.

8.9 DETECTOR TRANSFER FUNCTIONS

Whether a detector is scanned or staring, the detector integrates the incident flux over the spatial extent of the detector. That is, the output voltage of a detector can be determined by

$$V = \int_{\lambda_1}^{\lambda_2} \int_{-\infty}^{\infty} \int_{-\infty}^{\infty} i(\lambda, x, y) R(\lambda, x, y) dx dy d\lambda \quad [V] \tag{8.46}$$

where $i(\lambda, x, y)$ is the incident image irradiance on the detector corresponding to the spatial image and $R(\lambda, x, y)$ is the detector responsivity. From here, we are investigating the spatial transfer, so we drop the wavelength dependence where it is understood that we have the integrated flux for the output voltage. Consider the rectangular detector in Figure 8.22, centered at $[x', y']$.

The detector integrates the incident image flux and the output voltage is sampled. A single-output value represents the image flux integrated by the detector:

$$o(x', y') = \int_{-\infty}^{\infty} \int_{-\infty}^{\infty} i(x, y) rect(\frac{x-x'}{a}, \frac{y-y'}{b}) dx dy \tag{8.47}$$

resulting in a single voltage value located at $[x',y']$. Equation (8.47) is similar to a convolution where the output signal can be represented as

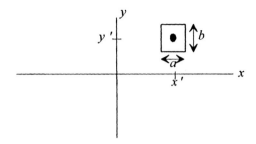

Figure 8.22 Detector spatial integration.

$$o(x',y') = i(x,y) * *rect(\tfrac{x}{a}, \tfrac{y}{b})|_{x=x', y=y'} \qquad (8.48)$$

where the substitution is performed only after the convolution is performed. The limitation on the single value can be accomplished by sampling. The evaluation at the single point is a single sample that can be obtained by the multiplication with $\delta(x-x', y-y')$ and then integrated (see the sifting property in Chapter 2).

For a staring array, scanning detector, or scanning linear array, the detector integrates the incident flux and, for now, we assume that the output is sampled at certain locations. Consider the detector sampling geometry of Figure 8.23.

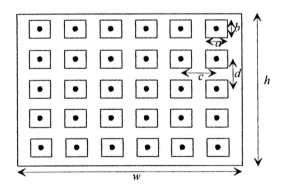

Figure 8.23 Detector sampling geometry.

The detector dimensions are a by b and are sampled at distances of c by d. The array size is limited by width w, and height h. This geometry describes the majority of detector configurations including the scanned types mentioned in the previous section. The sampling distances c and d are simply a/N_{ss} and b/N_{os}, where the sampling distances can describe detector overlapping. The output from the sampled system is a set of discrete values that can be represented by

$$o(x,y) = \{[i(x,y) * *rect(\tfrac{x}{a}, \tfrac{y}{b})]comb(\tfrac{x}{c}, \tfrac{y}{d})\}rect(\tfrac{x}{w}, \tfrac{y}{h}) \tag{8.49}$$

To understand the image transfer in linear system terms, we take the Fourier transform of (8.49):

$$O(\xi, \eta) = \{[I(\xi, \eta)ab\,sinc(a\xi, b\eta)] * *cd\,comb(c\xi, d\eta)\} * * wh\,sinc(w\xi, h\eta) \tag{8.50}$$

(8.50) describes many aspects of detector sampling and provides a good deal of guidance in system design. If we assume an infinite detector array (not limited by w and h), then the output spectrum is the image spectrum multiplied by a *sinc* function and convolved with a *comb*. Figure 8.24 shows a representation of the spectrum in the horizontal direction.

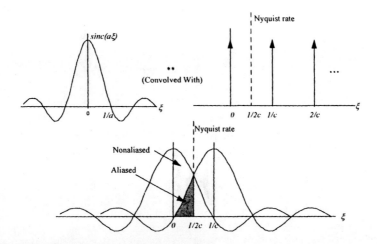

Figure 8.24 Detector output signal spectrum.

The *sinc* function has a width of $2/a$ to the first zeroes. It is generally assumed that the energy past the first zeroes is insignificant, but in reality it should be given consideration. If this function is convolved with the *comb* function as in Figure 8.24, overlapping occurs (i.e., aliasing) if $1/a$ is larger than $1/2c$. Also, the figure shows the case where $1/a$ is equal to $1/c$ (this is the case where the samples are spaced at exactly the detector width) and significant aliasing occurs. The shaded region shows the folded detector spectrum that corresponds to high spatial frequencies being represented as aliased lower frequency signals. This case corresponds to a nonmicroscanned staring array with spacings equal to the detector widths. To avoid or control aliasing and spurious responses, three characteristics can be exploited.

The first characteristic that we discuss is the least likely to be controllable. If the input scene (input to the sensor) has a spatial frequency bandlimit that ensures the highest spatial frequencies are less than $1/2c$ and $1/2d$ in cycles per meter (note that $c = N_{ss}a$ and $d = N_{os}b$) or less than N_{ss}/α and N_{os}/β in cycles per radian, very little aliasing occurs. This requires that the scene viewed by the sensor has negligible spatial frequencies above these requirements. For high-altitude surveillance sensors, this is extremely unlikely. For tactical close engagements, it is more likely. Closer objects have a lower spatial frequency content.

A better approach is to limit the input spatial frequencies by the optical design. This is to say that the optical MTF has cutoff frequency of d_{optics}/λ that matches N_{ss}/α or N_{os}/β in cycles per milliradian. Finally, the best approach is to oversample the detector output with at least two samples per DAS in both directions. This ensures that little aliasing and few spurious responses occur. In this situation, the limiting spatial frequencies are no longer N_{ss}/α and N_{os}/β, they are the first zeroes of the *sinc* function, $1/\alpha$ and $1/\beta$. The best design includes an oversampled detector with an optical design that matches these spatial frequencies.

With any of the three above requirements met, the transfer function of the detector can be approximated by

$$H_{det}(\xi, \eta) = sinc(\alpha\xi, \beta\eta) \tag{8.51}$$

where the DAS are given in milliradians and ξ and η are given in cycles per milliradian. In using (8.51), be careful to meet aliasing requirements. This equation is commonly used with systems that inherently have significant aliasing, thus providing poor results in the estimation of system performance.

It is difficult to ensure meeting nonaliasing requirements. For commercial CCDs, infrared staring arrays, and even for second-generation FLIRs, oversampling by a factor of two cannot be achieved so the sensor design results in limited aliasing. The reduction in input spectrum by the optics effectively reduces the resolution in the output image. Some aliasing can be tolerated and image quality is a tradeoff between resolution and aliasing. Some guidelines are given in Chapter 10 for these tradeoffs in terms of human perception of imagery.

Finally, we did not consider the last function in (8.50), the window function that describes the number of detector samples in the spatial array. Note that for a large array, the *sinc* function width is small. The convolution of any function with a function of small width decreases the resolution of the function only by a small amount. Remember that convolution with the zero-width delta function yields the exact function. A staring array of 1,000 by 1,000 detectors, where the detector spacing is very close to the detector width, produces a *sinc* function 1/1,000th the width of the detector *sinc*. The convolution of the output spectrum with the window *sinc* results in very little resolution effect. With an array of 4 detectors by 4 detectors, the convolution could affect the resolution significantly.

Example

A longwave (assume a 10-μm wavelength) infrared sensor has an entrance aperture diameter (entrance pupil) of 6 cm and a horizontal detector angular subtense of 0.1667 mrad. The horizontal sampling frequency is 6 samples per milliradian. If the system images a point source, determine the percent of horizontal aliasing of the signal.

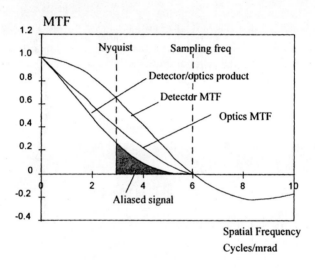

Figure 8.25 Example sensor.

The solution (Figure 8.25) can be determined by representing the point source as a *delta* function. Therefore, the input is $i(x,y) = \delta(x,y)$. This is a separable function so that $i(x) = \delta(x)$. The spectrum of the input is determined by the Fourier transform of the spatial input, so that $I(\xi) = 1$. That is, the spectrum is uniform over all frequencies. The detector output signal is

$$o(x) = [i(x) * h_{optics}(x) * \tfrac{1}{\alpha}rect(\tfrac{x}{\alpha})]comb(\tfrac{x}{\delta_x})$$

where h_{optics} is the optics impulse response, $\tfrac{1}{\alpha}rect(\tfrac{x}{\alpha})$ is the detector impulse response, α is the horizontal DAS, and δ_x is the angular distance between samples. The only limit to the output spectrum of the detector is the optics MTF and the detector MTF, before detector sampling. In the frequency domain, the output spectrum is

$$O(\xi) = [I(\xi)MTF_{optics}(\xi)MTF_{det}(\xi)] * \delta_x comb(\delta_x \xi)$$

The optics MTF is assumed to be diffraction-limited (from Chapter 7) and is plotted in Figure 8.25. The detector MTF is plotted in the same figure for the given detector angular subtense. The optics and detector MTFs are multiplied before the sampling function. The sampling is characterized by the *comb* function (ref. Chapter 2), where the comb spikes are located at the origin and then every 6 cycles per milliradian apart. If the detector output spectrum is greater than 3 cycles per milliradian apart (this is the spatial Nyquist rate associated with the system), the convolution of the detector output spectrum results in an aliased signal. The amount of aliased signal, for the image of the point source, is the shaded area shown. This area divided by the total area of the output spectrum is calculated to be around 9%.

We assume here that the atmospheric MTF is negligible. Because the sampling occurs after the optics MTF and the detector MTF (i.e., the sensor front end), the signal is aliased at this point in the system MTF cascade. The optical MTF, the detector MTF, and the sample spacing can be adjusted to reduce or eliminate aliasing. This is a common practice in sensor design, where the optics, detector, and sampling characteristics are matched to reduce aliasing while providing good image transfer. The electronics, display, and human perception MTFs are performed after the scene is sampled and cannot eliminate the aliasing.

8.10 INFRARED DETECTORS

Research into infrared detection began over 50 years ago before World War II, although few resources were devoted to this area, as a significant amount of research funds was devoted to radar technology. While research continued over the years, it was not until the 1960s that the first FLIR sensors were developed and fielded. These earliest FLIRs were serial scanners, which were discussed in Section 8.8. The technology continued to mature in the 1970s and 1980s, which resulted in the common module or first generation FLIR. The sensors were based on linear mercury cadmium telluride (HgCdTe) detector arrays that contained 60, 120, or 180 elements. These detector arrays are characterized by low quantum efficiency, limited dynamic range and sensitivity, single-band operation (8 - 12 µm), and are sensor-noise-limited.

The late 1980s and early 1990s saw the development of the second generation FLIR. These were typically based on an array that was 480 elements long and two or more detectors in the horizontal direction for TDI. These FLIRs provided a number of improvements over first-generation sensors, including improved resolution, sensitivity, dynamic range, uniformity, and detector performance approaching that of BLIP.

Third generation FLIRs are still in the research-and-development phase, with only brass-board prototypes completed. The third-generation sensors are primarily defined by large format arrays (e.g., 640 by 480 detectors) operating either in the MWIR or LWIR. These sensors will provide increased performance over second-generation FLIRs in the areas of dynamic range, uniformity, sensitivity, and resolution.

All three detector arrays discussed above require cryogenic cooling. The future growth for infrared detectors is expected to included multicolor arrays (i.e., a detector array that can detect in both the midwave and the longwave) and increasing usage of uncooled detectors (both pyroelectric and bolometric) as their performance continues to improve in resolution, responsivity, response time, and inherent noise.

8.11 ELECTRO-OPTICAL SYSTEMS

CCDs are currently the detector of choice for EO systems. Since they were invented in 1970, they have replaced photoemissive tube devices and have evolved to a sophisticated level of performance. They are likely to progress for many years to come, however Fossum [14] states that they are likely to be replaced in the long term by active pixel sensors (APS). APSs are defined as detector arrays that have at least one transistor within the pixel unit cell. APS sensors will eliminate the need for perfect charge transfer. That is, amplification occurs before the transfer of charge. APS sensors have been constructed at Toshiba that have 640- by 480-element arrays with good performance.

In the meantime, 2,048- by 2,048-pixel CCDs have been constructed [15] with dual-color focal plane arrays that operate in both the 400- to 640- and 640- to 800-nm bands. In fact, the world's largest singleband CCD was recently constructed [16] by Phillips at 7,000 by 9,000 pixels on a single wafer. The charge transfer efficiency (CTE) is currently 0.9999995 for a 1,620-electron charge packet [17]. Readout noise is down to 2- to 3-electron rms for systems with on-chip amplifiers. The largest arrays sizes that are physically possible (assuming current wafer sizes and 5-μm pixels) is 16,000 by 21,000. Also, the quantum efficiency is better than 0.5 over most wavelengths of interest.

The near term will bring a large number of improvements to CCDs. A 4,096- by 4,096-CCD array is being developed (the cinema CCD) to replace film in motion pictures. A 4,096- by 4,096-detector camera is also being developed for deployment on the Hubble telescope. The pixel dimensions for both of these CCDs will be 9 μm on a side. Dark current will be reduced further and the well capacity will be further optimized for particular applications. Finally, high-speed clocking will continue to be developed.

The pace of technology today yields many surprising developments in extremely short periods. EO systems have an added development thrust (over infrared systems) in that they are used widely in commercial and consumer applications. An example is the digital photographic camera, where the market continues to grow and the price of the system continues to decrease. These and many other EO systems, will continue to improve at rapid rates.

8.12 NOISE

Detector noise was treated in a general sense in this chapter, with detectivity providing the means to calculate the noise signal on the output of a single detector. Overall system noise includes photon noise (from both the signal and the background), fixed-pattern noise, generation-recombination noise, shot noise, Johnson noise, $1/f$ noise, and many other noise sources. Usually, one of these noise sources dominates the SNR of the system. The cause and impact of each of these are very different.

Photon noise is the fluctuation in detector output signal due to the discrete arrival of photons, and the corresponding electron state transition. For scanning single- and linear-detector infrared systems, the photon noise from the background flux is usually the performance-limiting noise source. These scanning systems account for a large majority of longwave infrared systems. However, a large number of midwave infrared systems are currently built in the staring-array configuration. These systems are typically performance-limited by fixed-pattern noise. Fixed-pattern noise is the spatial "fixed" noise caused by the nonuniformity in the detector (and electronics) responses over the array. Each of the detectors in an array has its own input flux to output voltage characteristic. These characteristics are caused by detector material variations, impurities, imperfections, electrical circuit tolerances, and so on. The result is a fixed, noisy pattern on the output of the sensor when viewing a uniform scene. In the infrared, the fixed-pattern noise is treated as an increase factor of the background-limited case. In the EO wavelengths, the fixed-pattern noise is treated as an rms electron count in the output of a CCD charge transfer. The other noises described above are those associated with readout electronics (generation-recombination noise, shot noise, Johnson noise, and $1/f$ noise) and are described in the following chapter dealing with electronics.

Noise is treated differently in EO systems and infrared systems. In EO systems, the dominant noise sources are readout noise (includes Johnson, $1/f$ noise, and other electronic noises) and fixed-pattern noise. In infrared systems, the dominant noise source is the background photon noise (i.e., BLIP). Also, the approach to noise analysis in EO systems is in equivalent rms electrons in a charge packet. In the infrared, detectivity is used to determine an NETD and a minimum resolvable temperature difference (MRT). For fixed-pattern-noise-limited infrared systems, a three-dimensional noise analysis is performed that modifies the NETD values. Because the noise treatments are different in EO and infrared systems, we reserve the treatments until Chapter 11 ("Infrared Systems") and Chapter 12 ("Electro-Optical Systems").

EXERCISES

8.1 Describe the differences between photon and thermal detectors. Provide a list of applications for both photon and thermal detectors.

8.2 Determine the bandgap energy of a detector material required to detect 10-μm monochromatic light. What occurs with a larger bandgap? A smaller bandgap?

8.3 A Mercury cadmium teluride (HgCdTe) detector has intrinsic concentration such that n_n and n_p are both 1×10^{13} per cm^3. The detector has a quantum efficiency of 60% once it is cooled to 77 deg K. For a 50-μm detector depth, determine the change in voltage with respect to incident irradiance.

8.4 Determine the gain for a photomultiplier with six stages and a secondary emission ratio of 5.

8.5 Describe the difference between radiant and photopic responsivity. Why is photopic responsivity used and what are the risks associated with its use?

8.6 A round InSb detector is 1 cm in diameter with a perfect output filter of 1 kHz in bandwidth. Determine the noise equivalent power of the detector. State your assumptions.

8.7 Derive the SNR equations for the resolved and unresolved source cases where the detector is square and the source is square.

8.8 List all possible noise-reduction activities that apply to both the resolved and unresolved source cases.

8.9 Calculate the vertical and horizontal detector angular subtenses for a 30- by 40-μm detector located at the image plane of a 25-cm focal-length lens. Given that the detector is sufficiently sampled in both directions, how can the detector modulation transfer function be improved?

8.10 Explain why second-generation infrared sensors are BLIP limited as compared with first-generation sensors.

8.11 For a bidirectional scanning sensor system that has a 60-Hz field rate (30-Hz frame rate) and 480 samples in the scan direction, determine the detector dwell time. (Assume that the scanner efficiency is unity.)

REFERENCES

[1] Pinson, L., *Electro-Optics,* New York: Wiley, p. 103, 1985.

[2] *The Photonics Dictionary,* Pittsfield, MA: Lauren Publishing Company, 1996.

[3] Dereniak, E., and G. Boreman, *Infrared Detectors and Systems,* New York: Wiley, p. 86, 1996.

[4] Crowe, D., P. Norton, T. Limperts, and J. Mudar, *Detectors in the Electro-Optics Components,* Vol. III of the *Infrared and Electro-Optics Handbook,* Bellingham, WA: SPIE and ERIM, p. 177, 1993.

[5] Streetman, B., *Solid State Electronic Devices,* Englewood Cliffs, NJ: Prentice Hall, p. 65, 1980.

[6] Hergert, E., "Expanding Photodetector Choices Pose Challenges for Designers," *The 1996 Photonics Design and Applications Handbook,* Pittsfield, MA: Lauren Publishing Company, p. 119, 1996.

[7] Grum, F., and R. Becherer, *Optical Radiation Measurements,* Vol. 1, Academic Press, 1979.

[8] Finney, P., "IR Imaging With Uncooled Focal Plane Arrays," *Sensors, The Journal of Applied Sensing Technology,* pp. 36-52, Oct. 1996.

[9] Saleh, B., and M. Teich, *Fundamentals of Photonics,* New York: Wiley, p. 664, 1991.

[10] Holst, G., *CCD Arrays, Cameras, and Displays,* Winter Park, FL: JCD Publishing, 1996.

[11] Aikens, R., "Replacing Charge-Coupled Devices in Many Imaging Applications," *The Photonics Design and Applications Handbook,* Pittsfield, MA: Lauren Publishing, 1996.

[12] Dereniak, E., and G. Boreman, *Infrared Detectors and Systems,* New York: Wiley, p. 152, 1996.

[13] Shumaker, D., J. Wood, and C. Thacker, *FLIR Performance Handbook,* DCS Corporation, 1988.

[14] Fossum, E., "Active Pixel Sensors and Are CCDs Dinosaurs?" *SPIE Proceedings: CCD and Solid State Optical Sensors,* San Jose, CA, 1993.

[15] Stubbs, C., et al., "A 32 Megapixel Dual-Color CCD Imaging System," *SPIE Proceedings: CCD and Solid State Optical Sensors,* San Jose, CA 1993.

[16] Holloran, M., "7,000 by 9,000 Imaging on an Integrated CCD Wafer," *Advanced Imaging,* Jan. 1996.

[17] Janesick, J., and T. Elliott, "Sandbox CCDs," *SPIE Proceedings: CCD and Solid State Optical Sensors 5,* San Jose, CA 1995.

Chapter 9

Electronics

The function of electronics is to transform the detector output into a signal that can be viewed or processed (Figure 9.1). This transformation must be accomplished with minimal degradation of system performance. Issues of primary importance are low noise, high gain, low-output impedance, large dynamic range, and good linearity. While there are entire books written on sensor electronics, we will provide an introduction along with simplistic models that will permit the inclusion of electronics in a system-performance estimate.

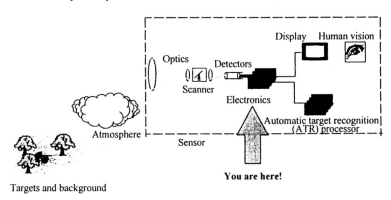

Figure 9.1 System electronics component.

9.1 DETECTOR CIRCUITS

A large number of detector circuits are used to provide a voltage or current that is proportional to the irradiance on a detector. Bipolar, JFET, and MOSFET technologies are all used in detector amplification. We focus here on operational amplifiers (op-amps) because they are extremely common in detector circuit design. The circuits given here are useful as amplifiers for photovoltaic, photoconductive, bolometer, and pyrometer detectors.

For photovoltaic detectors, there are two types of circuits that can be used as detector preamplifiers: the *voltage-mode circuit* and the *current-mode circuit*. The photovoltaic detector can be modeled with a voltage-current relationship that is very similar to that of a diode. The difference between the light-sensitive diode and the typical diode is that the voltage-current relationship shifts with detector illumination. The magnitude of the voltage is related to the number of incident photons on the detector. This voltage-current relationship is the nonlinear diode equation

$$I = I_s[e^{\frac{eI'}{\beta kT}} - 1] \qquad [\text{Amps}] \qquad (9.1)$$

where

I_s is the detector saturation current in amps
e is the charge on an electron (1.6×10^{-19} coulombs)
β is an efficiency factor (1 for ideal, and 2 or 3 for the real case)
k is Boltzmann's constant (1.38×10^{-23} J/deg K)
T is the detector temperature in degrees Kelvin.

While voltage is proportional to the number of incident photons, current is not linear with the number of photons.

Consider the voltage-current relationship and the voltage-mode circuit shown in Figure 9.2. The circuit is the standard noninverting op-amp circuit where the input current is negligible (recall that one of the ideal op-amp characteristics is that no current enters the op-amp). When the current is held to zero, there is a voltage change when the detector is illuminated. (This is illustrated in the voltage-current relationship of Figure 9.2.)

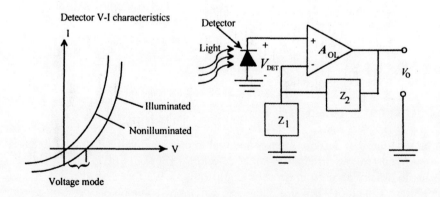

Figure 9.2 Voltage-mode detector circuit.

The ideal op-amp has an infinite open-loop gain. When the op-amp gain is sufficiently large (i.e., much larger than the closed-loop gain), the gain of the circuit can be approximated by the closed-loop gain equal to

$$A_v = \frac{V_0}{V_{Det}} = \frac{z_1 + z_2}{z_1} \qquad \text{[unitless]} \qquad (9.2)$$

where z_1 and z_2 are the impedances shown in the blocks of Figure 9.2. For an op-amp with an open-loop gain that is not much larger than the closed loop gain, the voltage gain of the circuit is

$$A_v = \frac{V_0}{V_{Det}} = \frac{z_1 + z_2}{z_1 + \frac{z_1 + z_2}{A_{OL}}} \qquad \text{[unitless]} \qquad (9.3)$$

and A_{OL} is the op-amp open-loop gain. The output voltage of this circuit is in phase with the input voltage. Also, the voltage-mode circuit is desirable when a high-input impedance and a low-output impedance is desired.

The second type of photovoltaic detector circuit is the current-mode detector circuit shown in Figure 9.3. Recall that another ideal op-amp characteristic is that the voltage across the input terminals of the op-amp is essentially negligible (i.e., grounded in the configuration shown). Forcing the voltage to approach zero causes the detector to establish a current when the detector is illuminated, as pointed out on the detector voltage-current relationship graph. The input impedance of the detector is not used in the determination of the gain. For an ideal op-amp, where the open-loop gain is large compared with the closed-loop gain, the amplifier voltage gain is

$$A_v = \frac{V_o}{V_{Det}} = -\frac{z_2}{z_1} \qquad \text{[unitless]} \qquad (9.4)$$

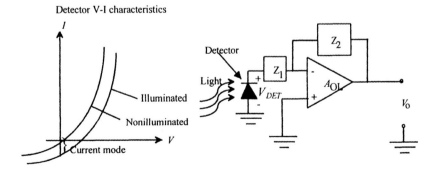

Figure 9.3 Current-mode detector circuit.

The gain for a nonideal op-amp with a lower open-loop gain is

$$A_v = \frac{V_o}{V_{Det}} = -\frac{Z_2}{Z_1}\frac{A_{OL}Z_1}{(1+A_{OL})Z_1+Z_2} \quad \text{[unitless]} \quad (9.5)$$

This type of circuit is used for high-gain, nominal-input impedance, and low-output impedance. However, there is a signal inversion (i.e., the signals are 180 deg out of phase) from the detector voltage to the output voltage.

Example

Determine the voltage gain for the detector amplifier shown in Figure 9.4. Assume that the operational amplifier is an ideal amplifier (i.e., large open-loop gain). The solution is given as the current mode gain of (9.4), where z_1 is the impedance of R_1 and C_1 in parallel. The impedance z_2 is R_2 and C_2 in parallel. The impedance of a resistor and capacitor in parallel is

$$z_1 = \frac{R_1}{1+j\omega R_1 C_1}$$

where ω is the angular electrical frequency. The voltage gain of the amplifier is

$$A_v = -\frac{z_2}{z_1} = -\frac{\left(\frac{R_2}{j\omega R_2 C_2+1}\right)}{\left(\frac{R_1}{j\omega R_1 C_1+1}\right)} = -\left(\frac{R_2}{R_1}\right)\left[\frac{j\omega R_1 C_1+1}{j\omega R_2 C_2+1}\right]$$

Note that when the frequency is small, the voltage gain is $-R_2/R_1$, and when the frequency is large, the voltage gain is $-C_1/C_2$.

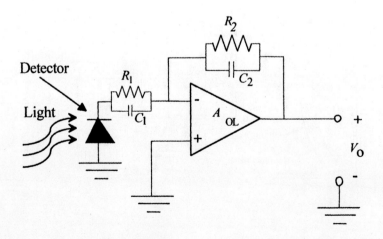

Figure 9.4 Example detector circuit.

The photoconductive detector provides a change in conductivity with incident photons. The change in conductivity is inversely proportional to the change in resistivity, so the detector can be modeled as a resistor. Therefore, the detector has a variable resistance that changes inversely proportional to the number of incident photons. The detector circuit is shown in Figure 9.5.

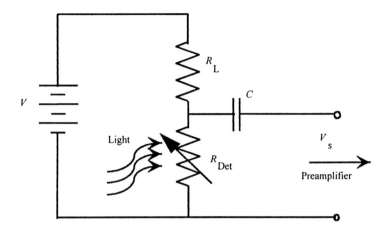

Figure 9.5 Photoconductor circuit.

If the circuit is operated in constant source current mode [1] and $R_L \gg R_{Det}$, the output voltage is proportional to the change in detector resistance:

$$V_s = \frac{V \Delta R_{Det}}{R_L + R_{Det}} \qquad [V] \qquad (9.6)$$

(9.6) can be written in terms of the detector parameters given a sinusoidal irradiance incident on the detector:

$$V_s = \frac{V R_{Det}}{R_L + R_{Det}} \frac{A_d \eta_q E_{Det} t}{N(1 + \omega^2 t^2)^{1/2}} \qquad [V] \qquad (9.7)$$

The detector characteristics are: A_d is the area of the detector, η_q is the quantum efficiency of the detector in converting photons to electrons, E_{Det} is the incident photon flux on the detector in photons per square centimeter per second, t is the average free-carrier lifetime, N is the total number of free charges in the element when there is no incident photon flux, and ω is the angular modulation frequency. The circuit has a capacitor on the output so that the circuit is ac-coupled. That is, the output voltage only represents the changes in the detector resistance. The capacitor can be removed to provide a signal proportional to the detector incident flux.

The bolometer can also be modeled as a resistor, but the resistance does not change with a photon-level conversion. The resistance is a measure of resistive material temperature (see thermal detectors in Ch. 8). At any rate, the circuit shown in Figure 9.4 can also be used for the bolometer circuit. The capacitor defines the time constant of the system and must be sized accordingly, taking into account the desired cutoff frequency. The pyrometer is modeled with a capacitor, where the capacitance changes with the temperature of the capacitor. To detect the change in capacitance, the light is chopped with rotating blades. A typical circuit for the pyrometer is shown in Figure 9.6.

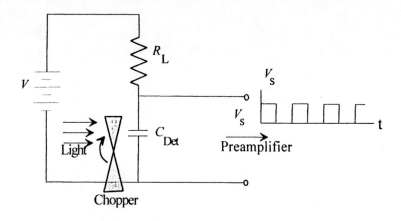

Figure 9.6 Pyrometer circuit.

The photovoltaic circuits shown adequately amplify the input signals, but the other circuits discussed require additional amplification. This can be accomplished by placing the outputs of the circuits at the terminals of the photovoltaic detector. That is, the output of the bias circuits in Figures 9.5 and 9.6 can be considered inputs to the photovoltaic amplifiers in Figures 9.2 and 9.3 (i.e., either the voltage or current mode). This first amplifier is usually called the *preamplifier* because there are other amplifiers in the total system electronics. The preamplifier is the most important circuit in the entire electronics network. The noise associated [2] with the first stage in a network has the predominant effect on the overall noise figure for the network. The system designer should always try to minimize the noise produced in the first stage.

9.2 CONVERSION OF SPATIAL AND TEMPORAL FREQUENCIES

For scanned detectors, there is a relationship [3] between the electronic temporal frequency and the system spatial frequency. This relationship depends on the scan velocity of the detector across the image (or the image velocity across the detector). There are two conversions: one is a function of metric spatial frequency (cycles per meter) and the other is a function of angular spatial frequency (cycles per milliradian). Consider the cases shown in Figure 9.7. Regardless of whether the detector is serial-scanned or parallel-scanned, it takes a particular amount of time for the detector to traverse the image. In the first case, the detector traverses the horizontal FOV in a time t_{scan}. The conversion from spatial frequency to electronics temporal frequency is

$$f_e[Hz] = \xi[cyc/mrad]\frac{FOV[mrads]}{t_{scan}[sec]} \qquad [Hz] \qquad (9.8)$$

The relationship is usually inverted to give the electronics transfer function in terms of spatial frequency.

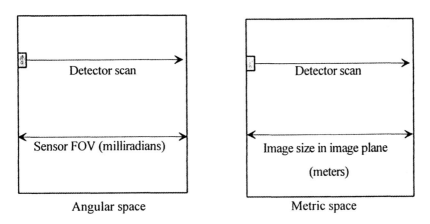

Figure 9.7 Detector scans across image space.

The second case of Figure 9.7 shows a detector scanning across the image plane, where the image plane is given in dimensions of meters. Sometimes it is convenient to work in the spatial frequency domain where spatial frequency is given in cycles per meter in the image plane. For this case, the conversion is

$$f_e[Hz] = \xi[cyc/meter]\frac{ImageSize[meters]}{t_{scan}[sec]} \qquad [Hz] \qquad (9.9)$$

In general, the electrical frequency f_e can be expressed in terms of the scan velocity

$$f_e = v\xi \qquad [Hz] \qquad (9.10)$$

where the velocity is in meters per second or milliradians per second and the spatial frequency is in cycles per meter or cycles per milliradian, respectively. One of the basic understandings of an EO engineer is the relationship between spatial and temporal frequencies.

The scan velocity can also be written in terms of the detector angular subtense (DAS) and the detector dwell time:

$$v = \frac{DAS}{t_{dwell}} \quad \text{[m/s or mrad/s]} \tag{9.11}$$

The DAS is the detector size in the scan direction divided by the system focal length. DAS is the angle subtended by the detector onto the angular object space. The dwell time (see Chapter 8) is the time required for a target edge to scan across the detector element.

Example

The boards and spaces on a picket fence subtend a fundamental spatial frequency of 1.5 cycles per milliradian (as seen from a sensor's point of view) in the horizontal scanning direction. The sensor has a 5-deg (87.3 mrad) FOV and operates at 30 frames/sec. Assuming a 100% scan efficiency, determine the electrical temporal frequency on the output of the detector that corresponds to the picket-fence fundamental frequency. The solution is given by (9.10) if the scan velocity can be determined. With a 100% scan efficiency, the 30 frames/sec requires that $(87.3 mrads) \times 30 / \sec$, or 2,618 mrad/s is the scan rate. With a picket fence fundamental of 1.5 cycles per milliradian:

$$f_e = (2,618mr/s)(1.5cy/mr) = 3,927Hz \tag{9.12}$$

or just under 4 kHz. Higher spatial frequencies require higher electronic frequencies, and lower spatial frequencies require lower electronic frequencies.

Now that temporal frequencies can be converted to spatial frequencies, we can address the image blur associated with the detector integration time as the detector is scanned across the FOV. The detector integration (sometimes called *detector sample-and-hold*) can be performed on the detector chip or off the detector chip on a circuitboard. The detector integration circuit sums the detector signal for some integration time and then is reset for the next integration time. Image blur due to this integration is a rectangular function only in the scan direction with a blur size, in time, equal to the integration time t_{int}. The temporal blur (in milliradians) is converted to a spatial blur with the scan velocity, $\alpha_{int} = v t_{int}$. The spatial blur due to detector integration time is present only in scanned imaging systems (not staring systems as the detector remains stationary for the integration time) and can be described with an impulse response:

$$h_{int}(x,y) = \frac{1}{\alpha_{int}} rect(\frac{1}{\alpha_{int}}) \tag{9.13}$$

where the corresponding detector integration transfer function is

$$H_{int}(\xi, \eta) = sinc(\alpha_{int}\xi) \tag{9.14}$$

The image blur only occurs in the scan, or horizontal, direction. The function in (9.13) can be considered a separable function where $h(y) = \delta(y)$. The transfer function is also separable where $H(\eta) = 1$.

9.3 ELECTRONICS TRANSFER FUNCTION

The electronics transfer function for a particular sensor describes the frequency limitations of the electronic amplifiers and the corresponding filters. Usually, the electronics transfer function provides bandwidth well beyond any other component in the system, so filters can be added to bound the noise content without reducing system performance.

A common method for modeling the electronic filter transfer functions is to consider the low-frequency response separately from the high-frequency response. The independent transfer function variables are then converted from temporal frequency to spatial frequency and applied as components of the horizontal, or scan-direction, transfer function of the system.

A typical low-pass amplifier filter design [4] is the lagging (output voltage lags the input voltage) low-pass single pole filter as shown in Figure 9.8(a). The transfer function for this filter can be written in terms of its single pole response:

$$H(f_e) = \frac{p}{f_e + p} \qquad \text{[unitless]} \tag{9.15}$$

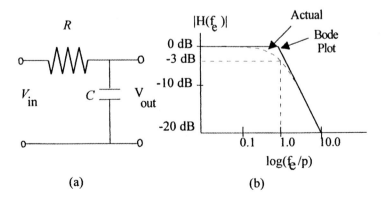

Figure 9.8 Low-pass filter (a) circuit; (b) transfer function.

where the pole is $p = 1/(2\pi RC)$. With some mathematical manipulation, the magnitude of the transfer function can be written as

$$|H(f_e)| = \frac{1}{\sqrt{1+(\frac{f_e}{p})^2}} \qquad \text{[unitless]} \qquad (9.16)$$

The magnitude of the transfer function for this filter is shown in Figure 9.8(b). The magnitude in decibels can be calculated by

$$|H(f_e)|_{dB} = 20 \log |H(f_e)| \quad \text{[unitless]} \qquad (9.17)$$

The transfer function can be easily converted to the spatial frequency domain for application as a system component simply be modifying p to a spatial pole $1/(2\pi vRC)$ and f_e with ξ in (9.15). Also note that v is the scan velocity in milliradians per second. The MTF for the filter can then be written as

$$MTF_{LowPass}(\xi) = \frac{1}{\sqrt{1+(\frac{\xi}{p})^2}} \quad \text{[unitless]} \qquad (9.18)$$

The order of the filter can be increased using the same filter cascaded (the output of one filter feeds the input of the next filter). These are called *ladder filters*. There are a large number of different ladder circuits that have been developed, including both Butterworth and Chebyshev filters. The spatial frequency equivalent MTF corresponding to the magnitude function [5] for the nth order Butterworth filter is

$$MTF_{LowPass}(\xi) = \frac{1}{\sqrt{1+(\frac{\xi}{p})^{2n}}} \quad \text{[unitless]} \qquad (9.19)$$

A similar filter can be designed for high-pass applications. This is the case for ac-coupled systems were the dc signals are removed from the output of the detector. In some cases, dc is added back to the ac signals for later display. These types of systems are called dc-restored systems. A simple, single-pole high-pass filter is shown in Figure 9.9(a) and the corresponding Bode plot is shown in Figure 9.9(b). The circuit shown in Figure 9.9 is a leading high-pass filter where the transfer function can be written in terms of the pole:

$$H(f_e) = \frac{f_e}{f_e+p} \qquad \text{[unitless]} \qquad (9.20)$$

where the pole is again at $p = 1/(2\pi RC)$. We are more interested, however, in the magnitude of the signal as it transfers through the system.

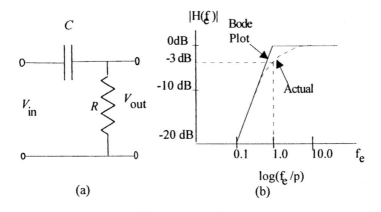

Figure 9.9 High-pass filter (a) circuit; (b) transfer function.

With some algebra, the magnitude of the function given in (9.20) is

$$|H(f_e)| = \frac{\frac{f_e}{p}}{\sqrt{1+(\frac{f_e}{p})^2}} = \frac{1}{\sqrt{1+(\frac{p}{f_e})^2}} \quad \text{[unitless]} \quad (9.21)$$

There are a large number of high-pass filters, with the Butterworth and Chebyshev filters being the more common. The transfer functions can be converted to the spatial frequency domain by changing the temporal frequency to a spatial frequency along with changing the pole to a spatial frequency with the scan velocity term $p = 1/(2\pi vRC)$. The high-pass filter MTF for an nth order Butterworth filter is

$$MTF_{HighPass}(\xi) = \frac{1}{\sqrt{1+(\frac{p}{f_e})^{2n}}} \quad \text{[unitless]} \quad (9.22)$$

The combination of the high pass and the low pass can implemented simply by multiplying their MTFs. In circuit design, the output of one filter feeds the input of the other filter. From Chapter 3, we know that in the time domain, the input signal of the first filter is convolved with the filter impulse response to result in the filter output signal. The output signal is then convolved with the impulse response of the second filter. The output of the second filter is the output of the filter system. Care must be taken in the characterization of the loading effects at each stage of analysis. In most cases, it is easier to work in the frequency domain where the transfer functions multiply.

9.4 NOISE

Entire books have been written on noise analysis in circuits. A complete treatment of circuit noise here is beyond the scope of this work; however, a cursory overview of the noise associated with detector electronics is appropriate. The noise components associated with the detector are described in Chapter 8. Noise components that are specific to EO and I²R systems are presented in Chapters 11 and 12, respectively. The noise components associated with the detector circuit and system electronics are Johnson, $1/f$ (or flicker noise), shot, microphonics, readout, and quantization noise. Each of these is addressed below.

Johnson Noise

Johnson [6] noise exists because all conductors exhibit thermal noise. Any material over the temperature of 0 deg K exhibits electrical noise from the thermal activity of the electron states. A resistor at some temperature, T, provides a noise level that is related to its resistance and temperature. In theory, capacitors and inductors do not exhibit thermal noise. In practice, even high-quality capacitors and inductors generate some noise. Thermal noise sources associated with resistors can be modeled as either a voltage source or a current source, as shown in Figure 9.10.

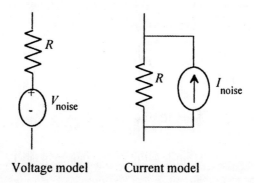

Voltage model   Current model

Figure 9.10 Johnson noise models.

The value of the rms noise voltage for the voltage model shown is

$$v_{Johnson} = \sqrt{4kTR\Delta f} \quad [V] \tag{9.23}$$

where k is Boltzmann's constant of 1.38×10^{-23} J/deg K, T is the temperature of the resistor in deg K, R is the resistance of the resistor, and Δf is the bandwidth over which the noise is measured. The equivalent current value for the second model is

$$i_{Johnson} = \sqrt{4kT\Delta f(1/R)} \quad [A] \tag{9.24}$$

Example

Determine the noise voltage for a 10 kOhm resistor at room temperature (300 deg K). The noise bandwidth is 10 kHz. The solution is given by (9.23), where

$$v_{Johnson} = \sqrt{4(1.38x10^{-23}J/K)(300K)(10000Ohms)(10000Hz)} = 1.29\mu V$$

Note that the rms thermal noise of the resistor is around a microvolt. A reduction in resistance, temperature, or bandwidth decreases the noise voltage.

1/*f* Noise

1/*f* noise, or *flicker noise*, accompanies any system where electron conduction is present [7]. This noise is due to surface imperfections caused during the fabrication process. The noise has a power spectrum that decreases with frequency, hence its name, and is more important at lower frequencies (from 0 to 100 Hz). The long-term drift of transistor amplifiers is usually the result of 1/*f* noise. Flicker noise can be described by an rms current:

$$i_{1/f} = \sqrt{KI_{DC}\frac{\Delta f}{f}} \quad [A] \tag{9.25}$$

where K is a constant that is specified for a semiconductor device, I_{DC} is the average (i.e., dc) current through the device, and Δf is the bandwidth.

Shot Noise

Shot noise in the electronics is the result of random current fluctuations caused by the discreteness of charge carriers when diffused across a semiconductor junction. The rms value for shot noise current is

$$i_{shot} = 2eI_{DC}\Delta f \quad [A] \tag{9.26}$$

where e is the charge of an electron, 1.6 x 10^{-19} coulombs. Both shot noise and Johnson noise have a power spectrum that is approximately constant across the frequency band. These are examples of *white noise*.

There is a difference in the way noise sources add versus typical voltage and current sources. DC voltages and currents are additive, and ac voltages and currents add vectorally (with amplitude and phase). However, noise sources add constructively. For two-noise voltage sources in series:

$$v_{total}^2 = v_1^2 + v_2^2 + 2\alpha v_1 v_2 \quad [V] \tag{9.27}$$

where α is the correlation coefficient for the noise sources. For uncorrelated noise sources, which includes the Johnson noise and the majority of other noise cases, the third term is zero and the noise sources add in quadrature. Two identical waveforms have a correlation coefficient of 1. In a few circumstances, noise sources are correlated, as in the case of ground-loop pickups of stray signals. The majority of sensor noise contributors are assumed to be uncorrelated.

There are many other types of noise. Diode noise, BJT noise, and FET noise are all combinations of shot and $1/f$ noise. Other noise sources include power source leakage, ground-loop pickup, and cable pickup (of electromagnetic fields). Some general guidelines in the noise reduction process are:

- Use filtering to limit the noise bandwidth.
- Match the input resistance of the amplifier to the detector.
- Reduce lead lengths as much as possible.
- Keep the power source clean. Decouple and regulate the power input to each board.
- Minimize any ground impedances. Ground planes are essential to isolate digital circuits from sensitive analog circuits.
- Keep digital grounds separate from analog grounds. They should connect only at one point (the point of lowest potential).
- Isolate high impedances, high-gain inputs from strong drive currents. This usually means shielding.
- Minimize magnetic loops. Reduce the loop area of wires, preferably with twisted pairs.

While the minimization of noise is, in general, frustrating, these general guidelines can simplify the noise-reduction process.

The *noise bandwidth* is defined differently than a network transfer function. It is not identical to the system bandwidth but describes the characteristics of the noise. The noise bandwidth is the frequency span of a rectangular-shaped power-gain curve equal in area to the area of the actual power gain versus frequency function. Consider the power spectrum (or power spectral density-PSD), $G(f)$, of the noise shown in Figure 9.11.

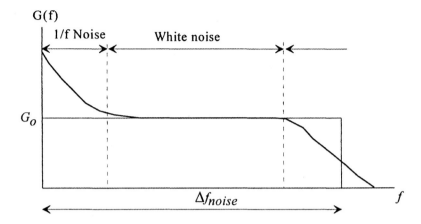

Figure 9.11 Noise power spectrum and noise bandwidth.

The noise bandwidth can be calculated by

$$\Delta f_{noise} = \frac{1}{G_o} \int_0^\infty G(f) df \quad [\text{Hz}] \tag{9.28}$$

Once the noise bandwidth is calculated, the amount of rms noise voltage in a 1-Hz bandwidth can be estimated:

$$v_{rms} = \sqrt{G_o \Delta f_{noise}} \quad [V/\sqrt{Hz}] \tag{9.29}$$

Two parameters that describe the noise associated with an amplifier or filter stage are the noise factor and the noise figure. The noise factor is defined as the input SNR normalized by the output SNR

$$F = \frac{S_i/N_i}{S_o/N_o} \quad [\text{unitless}] \tag{9.30}$$

The noise factor provides the noise figure in decibels. The definition for noise figure is

$$NF = 10 \log F \quad [\text{dB}] \tag{9.31}$$

An amplifier or filter stage with no noise will have an *NF* of zero. A well-designed amplifier should have an *NF* of less than or equal to 3 dB.

The noise factor allows the determination of critical design guidance in the staging of amplifiers and filters. Consider the cascaded network shown in Figure 9.12.

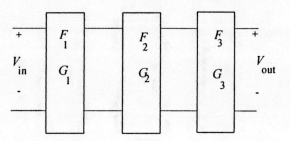

Figure 9.12 Cascaded network.

Let G describe the voltage gain and F describe the noise factor for a particular circuit in the cascaded network. The noise factor for the entire cascaded network can be estimated to be

$$F_{123} = F_1 + \frac{F_2 - 1}{G_1} + \frac{F_3 - 1}{G_1 G_2} \tag{9.32}$$

The impact of the first stage on overall system noise is higher given that the cascaded gains are larger than 1. Each stage should have a gain greater than 1 with the highest gain occurring at the first stage, where the sensor noise dominates.

9.5 MTF BOOST FILTER

The *MTF boost filter* is an active filter that provides gain in the compensation of MTF rolloff. The boost filter allows a boost to particular spatial frequencies while maintaining a unity transfer for low and high frequencies. Boost [8] is available from a variety of circuits. Here, we present a common representation:

$$MTF_{boost}(f_e) = 1 + (\frac{K-1}{2^N})[1 - \cos(\pi \frac{f}{f_{boost}})]^N \tag{9.33}$$

where K is the boost amplitude, N is the boost order, f is the temporal frequency of the circuit, and f_{boost} is the frequency that benefits the most from the boost. Figure 9.13 shows the boost gain as a function of temporal frequency for various boost amplitudes with an $N = 1$. The boost filter can be converted to spatial frequency using the temporal-to-spatial conversion given in Section 9.2 to yield

$$MTF_{boost}(\xi) = 1 + (\frac{K-1}{2^N})[1 - \cos(\pi \frac{\xi}{\xi_{boost}})]^N \tag{9.34}$$

The boost filter provides little gain at low frequencies and little gain at high frequencies. At the boost frequency, the signal is boosted by a factor of K. The spatial frequency version has the same shape and boost amplitude with a change in the independent variable.

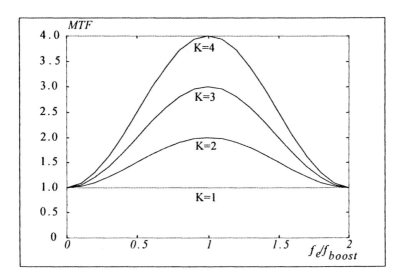

Figure 9.13 MTF boosting filter.

9.6 EO MUX MTF

The electro-optical multiplexer (EO mux) is an image converter. It provides infrared detector output signals from a linear array and their corresponding amplifiers to a visible linear light emitting diode (LED) array. The infrared signals light up the LEDs to an intensity (in the visible wavelengths, hence EO mux) proportional to the signal voltage. Consider the EO mux shown in Figure 9.14. The EO mux shown has a linear array of five infrared detectors, corresponding electronics, and LEDs to show the concept. In reality, common module FLIRs have 60, 120, or 180 detectors in a linear array.

A two-dimensional image is formed by the infrared lens onto an image plane. The front side of the scanner is reflective in the infrared wavelengths, and the scanner sweeps the image across the linear detector array in one direction. When the edge of the image is reached, the scanner reverses direction and sweeps the image back across the linear array. This backscan is accompanied by a small tilt of the scan mirror in the vertical direction to fill in between the forward scan lines to compensate for the gap between detector elements. The output voltages are taken from the infrared detectors, amplified, and fed to the visible LED array. The LED array is imaged by a visible lens and reflected off the backside of the scanner converging to a visible image plane. The image plane can be viewed directly by a human, or it can be imaged onto a vidicon tube for conversion to video output.

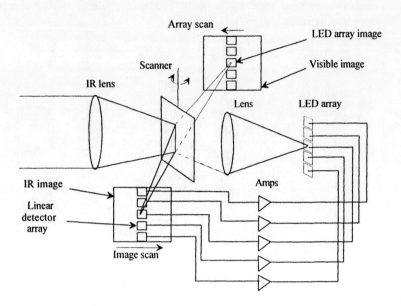

Figure 9.14   EO multiplexer.

The LED spatial extent has an MTF associated with it. The EO mux display is continuous in the horizontal direction with a continuous voltage out of each diode. In the vertical direction, the output is sampled as there are a discrete number of LEDs, just as the detectors sampled the original infrared image. The MTF treatment of the EO mux LED spatial characteristics is discussed in Chapter 10.

9.7 DIGITAL FILTER MTF

There are two major classes of digital filters: *infinite impulse response* (IIR) and *finite impulse response* (FIR). IIR filters have excellent amplitude responses but are more difficult than FIR filters to implement. FIR filters usually have more ripple than IIR filters. We focus here on FIR filters. We do not derive the transfer functions for these digital filters as there are references [7] that include these derivations. However, we are interested in the transfer functions as they affect the overall performance of our system.

The filters are shown in Figure 9.15 operating on a linear stream of pixel values. The output pixel signal level of the odd filter, in the case shown, depends on the value of five input pixels. The input pixel signal levels are multiplied by their corresponding coefficients and the products are summed to give an output pixel signal level. The input pixels are shifted by one pixel and the output pixel signal level is again calculated. This process continues through the stream of data.

There are artifacts at datastream edges (e.g., frame- or line-scan edges), where tricks such as doubling back data have to be played to reduce the artifacts.

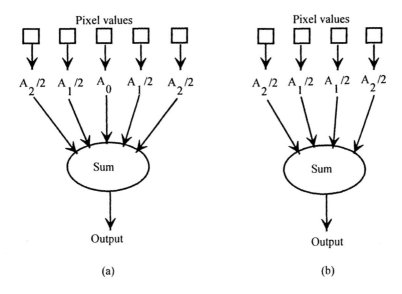

Figure 9.15 Filters with odd (a) and even (b) number of samples.

Note that the sum of the filter coefficients must be 1. Otherwise the average frame gain and offset change. The filter MTF in the filtering direction for an odd number of samples [9, 10] is

$$MTF_{dfilter}(\xi) = \sum_{k=1}^{N/2} A_k \cos[\frac{2\pi k \xi}{\xi_s}]$$ (9.35)

where $\xi_s = 1/S$ is in cycles per milliradian and S is the angular distance between pixel samples in milliradians. Note that with oversampling, S may be smaller than a DAS. The MTF for an even number of samples filter is

$$MTF_{dfilter}(\xi) = \sum_{k=1}^{N/2} A_k \cos[\frac{\pi(2k-1)\xi}{\xi_s}]$$ (9.36)

While these filters are written for one direction, they can be easily applied in the horizontal or vertical direction if separable (see Chapter 3) functions are used. Nonseparable two-dimensional filters are much more difficult to analyze.

9.8 CCDs

Most visible and some infrared staring arrays are CCDs. These CCDs comprise an array of detectors that sum the irradiance on the detectors for some integration time. The integration time is less than the frame time of typically around 1/30th of a second. The integrated charge is then moved out of the CCD along a predetermined path [11] under the control of clock pulses. The charge is stored and moved in a series of metal-oxide semiconductor (MOS) capacitors. Adapted from the *Infrared Handbook* [12], Figure 9.16 shows a typical three-phase readout cycle.

The electrode potentials at four different times are shown to depict the charge transfer. At time t_1, a low potential is held across the V_1 electrodes. At this time, the charge packets are located at the V_1 positions. A low potential is placed on the V_2 positions at t_2 and the potential is increased at the V_1 positions. This process is increased at t_3 causing even more of the charge to transfer to the V_2 positions. Finally at t_4, the only low potentials are located at the V_2 positions. This same process is followed to cause the charge packets to transfer to the V_3 positions.

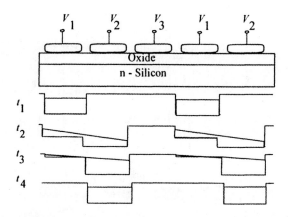

Figure 9.16   Three-phase CCD operation.

The process described above has a transfer efficiency that describes the completeness of charge packet transfer. Charge is typically left behind, causing a smearing effect. Holst [7] describes an MTF for the smearing effect:

$$MTF_{transfer} = \exp\{-N_{trans}(1-\varepsilon)[1-\cos(\frac{2\pi\xi}{\xi_{ts}})]\} \qquad (9.37)$$

N_{trans} is the total number of charge transfers from a detector to the output amplifier, ε is the transfer efficiency, and ξ_{ts} is the clocking spatial frequency. For horizontally clocked packets, where the horizontal FOV is much larger than a DAS:

$$\xi_{ts} \approx \frac{N_{trans}}{HFOV} \qquad (9.38)$$

Holst also points out that an average N_{trans} is half the maximal number of transfers. Transfer efficiencies range from 0.99 to 0.99999.

9.9 UNIFORMITY CORRECTION

In systems that have more than one detector, such as a scanned linear array or a staring array, more than one detector output signal provides the image. In these systems, the combination of the detectors, filters, and amplifiers may provide images that are not uniform in gain or offset. That is, the output images do not provide signals that are *uniform* functions of input irradiance. The output image in terms of gain and uniformity can be written as a function of the input image on the detector array:

$$O(x,y) = I(x,y)M(x,y) + B(x,y) \qquad (9.39)$$

where $M(x,y)$ is the gain and $B(x,y)$ is the offset. Equation (9.39) provides the equation for a line that gives the gain and offset for a particular pixel. Sometimes a *gamma* correction is required to force the throughput to be a line instead of a nonlinear input intensity-dependent gain and offset function. The gain can be considered the amplification of the signal and is sometimes known as *contrast* (in television systems). The offset is a standard background signal in order to control the level (or *brightness*). The gain depends on a number of contributors, including detector responsivity, amplifier gain, and filter calibration. The offset is more of an electronic source potential for ac-coupled systems and a combination of source potential and other contributors for dc-coupled systems.

For systems with staring arrays, each detector has a unique responsivity and some unique electronics. Staring arrays have been noted to be very nonuniform, especially in the infrared wavelengths. Figure 9.17 shows an image of a seashore with extremely nonuniform staring-array response. There are a number of techniques that are currently under investigation to correct for staring-array nonuniformities, including calibration and correction electronics. More extravagant solutions include retinal processors that adaptively correct the gain and offset based on the input imagery [13].

For scanned linear arrays, the detectors and electronics are common for each row. Therefore nonuniformities are seen more in line-to-line discrepancies. Figure 9.18 shows a nonuniform scanned image where the nonuniformities show up as streaks in the image. The correction for scanned imagers is typically a bank of amplifier and offset voltage adjustments or digital gain and offset equivalents.

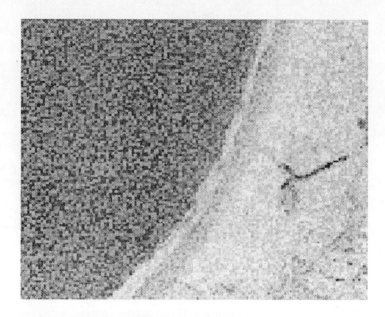

Figure 9.17 Nonuniform staring-array image.

Figure 9.18 Nonuniform linear-array image.

EXERCISES

9.1 Determine the transfer function and the 3-dB cutoff frequency for the following detector amplifier. Assume an ideal operational amplifier.

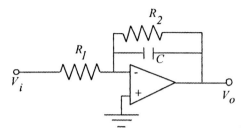

Figure 9.19

9.2 A HgCdTe photovoltaic detector has a resistance of 10 kOhms. Design a voltage-mode detector amplifier for the detector with a bandwidth of 5 Hz to 1 MHz and a closed-loop, midband gain of 30 dB.

9.3 A common-module FLIR system has 180 detectors that scan in the horizontal direction at a rate of 60 times per second (30 Hz and a 2:1 interlace pattern). The scan efficiency is 0.8 (20% of the time the scanner is performing some other task than scanning the image across the detector: turnaround time, stop time, retrace time, etc.) If the horizontal FOV is 2.75 deg and the detector scans across a picket fence with equally spaced boards 1 mrad apart, what is the

(1) Scan velocity.
(2) Temporal signal frequency corresponding to the fundamental harmonic of the fence.

9.4 Consider two resistors (R_1 = 50 kOhms and R_2 = 20 kOhms) that are connected in series. At a temperature of 400 deg K and a bandwidth of 5 MHz, calculate the rms noise voltage across each resistor and then across both resistors.

9.5 A system input SNR ratio is 100 and the system output SNR is 30. Determine the system noise factor and noise figure.

9.6 Plot the MTF for a boost filter with a K of 4 and a boost temporal frequency of 2 MHz. Assume a 50-mrad HFOV and a 52-μsec HFOV scan time.

9.7 An odd digital filter is described with the following coefficients: $A_o = 0.8$, A_1 $= 0.9$, $A_2 = -0.2$, and $A_3 = -0.5$. Sketch the MTF in terms of the normalized spatial frequency ξ/ξ_s.

9.8 Plot the MTF as a function of normalized spatial frequency (normalized to the clocking spatial frequency) for CCD transfer efficiencies of 0.99, 0.999, 0.9999, and 0.99999. Assume the number of transfers to be 300.

REFERENCES

[1]   Wolfe, W., and G. Zissis, *The Infrared Handbook*, Environmental Research Institute of Michigan, Office of Naval Research, Washington DC, pp. 11-32, 1993.

[2]   Krauss, H., C. Bostian, and F. Raab, *Solid-State Radio Electronics*, New York: Wiley, 1980.

[3]   Holst, G., *Electro-Optical Imaging System Performance*, Orlando, FL: JCD Publishing, p. 119, 1995.

[4]   Valkenburg, M., *Analog Filter Design*, New York: Holt, Rinehart, and Winston, p. 80, 1982.

[5]   Sedra, A., and K. Smith, *Microelectronic Circuits*, Philadelphia, PA: Holt, Rinehart and Winston, p. 771, 1991.

[6]   Watts, R., *Infrared Technology Fundamentals and System Applications: Short Course*, Environmental Research Institute of Michigan, June 1990.

[7]   Holst, G., *Electro-Optical Imaging System Performance*, Orlando, FL: JCD Publishing, p. 146, 1995.

[8]   Savant, C., M. Roden, and G. Carpenter, *Electronic Circuit Design*, Menlo Park, CA: Benjamin Cummings Publishing, p. A125, 1987.

[9]   *FLIR92 Thermal Imaging Systems Performance Model*, U.S. Army Night Vision and Electronic Sensors Directorate, p. ARG-6, Jan. 1993.

[10] Rabiner, R. L., and B. Gold, *Theory and Application of Digital Signal Processing*, Englewood Cliffs, NJ: Prentice-Hall, pp. 81 - 84.

[11] Streetman, B. G., *Solid-State Electronic Devices*, Englewood Cliffs, NJ: Prentice-Hall, NJ, 1980.

[12] Wolfe, W., and G. Zissis, *The Infrared Handbook*, Environmental Research Institute of Michigan and the Office of Naval Research, Ch. 12, 1993.

[13] Scribner, D. A., K. A. Sarkady, M. R. Kruer, and J. T. Caulfield, "Adaptive Retina-Like Preprocessing for Imaging Detector Arrays," *IEEE International Conference on Neural Networks*, Mar. 1993.

Chapter 10

Displays, Human Perception, and Automatic Target Recognizers

Displays are the interface between the I²R or EO sensor and the human vision system (Figure 10.1). The display converts the electrical signal from the I²R or EO sensor to a visible signal that is subsequently presented to the viewer. Occasionally, systems are designed where humans do not interpret the data, so displays are not required. Imaging missile seekers with automatic target trackers are a good example. Various levels of human interpretation of imagery are seen in the targeting community. One example that is increasing in success and popularity is the targeting sensor coupled to a computerized automatic target recognizer (ATR), automatic target cueing (ATC) system, or aided target recognizer (AiTR). We collectively refer to these automated target exploitation systems as ATRs.

The performance of displays can be characterized with a modulation transfer function (MTF), where the MTF depends on the resolution of the display. The human visual system also has a transfer function that is based on the resolution limits of the eye. Both these transfer functions are discussed; however, this chapter provides only an introduction on how to account for these "system" components.

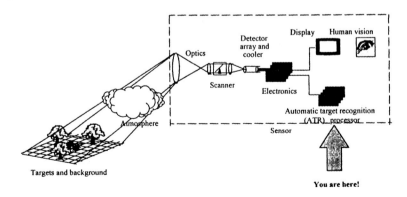

Figure 10.1 The last components of the system.

Automatic targeting systems are in early technology development, so the performance of these systems is difficult to quantify. An introduction to the ATR nomenclature is provided. ATR systems are typically nonlinear and do not lend themselves to linear systems modeling. Figure 10.1 identifies these last components in the EO and I^2R systems.

10.1 DISPLAYS

Much work is currently being performed in the analysis of displays. The evaluation of displays is still highly subjective because the primary basis of display design is viewer satisfaction. However, there is an increasing amount of work in the objective performance evaluation of these devices. Pinson [1] states that display criteria are usually given in terms of the probability that the viewer can perform specific tasks. These tasks involve extracting information from a displayed image. The probabilities are related to more tractable criteria, such as measurements of MTF, contrast, SNR, and resolution.

The magnification of a system depends on the sensor's imaging characteristics and the observer/display geometry. The definition of system magnification (which is different from the optics magnification) is the ratio of the angular image size seen by the observer to the angular size of the image as seen by the sensor input pupil (see Figure 10.2).

$$M = \theta_{image}/\theta_{object} \qquad (10.1)$$

This can be simplified so that the system magnification is not object dependent by writing

$$M = \frac{FOV_d}{FOV_v} \qquad (10.2)$$

where FOV_d is the display field of view in the vertical direction and FOV_v is the sensor input pupil vertical field of view. Note that the magnification is larger if the viewer moves closer to the display. However, the image becomes objectionable because the near-point limitation of the eye and the cognitive frame of the observer. Viewing distances are typically selected by observers to make the image display lines unnoticeable. In aviation systems, typical viewing distances vary from 20 to 28 in, depending on the height of the pilot.

System displays include cathode ray tubes (CRT), light emitting diodes (LED), and liquid crystal displays (LCD). These display systems are described in the following sections along with their corresponding resolutions and MTFs. Keep in mind that there are a large number of display types, each with its own MTF, that must be accounted for in the wide variety of sensor systems. The ones covered here are some of the more common displays.

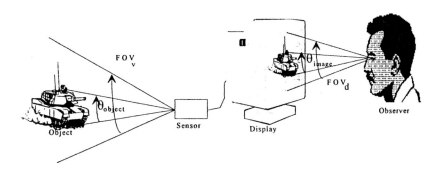

Figure 10.2 System magnification.

Example

A 3- by 4-deg sensor has an output image on a 15-cm-high display monitor. The observer is positioned 38 cm from the monitor. Determine the magnification of the system. The solution is given by (10.2) where the vertical FOV of the sensor is 3 deg. Typically, the horizontal FOV is larger than the vertical FOV and it is customary to specify vertical and then horizontal FOVs. The display vertical FOV is

$$FOV_d = \tan^{-1}\left(\tfrac{15}{38}\right) = 21.5 \qquad [\text{deg}]$$

The magnification is then 21.5/3 = 7.2. Note that a smaller sensor FOV or a larger display FOV gives a larger magnification.

10.2 CATHODE RAY TUBES

CRTs are probably the most common display system. A CRT comprises an evacuated tube with a phosphor screen. An electron beam is scanned across the phosphor screen in a raster pattern as shown in Figure 10.3. The beam direction is controlled with horizontal and vertical magnetic fields that bend the beam in the appropriate direction. The phosphor converts the electron beam into a visible point, where the visible luminance of the phosphor is related to the electron beam current (and voltage). The standard raster scan and interlace pattern are also shown in Figure 10.3. First the solid line shows a field pattern that is traced out on the screen. The dashed line shows a second field pattern that is interlaced between the first field lines. Both fields together provide 525 lines, where around 490 of the lines display information. The two fields in the standard 2:1 interlace pattern are collectively called a *frame*. The fields are presented at a rate of 60 Hz and frames are presented at 30 Hz.

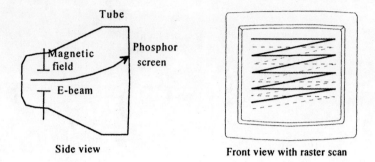

Side view   Front view with raster scan

Figure 10.3 Cathode ray tube.

The output luminance of the phosphor spot is related to the tube voltage in the linear region (i.e., the region that is not saturated) by

$$L = k(V - V_T)^\gamma \qquad (10.3)$$

where k is a constant, V_T is a threshold voltage, and γ is a display constant known as the display gamma. A high gamma provides more phosphor contrast between two different voltages.

A common CRT resolution assumption is that the electron beam spot and the corresponding luminescent spot is Gaussian in shape. The spot can be approximated by

$$S(x,y) = \frac{1}{2\pi\sigma^2} Gaus(\frac{\sqrt{x^2+y^2}}{\sqrt{2\pi}\,\sigma}) \qquad (10.4)$$

where x and y are the horizontal and vertical positions on the screen and σ describes the size of the spot (known as the spot size parameter). (10.4) can be considered the impulse response of the CRT. The MTF is then determined by taking the Fourier transform of this expression, yielding

$$MTF_{CRT}(\xi, \eta) = Gaus(\sqrt{2\pi}\,\sigma\sqrt{\xi^2 + \eta^2}) \qquad (10.5)$$

Gaussian functions are separable in x and y so that the MTF given in (10.5) can be separated to give an MTF in the horizontal and vertical directions:

$$MTF_{CRT}(\xi, \eta) = MTF_{CRT}(\xi)MTF_{CRT}(\eta) = Gaus(\sqrt{2\pi}\ \sigma\xi)Gaus(\sqrt{2\pi}\ \sigma\eta) \quad (10.6)$$

The spot size can be measured using the *shrinking raster* technique [2]. With this technique, the line spacing on the CRT is reduced until the observer can no longer resolve the scan lines. The distance between the lines l can be estimated by measuring the total height of all the lines and dividing by the number of lines. The spot-size parameter σ is related to the distance between the lines by

$$\sigma = 0.54l \quad [m] \quad (10.7)$$

Note that σ is in meters, so the MTF given in the above equations has an argument of cycles per meter. To provide an MTF that can be used in an angular system MTF estimate, the argument must be given in terms of cycles per radian or cycles per milliradian. This conversion is determined with the sensor FOV in milliradians and the size of the CRT display in meters. An example of this conversion in the vertical direction is

$$\sigma_{angular} = \sigma\frac{FOV_v}{MonitorSize_v} \quad (10.8)$$

where FOV_v is in milliradians. This angular spot-size parameter provides an MTF in the same spatial frequency domain as that of the other sensor components.

Example

The spot-size parameter σ has been determined to be 200 μm on a 15-cm-high CRT monitor using the shrinking raster technique. The monitor displays the output of a 5- by 7-deg FOV sensor. Plot the MTF of the monitor for system-related object space in units of cycles per milliradian. The solution is given by first converting the spot-size parameter from micrometers to milliradians:

$$\sigma_{angular} = 200\text{x}10^{-6}m\frac{87.3mrads}{15\text{x}10^{-2}m} = 0.116mrads$$

This angular spot size can be used in the horizontal component of (10.6) to give the horizontal MTF. The MTF is given by

$$Gaus[\sqrt{2\pi}\ \sigma_{angular}\xi] = e^{-\pi[\sqrt{2\pi}\ \sigma_{angular}\xi]^2} = e^{-2\pi^2\sigma_{angular}^2\xi^2}$$

which is shown below. If the *Gaus* function is written in terms of $Gaus[\frac{\xi}{\xi_{co}}]$ where ξ_{co} is the cutoff frequency, then it can be shown that $\xi_{co} = 1/(\sqrt{2\pi}\ \sigma_{angular})$. In this case, the cutoff frequency is 3.4 cycles per milliradian.

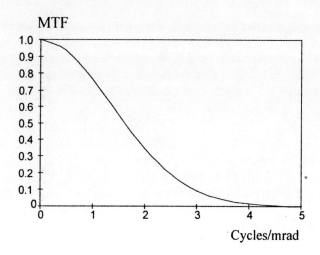

Figure 10.4 CRT example results.

Example Results

The CRT usually has a sample-and-hold circuit that gives a discrete number of horizontal pixels as the display spot-scans the screen in the horizontal direction. This sample-and-hold samples the horizontal signal on a scan line into an integer number of samples and then holds the phosphor spot voltage constant over this sample as the spot is scanned across the horizontal direction. For example, many CRTs have 480 active lines in the vertical direction (out of the 525 possible lines). With a 1.33 horizontal-to-vertical image aspect ratio, the horizontal scan across the CRT screen would be broken into 640 samples. If the CRT has this type sample-and-hold circuit, the psf for the sample-and-hold circuit is $h(x,y) = (FOV_h/640)rect[x/(FOV_h/640)]\delta(y)$ and the display sample-and-hold transfer function is $H(\xi,\eta) = sinc[(FOV_h/640)\xi]$. This transfer function must be accounted for in any system that includes a CRT display sample-and-hold circuit.

10.3 LIGHT EMITTING DIODES

LEDs are P-N junction devices that emit light when they are forward biased. Because LEDs [3] emit light, they are very visible in dark conditions and are less visible in bright conditions. LEDs are luminescent (self-emitting in visible wavelengths), where the luminescence is proportional to the current passing through the LED. The visibility of the LED depends on the emitted radiation and the external quantum efficiency of the eye at the LED emission wavelength. The efficiency of LEDs is limited because of the mismatch of refractive index between air and the luminescent material (index of refraction around 3.6). Therefore the emitted angle for total internal reflection is small. A lens can increase the efficiency by a factor of 2 to 3.

LEDs are typically arranged in a linear array (a single line of diodes) and are parallel-scanned across the observer's viewing plane. Consider the system shown in Figure 10.5. As the scan traverses across the image plane, a current is applied to each LED and the corresponding luminescent signals are traced out in lines. An eyepiece adjusts the LED image to a distance from the viewer that is comfortable.

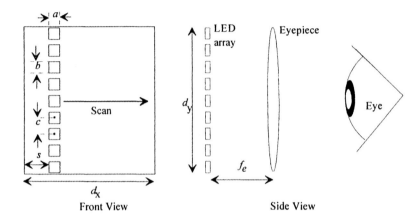

Front View   Side View

Figure 10.5 LED array display.

The scanning occurs at a rate higher than the rate at which flicker is seen by the human eye (over 20 Hz). Most LED displays, as used in I^{2}R systems, form the back end of the EO mux subsystem (as described in Ch. 9). Here, the scan occurs at the same rate as that of the infrared linear-detector array scan. The vertical angular size of the image depends on the array height and the eyepiece focal length:

$$\alpha_y = d_y/f_e \qquad (10.9)$$

The vertical image size is related to FOV$_v$ by the magnification

$$\alpha_y = M \ \text{FOV}_v \qquad (10.10)$$

In the system shown, a and b describe the size of the LEDs and c describes the distance between the centers of the LEDs in the vertical direction. The distance of the LED array from the left side of the image plane is described as s. Many scanned LED displays are analog in nature (i.e., the voltage and corresponding luminescent signal are continuous across the scan), so there is no sampling in the horizontal direction. Therefore, the spatial function for the scanned array shown is

$$o(x,y) = [i(x,y)\tfrac{1}{c}comb(\tfrac{y}{c})\delta(x-s)] * *rect(\tfrac{x}{a}, \tfrac{y}{b}) \qquad (10.11)$$

Here, the spatial parameters x and y are in meters in the image plane and must be converted to angular object space. This is performed using

$$o(x,y) = [i(x,y)\tfrac{d_y}{cFOV_v}comb(\tfrac{yd_y}{cFOV_v})\delta(x - \tfrac{sFOV_h}{d_x})] * *rect(\tfrac{xd_x}{aFOV_h}, \tfrac{yd_y}{bFOV_v}) \qquad (10.12)$$

where x and y are in radians (object space). In addition, d_x and d_y are the width and height of the displayed image. The spatial frequency domain can now be compared directly with all the other system contributors. The Fourier transform of (10.12) gives the spatial frequency representation of the display:

$$O(\xi, \eta) = [I(\xi, \eta) * *comb(\tfrac{c(FOV_v)\eta}{d_y})]\tfrac{ab(FOV_h)(FOV_v)}{d_x d_y} sinc(\tfrac{a(FOV_h)\xi}{d_x}, \tfrac{b(FOV_v)\eta}{d_y})e^{-j\tfrac{sFOV_h}{d_x}} \qquad (10.13)$$

If the input signal (the image to be displayed) is bandlimited to where all frequency components are less than half of $d_y/(cFOV_v)$, then no aliasing occurs and the MTF of the LED array can be written as

$$MTF_{LED}(\xi, \eta) = sinc(\tfrac{a(FOV_h)\xi}{d_x}, \tfrac{b(FOV_v)\eta}{d_y}) \qquad (10.14)$$

If the signal is not bandlimited, then aliasing occurs on the output image and artifacts are seen. Well-designed systems use the optics and detector MTFs to bandlimit the imagery so aliasing is controlled. Further discussion of acceptable image aliasing for human consumption is described later in this chapter.

10.4 LIQUID CRYSTAL DISPLAYS

The LCD [4] comprises a thin, clear layer of twisted nematic crystals placed between two conducting plates that are transparent. Some common LCDs use crossed polarizers as the two conducting plates. With an applied voltage, the LCD material (twisted nematic crystals) then turns the light polarization to pass through the crossed polarizer. The degree of polarization twist determines the shade of brightness that passes through the polarizer. The LCD panel is an aggregate of these cells that form an electronically addressable display. LCDs can be small, light, and inexpensive.

LCDs are passive devices that modulate passing light. Therefore, they work as well in bright, ambient light as they do in dim lighting. Their performance is strongly influenced, however, by the spatial distribution of lighting. Also, LCD displays are usually viewed directly by the observer. LCDs require very little power dissipation because the power is only required to provide dynamic scattering in the LCD fluid. LCDs are not as fast as LEDs and typically require tens of milliseconds to turn off or on compared with some LEDs in the nanosecond realm. The slow response time limits their utility in high-speed applications.

The spatial display function and the transfer function can be derived from a simple model shown in Figure 10.6. The LCD array is a rectangular grid of LCD cells that are surrounded by an inactive area. The ratio of the LCD active cell area to the total array area is called the *fill factor*. The spatial sampling of the input image and the display of the image on the rectangular functions can be written as

$$o(x,y) = [i(x,y)\tfrac{1}{cd}comb(\tfrac{x}{d},\tfrac{y}{c})] * *rect(\tfrac{x}{a},\tfrac{y}{b})$$ (10.15)

Taking this function to angular object space gives

$$o(x,y) = [i(x,y)\tfrac{d_x}{dFOV_h}\tfrac{d_y}{cFOV_v}comb(\tfrac{xd_x}{dFOV_h},\tfrac{yd_y}{cFOV_v})] * *rect(\tfrac{xd_x}{aFOV_h},\tfrac{yd_y}{bFOV_v})$$ (10.16)

where x, y, and the FOVs are in milliradians. This spatial function can be converted to the spatial frequency domain by taking the Fourier transform:

$$O(\xi,\eta) = [I(\xi,\eta) * *comb(\tfrac{d(FOV_h)\xi}{d_x},\tfrac{c(FOV_v)\eta}{d_y})]\tfrac{ab(FOV_h)(FOV_v)}{d_xd_y}sinc(\tfrac{a(FOV_h)\xi}{d_x},\tfrac{b(FOV_v)\eta}{d_y})$$ (10.17)

Note that this function is very similar to the spatial frequency representation of the LED array (10.13). The difference here is that the LCD array is sampled in both the horizontal and vertical directions. Also note that if the image spectrum is not bandlimited in both directions, aliasing occurs *before* the display of the imagery. If the display is bandlimited to half of the *comb* function spacing, then the MTF is identical to that described in (10.14).

10.5 SAMPLING AND DISPLAY PROCESSING

Any display that provides a sampled signal has an infinite theoretical replication of the image spectrum in the frequency domain. This replication is seen as the first term in the spatial frequency models of the LED (10.13) and the LCD (10.17) displays. For an LSI system to provide an image without aliasing, Goodman and Gaskill teach (see Ch. 3) that the image spectrum must be bandlimited to half the sampling frequency. Consider the sampled function in Figure 10.7.

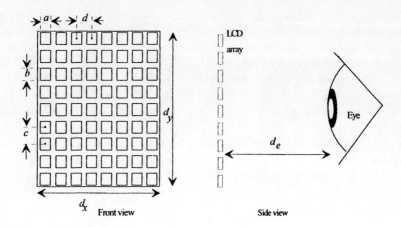

Figure 10.6 LCD display.

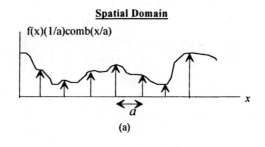

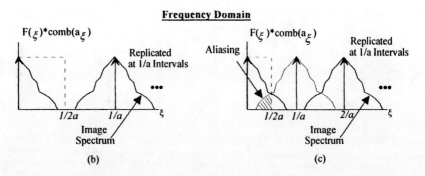

Figure 10.7 Sampling in space and frequency. Spatial domain (a), frequency domain with no spectra overlap (b), spectra overlap (c).

The function *f(x)* is sampled at a spatial distance of *a* meters (radians) and mathematically depicted by the product of *f(x)* and the appropriate *comb* function. The result is a set of samples that represent the original function. In the frequency domain, the spectrum of *f(x)*, represented by $F(\xi)$, is convolved with the transform of the original *comb* function. The result is a replication of $F(\xi)$ at intervals of 1/a cycles per meter (cycles per milliradian). Note that the location of the replicas depends only on the sampling distance *a*. To obtain the original function, *f(x)*, without sampling artifacts, a "reconstruction filter" must be applied to the spectrum to eliminate all the higher order replicas of $F(\xi)$. Again, the perfect theoretical filter is a *rect* filter that limits the spectrum to half the sampling frequency as shown by the dashed line in Figure 10.7(b). For spatial frequencies less than 1/2a, the required sampling rate is 1/a cycles per meter or cycles per milliradian. If the spectrum of $F(\xi)$ is bandlimited to 1/2a, then perfect reconstruction can occur. However, if $F(\xi)$ spills over past 1/2a, as depicted in Figure 10.7(c), then *aliasing* occurs. The $F(\xi)$ content that is included within the *rect* filter is unaliased signal. The signal content from the second replication that spills over into the *rect* is aliased. This aliasing is a spurious, high-frequency signal that takes on the identity of lower frequencies, hence the term alias. It can be visually objectionable if it is not properly controlled. This aliased signal is really the higher frequencies in the original $F(\xi)$ function that were "wrapped" back into lower frequencies because of the insufficient sampling rate. These lower frequencies were not present at this apparent contribution in the original image.

　　To determine the sources of aliasing in a sensor system, consider Figure 10.8. Imagery is degraded by the atmospheric MTF, the optics MTF, and the detector MTF, and then the image signal is usually sampled by the detectors. If the image is bandlimited, or these MTFs provide sufficient bandlimiting, or the sample rate is high enough, then aliasing will not occur. However, if the image spectrum has content above 1/2a by the time the signal gets to the detectors, then aliasing occurs. Optical and detector MTFs are usually designed with sampling rates to control aliasing.

　　Once the signal is sampled by the detector, the electronic MTF is applied and a display reconstruction filter may be applied (in the same manner as the MTFs). The discrete nature of the display makes it another sampling device. If the display is matched to the sampling characteristics of the detector, no reconstruction is required. However, if the display has a different sampling rate than that of the detector, then reconstruction is required. The reconstruction filter bandlimits the imagery for display at a lower resolution sampling grid or interpolates the signal for display on a higher resolution sampling grid. Finally, the display MTF and the eye MTF are applied to the image signal.

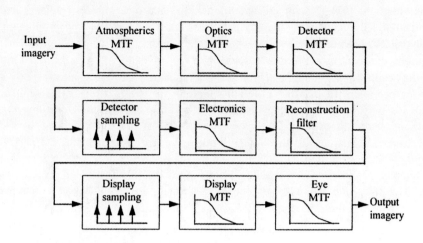

Figure 10.8 Imagery transfer.

Now that we have described the image transfer through the system, we know that aliasing can take place at two places: the detector sampling action and the display sampling action. Optics, detector, and detector sampling control the detector aliasing. Reconstruction filters (if necessary) control the display aliasing.

Imperfect sampling does not follow LSI principles, and Vollmerhausen [5, 6] addresses a number of reconstruction issues in this regard. First, it is true that the reconstruction function must be applied to the sampled spectrum to bandlimit the information for display. There are a number of methods for approaching this including a spectral filter similar to the *rect* bandlimiting function. In practical systems, the *rect* function in the frequency domain is a *sinc* function in the space domain that effectively has to be convolved with the sampled image. The input image is not infinite in width, so the ripple of the *sinc* tails at the edges gets folded back over and causes artifacts. There are more practical reconstruction functions including a *rect* convolved with a *Gaus* function. Vollmerhausen reveals that a number of reconstruction functions work fairly well and are not objectionable to human perception of the bandlimited imagery.

Second, image signals do not have to be bandlimited to half of the sampling rate. The sampling theorem in terms of the display of sampled imagery corresponds to an ideal case and is not practical in real systems. Vollmerhausen states that sampling at a rate double the point where the MTF reaches 10 to 40% is generally adequate for decent image quality.

There are three well-known criteria [7] for the design of reconstruction filters. We consider an input image spectrum, a presampling MTF, and a sampling frequency as shown in Figure 10.9.

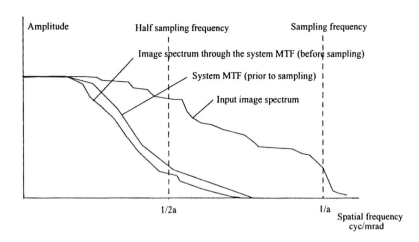

Figure 10.9 Image spectrum, presampling MTF, and sampling frequencies.

In Figure 10.9, an input image spectrum is shown that is well beyond the required sampling bandlimit for aliasing. Sometimes, this bandlimit, 1/2a, is called the *Nyquist limit* as frequencies higher than this are wrapped back into the lower frequencies. This wrapping around is not shown here to discuss aliasing control criteria. However, any frequency content above the bandlimit, 1/2a, is aliased. The input image spectrum shown results in significant aliasing if it is sampled directly. However, the presampling MTF (such as the optics and detector MTF before detector sampling) limits the input spectrum performing a signal conditioning function. This MTF bandlimiting action reduces the amount of signal that is aliased.

With respect to Figure 10.9, the three aliasing control criteria are *Legault's criterion, Sequin's criterion*, and *Schade's criterion*. Legault's criterion is the more strict in that less than 5% of the image spectrum through the system (i.e., the area of the curve shown in Figure 10.9) should be at frequencies greater than 1/2a. The Sequin's criterion states that the aliased signal should be no more than one-half of the nonaliased signal. The Schade's criterion states that the MTF (before sampling) should have a magnitude of less than 15% at the 1/2a frequency.

Finally, it is worth discussing the effects of phase and the finite width of the display. The sampling theorem is the solution to a signal that is sampled in an infinite time or space. For a finite-length signal (limited by the display width or height), the number of samples prescribed by the sampling theorem to replicate the signal are not sufficient. In fact, the smaller the length of signal, the larger number of samples is required to replicate an accurate rendition of the signal. In these cases, the phases or the locations of the equally spaced samples on the signal become an important factor in determining whether the signal can be faithfully reconstructed. Vollmerhausen develops a technique for determining the effects of sampling finite signals and discusses phasing between the samples and the signal.

It is beyond the scope of this introductory book to teach non-LSI systems or system components; however, we should note that the LSI approximations are not always sufficient. It could be that the display of sampled imagery is the EO or I^2R characteristic that is least appropriate for LSI modeling. Nevertheless, the LSI approach has been an effective tool for analyzing sensor systems for some time and will continue to be so. A suggestion here is to learn the LSI modeling technique as a first-order approach to sensor analysis and to then refine these approaches to include non-LSI effects. Also, it is our responsibility to learn the limitations of our analytical models.

10.6 HUMAN PERCEPTION AND THE HUMAN EYE

The observer must interpret the information that is presented on a display. To more fully understand the response of the eye to this information, we describe the eye in physical terms and then provide models that can be used to estimate the eye MTF.

The human eye is similar to a camera. It forms a real image on a light-sensitive surface called the *retina* (see Figure 10.10). Light enters the eye through a transparent layer called the *cornea*, then traverses through an anterior liquid chamber called the *aqueous humor*. The light from this anterior chamber is limited by the *iris,* which is the effective entrance pupil of the eye. The diameter of the iris changes in response to the amount of light received by the eye. In reality, the pupil is not that important in the adaptation of the eye to large variations in light level. The most popular theory is that the eye adapts to large changes in light levels through chemical changes in the photoreceptors. Some of the light passes through the iris to a crystalline lens that is an elastic material. The lens power is determined by the cilliary muscles that pull on the lens radially to change the lens curvature. This change in optical power allows image focus of near and far objects on the retina. After refraction by the lens, the light is imaged onto the retina through the vitreous humor.

The eye is a spherical jelly-like mass that is protected by a tough membrane called the *sclera*. The cornea is the only transparent part of the sclera; the rest is white and opaque. Inside the sclera is a dark pigmented layer called the *choroid*. The choroid is an absorber of stray light, similar to the black paint on the inside of electro-optical devices. A thin layer of light-sensitive photoreceptors, like detectors, covers the inner surface of the choroid. The eye has two kinds of photoreceptors (125 million in all): *rods* and *cones*. Rods have characteristics of high-speed, course-grain, black-and-white film and are extremely light sensitive. These photoreceptors can image light that is too dim for cones to process, but the images are not well defined. Cones are like low-speed, high-grain, color film that performs very well with bright light. The photoreceptor difference is one of the primary reasons that day and night vision provide two photometry curves:

photopic and *scotopic* (see Chapter 5). At the retinal center, a depression in the photoreceptor layer is called the *macula*. It is around 2.5 to 3 mm in diameter with a rod-free region in the center of about 0.3 mm in diameter called the *fovea centralis*. Hecht and Zajac [8] state that the moon subtends a spot of around 0.3 mm on the retina. In this region, the cones are closely packed and provide the sharpest detailed images. The photoreceptors are ac-coupled. The eye is continually moving the fovea centralis over objects of interest. The image is constantly shifted across the retina. If the image is held stationary on the retina, the image actually fades out.

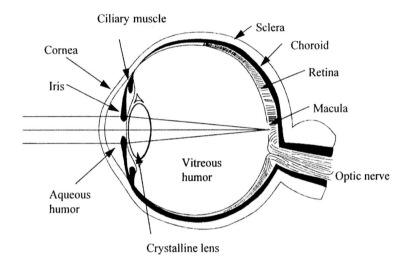

Figure 10.10 The human eye.

The radii of curvatures [9] for the cornea, crystalline lens first surface, and crystalline lens second surface are 7.8, 10, and 6.0 mm, respectively. The indices of refraction of the aqueous humor, the lens, and the vitreous humor are 1.336, 1.413, and 1.336. An interesting note is that one of the reasons humans do not see well under water is that the water refractive index is typically 1.33, very close to the eye indices. Recall that little change in the refractive index at a curved interface provides little focusing power of the input light. The crystalline lens is fascinating in that it is a graded index lens. The index is 1.406 in the center, 1.375 at the equator, and 1.387 (aqueous) and 1.385 (vitreous) at the vertices. Focusing the lens is called *accommodation* resulting in a change of the lens shape. The lens is almost spherical until pulled by the ciliary muscles, where the lens takes on a flatter shape. The front surface radius can change from 10 mm to 5.3 mm. The total power of the eye is around 60 diopters. The cornea-air interface accounts for around 42 diopters of the total power [10].

The age degradation of the crystalline lens and the ciliary muscles tends to affect eye performance in a significant way. The closest point that the eye can image is around 7 cm for a teenager, 25 cm for a young adult, and 100 cm for middle-aged people. Lenses are prescribed for people who cannot accommodate for the necessary power. Eyeglass power is prescribed in *diopters* (recall that power is the reciprocal of the focal length). Myopia, or nearsightedness, is the case where the eye provides too much power and a negative lens is prescribed to give a less overall system power. Hyperopia, or farsightedness is the case where the eye does not provide sufficient power to image on the retina, so a positive power prescription is the solution. Ablation of the corneal surface with excimer laser radiation to change the surface curvature is becoming a common solution to either of these accommodation problems.

The band of sensitivity for the eye ranges from roughly 360 nm to 780 nm. There have been cases where people have seen images outside these wavelengths. The typical resolution of a human eye under certain conditions can be estimated by using the pupil size and a 0.5-μm wavelength with any one of the angular resolution criteria in the optics chapter. These estimates provide ballpark values but are probably never realized because of imperfections in the eye. Typical angular resolutions of the eye range from 200 to 400 μrad.

10.7 THE MODULATION TRANSFER FUNCTION OF THE EYE

The modulation transfer function of the eye is taken from Overington [11] and is the product of three distinct transfer function characteristics: *optical refraction*, *retina*, and *tremor*. These components are covered separately but must be cascaded (multiplied) to obtain the overall MTF of the eye.

The optical refraction MTF component corresponds to the limiting resolution of the pupil diameter. The pupil diameter, however, is a function of the display light level and can be estimated by

$$d_{pupil} = 4.30 - 0.645 \log(ftL) \quad [\text{mm}] \tag{10.18}$$

where *ftL* is the luminance of the display in foot-lamberts. There are 0.292 foot-lamberts in 1 lumen/m^2-sr.

The optical MTF of the eye is estimated by

$$MTF_{eoptics}(\rho) = \exp[-(43.69\rho/\rho_o)^{io}] \tag{10.19}$$

where ρ_o and *io* are transfer function variables that are related to the pupil diameter of the eye. Here, ρ is the circularly symmetric spatial frequency in cycles per milliradian. Table 10.1 gives the transfer function variable values for given pupil diameters. The pupil diameters given are for use with one eye. When two eyes are used, the pupil diameter becomes around 0.5 mm smaller. Also, the MTF given is in the eye angular space. The spatial frequency parameter ρ is increased (division of ρ in (10.19): recall the scaling theorem from Chapter 2) by a factor of the system magnification M to convert the MTF to the sensor object space.

Table 10.1
Eye optical MTF variables for given pupil diameter

Pupil diameter (mm)	r_o	io
1.5	36	0.9
2.0	39	0.8
2.4	35	0.8
3.0	32	0.77
3.8	25	0.75
4.9	15	0.72
5.8	11	0.69
6.6	8	0.66

The second MTF parameter associated with the human eye is the MTF of the retina. This parameter is similar to a detector MTF in that it is associated with the size of the retinal receptors and the focal length of the eye. A good approximation for the MTF is

$$MTF_{retina}(\rho) = \exp[-0.375\rho^{1.21}] \qquad (10.20)$$

where the spatial frequency must be converted to the angular object space with the magnification of the system to use the MTF in a system manner. (10.20) gives the MTF of the eye in angular object space as seen by the eye. The sensor system angular object space is smaller by a factor of the system magnification M.

Finally, the last eye MTF component considered here is that of tremor, which can be estimated by

$$MTF_{tremor}(\rho) = \exp[-.4441\rho^2] \qquad (10.21)$$

where the MTF has to be corrected for the system magnification for placement in sensor object space. In (10.19) through (10.21), ρ is replaced with ρ/M to give the MTFs in sensor, or object, space. Tremor is associated with the normal movement of the eye. Eye movements comprise high-frequency tremor, low-speed drift, and flick. All these are small, involuntary movements that are necessary for vision. Experiments [10] have been performed where the eye was artificially stabilized with a contact lens projector. The conscious image appeared to fade out. Therefore, the eye can be considered an "ac-coupled system."

Example

Determine and plot the eye's optical MTF using the Overington model. Assume that an observer is viewing a monitor of 10-fL brightness. The solution is given by first determining the pupil diameter, using (10.19):

$$d_{pupil} = 4.3 - 0.645 \log(10) \qquad [\text{mm}] \qquad (10.22)$$

or 3.655 mm. Using Table 10.1, the MTF variables are determined. Interpolating for a 3.655-mm pupil diameter, $\rho_o = 26.2$ and $i_o = 0.754$. The optical MTF associated with the pupil size is then estimated by (10.19) as

$$MTF(\rho_o) = e^{-(43.69 \frac{\rho}{26.2})^{0.754}} \qquad (10.23)$$

This function is shown in Figure 10.11. Note that if two eyes were used, the pupil size would be smaller and the MTF would provide more degradation.

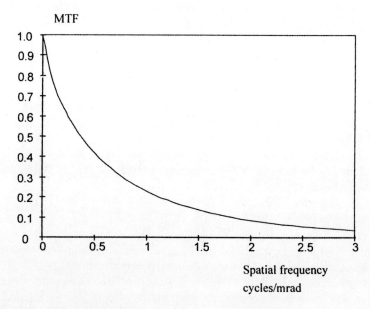

Figure 10.11 Example results.

10.8 CONTRAST THRESHOLD FUNCTION OF THE EYE

Blackwell [12] showed that the detection capability of the human eye is a strong function of target size, contrast, and brightness. His classic set of experiments included more than 200,000 observations by 19 women during World War II. Sources were presented that were circular targets against uniform backgrounds to determine a contrast threshold of 50% detection probability. Blackwell showed that the contrast threshold decreases with an increase in display brightness or target size. Many other experiments were performed that were similar to Blackwell's and bar targets and sine wave targets were eventually used to relate contrast threshold to spatial frequency. The contrast threshold function (CTF) was developed and defined as "the level of contrast required for an observer to detect the presence of a sine wave pattern with a 50% probability level as a function of spatial frequency." The CTF follows what is known as a standard J curve shown in Figure 10.12.

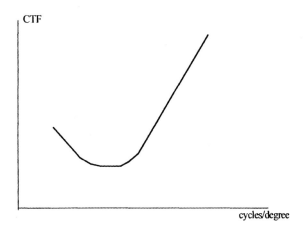

Figure 10.12 Contrast threshold function.

Essentially, the curve describes the minimum contrast for the human visual system to detect a spatial frequency within the eye's FOV. Karim [13] states that any system MTF that is below the CTF is not usable to the observer, so he describes a modulation transfer function area (MTFA) that is a measure of the usable contrast above the threshold value. Also, note that the units of CTF spatial frequency are in cycles per degree. This is an eye research convention where the minima of the J is around 3 to 8 cycles per degree. Keep in mind that these units must be converted to cycles per radian or cycles per milliradian to use the CTF as an analytical function within the sensor response. It then must be adjusted by the system magnification. Holst [14] describes the J function in two parts: spatial frequencies below the minima called the *inhibitory region* and spatial frequencies above the minima called the *excitatory region*. Many sensor performance estimates do not include the inhibitory region response because it corresponds to low frequencies. Most image details are captured in the higher frequencies. That is, edges and smaller objects contain significant energy in the high-frequency components of the spectrum. Ignoring the inhibitory region sometimes leads to poor sensor system performance estimates at low spatial frequencies. Holst also compares five eye models of the J curve and determines that the J can change significantly for observer head movement, viewing distance, and noise power spectral density.

Holst [15] also states that the eye MTF takes the shape of an inverted CTF. He points out that the Nill model and the Kornfeld-Lawson model are common models. The Nill model includes the inhibitory response and the Kornfeld-Lawson model does not. The Nill model approximates the eye MTF using

$$MTF_{eye}(\rho) = 2.71[0.19 + 0.81(\frac{\rho}{\rho_{peak}})]e^{-(\frac{\rho}{\rho_{peak}})} \tag{10.24}$$

where ρ_{peak} is the location in spatial frequency of the eye's peak response. In this case, units are arbitrary and can be cycles per degree or cycles per milliradian. The Kornfeld-Lawson model is

$$MTF_{eye}(\rho) = e^{-\Gamma(\frac{\rho}{17.45})} \tag{10.25}$$

where units of ρ are in cycles per degree. Γ is a light-dependent factor that can be estimated by

$$\Gamma = 1.444 - 0.344\log(B) + 0.0395\log^2(B) + 0.00197\log^3(B) \tag{10.26}$$

where B is the display brightness in fL. Figure 10.13 shows the Nill and Kornfeld-Lawson eye models.

The Kornfeld-Lawson model is used in a number of sensor performance models. It has errors at the lower spatial frequencies, however, due to the missing inhibitory part of the model. Holst points out that the model was validated with tank-sized targets that were generally in the mid-spatial frequency region. Finally, Holst states that the MTF should be set to 1 when the observer is allowed head movement to optimize vision for presented imagery. That is, the observer can move closer for small images and farther for large images.

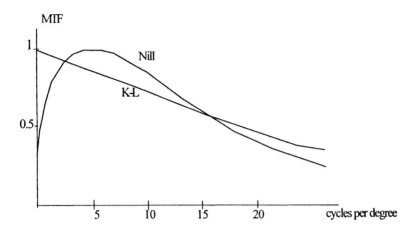

Figure 10.13 Nill and Kornfeld-Lawson eye models.

10.9 AUTOMATIC TARGET RECOGNITION

It has long been desired to automatically process the data provided by imaging sensors for a variety of functions. These functions range from such commercial applications as component inspection for manufacturing to military applications such as target detection and face recognition. The focus here is on military pattern recognition, though much of this material is applicable for both commercial and military systems. The terminology that is often used to describe automated pattern recognition in the military community is generically referred to as *automated target recognition* (ATR). ATR implies a sequence of mathematical operations where the result is the recognition of a target. The principle functions for the ATR sequence [16-18] are shown in Figure 10.14.

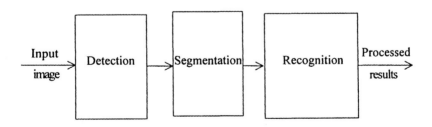

Figure 10.14 ATR process.

The definitions for each of the ATR functions are provided as follows.

Detection: Detection is a process whereby a portion of an image, usually called a *region of interest* (ROI), has been determined to contain an object of interest. Another definition is simply that an image successfully traverses through a prefilter (i.e., the detection process is a spatial screener). This process is usually carried out by stepping a window through the entire image. The window is approximately the size of the target class of interest. At each step, a variety of tests (mathematical operations) are performed to determine if an object is present. Typical parameters of the window include: contrast, various statistics, and power spectral density. Once a parameter is calculated, it is either compared with the background region around the window or compared with some predetermined threshold value. These values are determined based on some *a priori* knowledge of the target types of interest and by analysis of existing data that are similar to the test data. The primary purpose of detection is to eliminate most of the imagery data, as the processing power is usually not available to apply complex recognition algorithms to the large amount of imagery data. The real target decision is performed later.

Segmentation: Once a potential target is localized through detection, it is extracted from the background as accurately as possible. Segmentation is generically referred to as the extraction of both low- and high-level features that are used in the recognition stage. Typical features that are extracted include target silhouette and internal features of the vehicle. There are three methodologies that are used in segmentation: edge detection, thresholding, and region growing. Some segmentation approaches employ all three components. Basically, segmentation assumes that objects are distinguished from their surroundings by the presence of edges. Some segmentation methods employ thresholding to separate edges of the target from those of the background. A wide range of edge detectors are available, including the gradient, Laplacian, and Sobel operators and more recently, wavelets. Morphological operators such as erosion and/or dilation are sometimes employed to help improve the segmented image. Erosion makes a region smaller by removing pixels from the edges, while dilation makes them larger by adding pixels.

Classification: After segmentation, additional features are calculated, usually from combinations of features extracted during segmentation. They are used for categorizing the object to a specified class or specific identification. There are three categories of classification algorithms: statistical, template correlation, and neural networks. All these approaches require extensive knowledge of the target set. A pictorial representation and basic description of the three classification approaches is shown in Figure 10.15.

While the above process is a classical description of the ATR approach, advances in segmentation [19] and other ATR processes are making it more difficult to separate the steps shown in Figure 10.14. Detection is increasingly becoming a data elimination process. Segmentation is also becoming more a part of this process by using more sophisticated analytical techniques.

Stastical Classifiers use various features such as moments, frequency components, and stastical measures in order to distinguish one target from other targets in the same general class . This is done through probabilistic association by partioning the feature space into various regions.

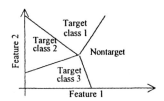

Template Correlation algorithms use a set of templates stored in a data base to develop correlations with the segmented object for purposes of classification. Very simply, the higher the correlation, the higher the probability of correction classification. The template data base can be developed either from training data or CAD models of the targets of interest.

Neural Networks are based on the use of a multitude of elemental nonlinear computing elements organized in a network reminiscent of the brain. The key components/ aspects of a neural network include: the input layer, hidden layer, output layer, a set of initial weights, and a learning algorithm.

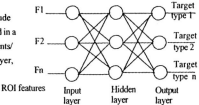

Figure 10.15 Classification approaches.

In evaluating an ATR algorithm, it is desirable to use measures that completely describe its performance. A wide range of factors must be considered including the environment in which the data was taken, the quality of the sensor data, the parameters of the sensor (resolution, sensitivity), and scene background clutter, just to name a few. A performance curve that is frequently used in the evaluation/design of ATR algorithms is shown in Figure 10.16. Historically, this curve has been known as the *receiver operating curve* (ROC). More recently, it has been called the *ATR operating curve* [20].

As can be seen from the graph, the probability of target detection (this could be recognition or identification) is plotted with respect to the false alarm rate (FAR). A false alarm occurs when the ATR incorrectly classifies a nontarget as a target. As the probability of target detection (P_d) improves, the FAR increases. Ideally, one would like to have a very high probability of detection and a very low FAR. It is up to the algorithm designer to choose an acceptable P_d along with an allowable FAR.

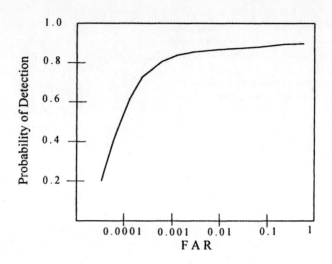

Figure 10.16 ATR performance evaluation curve.

In summary, there have been tremendous improvements in the supporting elements of ATR (sensors, processors, mathematics). However, the algorithms are still far from mature. Performance limitations can be attributed to the wide range of target signatures and backgrounds that vary tremendously depending on the test location and the environmental conditions. Despite its limitations, ATR is proving to be extremely useful in cueing an operator to an area of an image that contains an important target. This cueing and partial recognition is important for many military applications where timelines are critical and a large amount of imagery is involved. The commercial sector has had better success with optical character recognition (OCR) for typed pages and component inspection in manufacturing. The success in the commercial arena can largely be attributed to having a controlled environment.

EXERCISES

10.1 An imaging system has a vertical FOV of 2 deg and the imagery is displayed to a human observer. Assuming a typical viewing monitor angle, determine the system magnification.

10.2 A CRT display is a 525-line, 14-in monitor that is given the shrinking raster test. The shrinking raster yields a total line height of 25 cm. Sketch the MTF of the CRT display in cycles per meter (or cycles per millimeter). Assuming that the monitor displays imagery from a 5-deg vertical FOV sensor, determine and sketch the CRT MTF in cycles per milliradian so that it can be compared with other system MTFs.

10.3 For the example given in Section 10.2, provide the necessary spot-size parameter for a cutoff frequency of 10 cycles per milliradian given the same system.

10.4 Show that the cutoff frequency for the CRT is $1/(\sqrt{2\pi}\,\sigma)$.

10.5 Sketch the horizontal MTF for an LED display with an LED horizontal dimension of 0.05 mm, an LED scan distance of 2 cm, and a horizontal FOV of 5 deg. Sketch the MTF as a function of spatial frequency in cycles per milliradian.

10.6 Using the Overington model, determine the MTF of the eye that is viewing a display brightness of 20 fL. Sketch the results as a function of spatial frequency in cycles per milliradian. Compare these results with the MTFs of the retina and tremor.

10.7 Discuss the best conditions for each ATR classifier approach. What would the best approach be for a manufacturing visual inspection? A desert battlefield with little clutter? An extremely cluttered and smoke-filled battlefield environment?

10.8 Of the three display devices described in this section, which one would lend itself more to a handheld device for field use? An aircraft cockpit?

REFERENCES

[1]   Pinson, L., *ElectroOptics*, New York: Wiley, p. 240, 1985.
[2]   Waldman, G., and J. Wootton, *Electro-Optical System Performance Modeling*, Boston, MA: Artech House, p. 170, 1993.

[3]   Biberman, L., "Image Display Technology and Problems With Emphasis on Airborne Systems" in the *Infrared and Electro-Optical Systems Handbook,* ERIM and SPIE Press, 1993.

[4]   Goodman, L. A., *The Relative Merits of LEDs and LCDs,* Proceedings for Society of Information Display, 16(1), 1975.

[5]   Vollmerhausen, R., "Impact of Display Modulation Transfer Function on the Quality of Sampled Imagery," *SPIE Proceedings of Aerospace/Defense Sensing and Controls,* Orlando, FL, Apr. 1996.

[6]   Vollmerhausen, R., *Application of the Sampling Theorem to Solid State Cameras and Flat Panel Displays,* U.S. Army Night Vision and Electronic Sensors Directorate Report NV-2-14, Ft. Belvoir, VA, Feb. 1989.

[7]   Barbe, D., and S. Campana, "Imaging Arrays Using the Charged Coupled Concept," in *Image Pickup and Display,* Vol 3, B. Kazan, Editor, Academic Press, 1977.

[8]   Hecht, E., and A. Zajac, *Optics,* Reading, MA: Addison-Wesley, p. 138, 1979.

[9]   Meyer-Arendt, J. R., *Introduction to Classical and Modern Optics,* Englewood Cliffs, NJ: Prentice-Hall, 1984.

[10]   Yu, F. T., and I. C. Khoo, *Principles of Optical Engineering,* New York: Wiley, 1990.

[11]   Overington, I., *Vision and Acquisition,* New York: Crane, Russak and Co., 1976.

[12]   Blackwell, H., "Contrast Thresholds of the Human Eye," *Journal of the Optical Society of America,* Vol. 36, 1946.

[13]   Karim, M., *Electro-Optical Displays,* New York: Marcel-Dekker, 1993.

[14]   Holst, G., and A. Taylor, "What Eye Model Should We Use for MRT Testing," *Infrared Imaging Systems: Design, Analysis, Modeling, and Testing,* SPIE Vol. 1309, 1990.

[15]   Holst, G., *Electro-Optical Imaging System Performance,* Orlando, FL: JCD Publishing, p. 130, 1995.

[16]   Haykin, S., *Neural Networks: A Comprehensive Foundation,* Maxwell McMillan International, 1994.

[17]   Keinosuke, F., *Introduction to Statistical Pattern Recognition,* Academic Press, 1972.

[18]   Madler, M., and E. Smith, *Pattern Recognition Engineering,* New York: Wiley, 1993.

[19]   Morel, J., and S. Solimini, *Variational Methods in Image Segmentation,* Boston, MA: Birkhauser, 1994.

[20]   Sherman, J., D. Spector, C. Swauger, L. Clark, E. Zelnio, M. Lahaut, and T. Jones, "Automatic Target Recognition Systems" in the *Infrared and Electro-Optical Systems Handbook,* ERIM and SPIE, p. 369, 1993.

Part 3

Systems

Chapter 11

Infrared Systems

Waldman and Wootton [1] state that infrared systems underwent initial development just before World War II. Due to the success of radar, imaging infrared (I²R) systems were investigated primarily in the laboratory until the 1960s. Once developed, its highest value was identified as providing battlefield observation in the dark. Infrared sensors allowed both targeting and fire control with complete day and night coverage. Huge successes were seen in Desert Storm with the night superiority provided by I²R systems. The I²R techniques presented in this chapter are the same as those used for the design and analysis of these military systems.

The *forward-looking infrared* (FLIR) receiver is a military version of the I²R sensor. Both terms, FLIR and I²R, are used interchangeably in the tactical and strategic sensor communities. The progress in infrared imaging technology has been described in terms of the FLIR. The first-generation FLIR is widely fielded on may platforms including tanks, helicopters, and rifles (also, hand-held sighting systems). The first-generation FLIR is generally called a *common-module FLIR*. This stems from the use of system components made up of modules designed to be configured many different ways to be compatible with the platform constraints. The modules or building blocks allow system versatility in design while minimizing system uniqueness and, therefore, major expense throughout the life cycle of the equipment. Minimized logistic cost are realized as many of the components can be interchanged with similar fielded common-module systems. Due to specific system weight, power, and size constraints, some of the common modules are unique and cannot be interchanged. For example, there is a large IR imager module and a small IR imager module. The first-generation FLIR may comprise a linear array of detectors that are optically swept across the sensor FOV. Three detector array modules consist of 60, 120, and 180 detectors each. The 120- and 180-element modules are interchangeable, whereas the 60-element module is unique to itself and is used for rifle and hand-held applications. The 120-element module is typically used for ground vehicle platforms, whereas the 180-element module is used for airborne applications. There are two unique and noninterchangeable scanner modules. One for the small 60-element detector module and the other for the 120- and 180- element detector modules. The scanners are designed in such a way that the scanning mirror tilts on successive scans, thus providing successive interlace fields to the infrared imagery.

The scanners are bidirectional in operation. All the electronic amplifiers and filters are analog. The infrared-to-visible-light conversion is performed with an electro-optical multiplexer (EO mux). The first-generation FLIR was very successful in Desert Storm. First-generation FLIRs have been fielded in Apache helicopters, Light Observation helicopters, M1A tanks, Bradley Fighting Vehicles, F-16 fighters, with troops (the AN/TAS-4A), and the Night Observation Device-Long Range (NODLR), to name a few.

Second-generation FLIRs have been under development for the last 10 years. They are well defined and have been patented [Blecha, et. al., U.S. Patent Number 5,510,618]. While the second-generation FLIR has been successfully developed and characterized for some time, the production and mass fielding of these systems have only recently begun. The systems are intended to replace the fielded first-generation systems initially, and then become integrated components in new weapon system platforms. The major differences are that the detector has the ability to perform time-delay-integration (TDI) processing with a number of detectors in a single scan line. Typically, the detector is 480 by 4, where the four-detector width is scanned and read out serially to perform the TDI function. In short, each of the four detectors samples the FOV at the same point and the signal is integrated to increase its fidelity. The signal adds directly and the noise adds in quadrature giving an increased signal-to-noise ratio (SNR) by a factor of 2. On-chip electronics are still analog, but digital processing is performed off the chip. Second-generation FLIRs are still single-band systems that either operate in the midwave or longwave spectral bands.

The third-generation FLIR is currently under development. It is not yet defined to the point that a patent has been issued. The third-generation FLIR technologies are listed in Figure 11.1; however, whether these technologies are included in the third-generation FLIR is only speculation. It is widely accepted that the third-generation FLIR will include a large format staring array. The details about digital technology on the chip are not currently known. Finally, there is some chance that the third-generation FLIR will include multiple spectral-band detectors on the same chip. These bands could be both midwave and longwave or a combination of subsets of these spectral bands.

Lloyd [2] points out that the imaging process has several different dimensions: intensity, time, wavelength, polarization, and the three spatial dimensions. With the number of variables contained in these dimensions, there are many correct solutions for a given imaging problem. Unfortunately, a large number of incorrect parameter sets can also be taken as solutions to a particular situation. Analysis and design go hand-in-hand; they form an iterative process. We assume that the analysis lends itself to linear-shift invariant principles in the development of the response for an infrared sensor design.

1 st Generation (common-module)	2 nd Generation	3 rd Generation
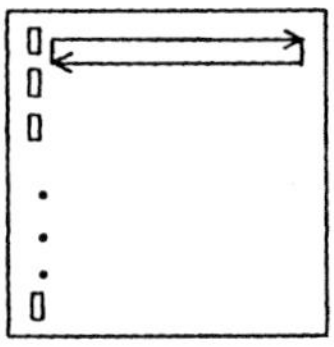	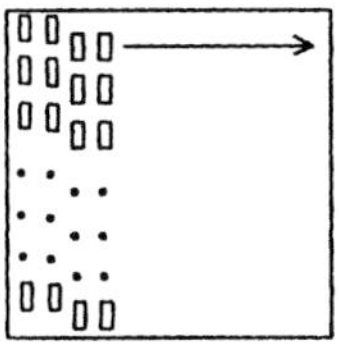	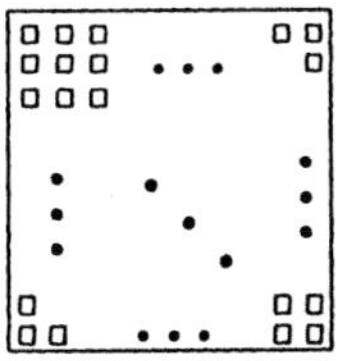
Bidirectional linear array	Unidirectional TDI x 4 Array	Large format array
Analog electronics	Analog electronics on chip, digital off chip	Digital electronics on chip
EO-MUX E-MUX Analog filtering	Digital signal processing	On-chip processing Digital signal processing
Single-wave band	Single-wave band	Multispectral

Figure 11.1 FLIR generations.

Performance measures are an excellent method for representing the collective response of a sensor system. However, infrared sensor performance measures do not include all the necessary information to determine how well a sensor will perform in an overall imaging environment (e.g., a tactical or strategic scenario). That is, the I^2R system performance measures do not explicitly include target, background, or atmospheric characteristics. The measures only include the sensor components as outlined by the dashed box in Figure 11.2. While the sensor system does not include the target, background, and atmospheric components, it does include the display and human vision components (if they are intended to process the data).

The idea here is to characterize the sensor with a number of system-level performance parameters that describe the fidelity of the infrared to visual transformation. These system-level metrics include the response of each sensor component. They can be used to determine how well a sensor performs in an overall imaging system scenario for particular targets, backgrounds, and atmospheric conditions allowing a quick evaluation of the sensor in different environments.

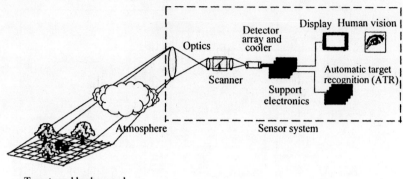

Figure 11.2 I²R sensor system.

The system-level performance measures describe the sensor in terms of sensitivity and resolution. Noise equivalent temperature difference (NETD) and three-dimensional noise parameters describe the sensor's general sensitivity. The system modulation transfer function (MTF) describes the imaging resolution of the sensor. However, sensitivity and resolution of a sensor are not separable. The resolution of an infrared sensor is strongly dependent on the sensitivity of the sensor and vice versa. Therefore, a combined sensitivity and resolution performance parameter was developed called the minimum resolvable temperature difference (MRTD, or just MRT) that accurately describes the interrelationship for a particular sensor. MRT is used by many engineers and scientists, especially tactically oriented (fire control and targeting) organizations, as the primary performance measure.

Many parameters are discussed in this chapter. The material is intended to pull together all the sensor components presented in the previous chapters to culminate in a system-level sensor description. This is then used along with the target and atmospheric parameters to give a probability of object discrimination.

11.1 SENSITIVITY AND RESOLUTION

The two general parameters of performance for any I²R or EO sensor are *sensitivity* and *resolution*. Sensitivity refers to how well a sensor can discriminate small radiance changes in the object space. Formally, sensitivity can be defined as the differential radiance which produces a unity SNR. For infrared sensors, this is usually described in terms of an equivalent blackbody temperature (i.e., the temperature of a ideal blackbody that delivers the prescribed radiance). Ideally, an infrared sensor would be able to resolve the radiant changes in targets and backgrounds to an infinite number of equivalent blackbody temperatures.

However, system noise and sensor dynamic range eliminate any chance of infinite sensitivity. NETD is a good measure of sensitivity, but it is a gross value that lumps noise into an equivalent bandwidth. More important, sensitivity is a function of resolution. MRT describes sensitivity as a function of spatial frequency (i.e., resolution), producing a more comprehensive characterization.

Resolution refers to how well a sensor can "see" small spatial details in the object space. Resolution is characterized by the MTF of the system. However, the entire system MTF is not useful. Some MTF values decrease signals to less than the noise level of the system (for particular spatial frequencies). So, again, we find ourselves in a position where the true useful resolution of the system depends on noise (and therefore sensitivity). MRT was developed to address the need for a function relating the two.

Because sensitivity and resolution are related, changes in sensor resolution affect sensor sensitivity. Most of the possible changes in sensor components give conflicting changes in sensitivity and resolution. For example, an increase in a sensor's focal length (with all other sensor parameters held constant) may increase resolution and decrease sensitivity. Such a parameter change can give a sensitivity and resolution relationship similar to the one shown in Figure 11.3.

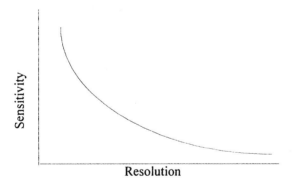

Figure 11.3 Sensitivity and resolution relationship.

With such a parametric analysis, a sensor designer or analyst needs to determine an appropriate point to set the parameter. The decision may be a simple one because of the sensor use. For example, the sensor may be used to view rocket plumes where plenty of signal is present, but high resolution is desired. The process may be an iterative one requiring convergence to a compromise in requirements.

Not all parameters are conflicting in sensitivity and resolution. There are a few such as entrance pupil diameter that usually enhance both sensitivity and resolution. For a larger entrance pupil diameter, the resolution of a sensor may be increased because of a smaller diffraction spot (or psf) and the sensitivity of the sensor may be increased because of collection efficiency (i.e., flux throughput). While this sounds like a great way to beat both parameters, imaging optics usually have a practical f-number lower limit of around 1, resulting in a limit on entrance pupil diameter. Also, optics with very low f-numbers tend to be accompanied by significant aberrations, so the resolution of the system may actually suffer. It is well known in the airborne sensor communities (both tactical and intelligence, surveillance, and reconnaissance [ISR]) that payload customers want sensors with infinite resolution, infinite sensitivity, and an infinite FOV. The bottom line is that sensor parameters involve significant tradeoffs in sensitivity, resolution, and area coverage. The following sections provide an introduction to the sensitivity and resolution parameters of I^2R sensors, the basis of most tradeoffs. We begin with the sensitivity parameter of NETD.

11.2 NOISE EQUIVALENT TEMPERATURE DIFFERENCE

NETD is a sensitivity parameter that is defined [3] as the target-to-background temperature difference in a standard test pattern that produces a peak-signal-to-rms-noise ratio of unity at the output of a reference filter (recent measurements use the system noise bandwidth as the linearity filter) when the system views a test pattern. The NETD is a measure of the rms noise amplitude in terms of target-to-background temperature differentials. The NETD is typically measured with an oscilloscope on the output of a detector while the infrared imager views a square target of differential temperature ΔT that produces a signal-to-background differential voltage V_s. The noise voltage on the output of the detector is then measured with a true rms voltmeter V_n. The corresponding NETD of the detector signal is determined by

$$NETD = \frac{\Delta T}{V_s/V_n} \qquad (11.1)$$

The overall frame NETD can then be taken as the average, or some other function [4], of the detector NETDs. There are actually a number of different techniques for measuring NETD that can lead to errors [4]. However, the basic concept is that NETD is a temperature equivalent signal that corresponds to system rms noise output.

The following derivation of NETD is provided by Lloyd [3] with the following assumptions:

1. Detector responsivity is uniform across the detector's sensitive area.
2. Detector detectivity is independent of other parameters in the NETD equation.
3. NETD equivalence is in blackbody signal levels.

4. The detector angular subtense and system f-number can be expressed by small angles.
5. Electronic processing introduces no noise.

Consider the sensor system in Figure 11.4 that views part of a large blackbody source. The blackbody source has a spectral radiance of

$$L(T,\lambda) = \frac{M(T,\lambda)}{\pi} \qquad \text{[W/(cm}^2\text{-sr-mm)]} \qquad (11.2)$$

The flux (or power) on the detector, whether the detector is scanned or staring can be expressed as

$$\Phi(T,\lambda) = \frac{M(T,\lambda)}{\pi}\frac{A_o}{R^2}(\alpha R)(\beta R)\tau_o(\lambda) = \frac{M(T,\lambda)}{\pi}A_o\alpha\beta\tau_o(\lambda) \quad \text{[W/mm]} \qquad (11.3)$$

where $\alpha = a/f$ (horizontal detector angular subtense), $\beta = b/f$ (vertical detector angular subtense), A_o is the area of the optics entrance pupil, and $\tau_{optics}(\lambda)$ is the transmission of the optics.

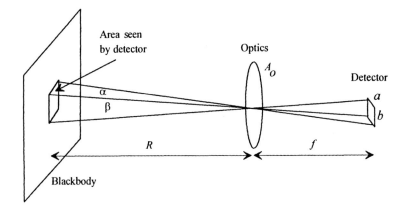

Figure 11.4 Blackbody flux to detector.

Because the detector signal responds to flux, we are interested in differential changes in flux with target temperature

$$\frac{\partial\Phi(\lambda)}{\partial T} = \frac{\alpha\beta}{\pi}A_o\tau_o(\lambda)\frac{\partial M(T,\lambda)}{\partial T} \quad \text{[W/(mm-deg K)]} \qquad (11.4)$$

The detector responsivity relates the flux $\Phi(\lambda)$ to the detector signal voltage by $V_n D^*(\lambda)/\sqrt{ab\Delta f}$, where $D^*(\lambda)$ is the detector detectivity and Δf is the detector electronics equivalent noise bandwidth. The change in voltage with the change in temperature can be written as

$$\frac{\partial V_s(\lambda)}{\partial T} = \frac{\alpha\beta}{\pi} A_o \tau_{optics}(\lambda) \frac{V_n D^*(\lambda)}{\sqrt{ab\Delta f}} \left(\frac{\partial M(T,\lambda)}{\partial T}\right) \quad [V/(mm\text{-deg }K)] \qquad (11.5)$$

Integrating with wavelength yields an expression that is equal to $\Delta V_s/\Delta T$ for small signal approximations:

$$\frac{\Delta V_s}{\Delta T} = \frac{\alpha\beta A_o V_n}{\pi\sqrt{ab\Delta f}} \int_0^\infty \frac{\partial M(T,\lambda)}{\partial T} D^*(\lambda)\tau_{optics}(\lambda)d\lambda \quad [V/\text{deg }K] \qquad (11.6)$$

NETD occurs when $\Delta V_s/V_n$ is equal to 1. Rearranging (11.6) to solve for the ΔT when $\Delta V_s/V_n = 1$ gives

$$NETD = \frac{\pi\sqrt{ab\Delta f}}{\alpha\beta A_o} \frac{1}{\int_0^\infty \frac{\partial M(T,\lambda)}{\partial T} D^*(\lambda)\tau_{optics}(\lambda)d\lambda} \quad [K] \qquad (11.7)$$

This equation gives a generalized form of NETD that can be applied to a number of different systems. (11.7) is an exact equation that is integrated in wavelength. NETD can be simplified further with a few assumptions or approximations. They are

(a) The transmission of the optics $\tau_{optics}(\lambda)$ is constant within the sensor band and zero outside the sensor band. An effective transmission for the band can be taken as

$$\tau_{optics} = \frac{\int_0^\infty \frac{\partial M(T,\lambda)}{\partial T} \tau_{optics}(\lambda)D*(\lambda)d\lambda}{\int_0^\infty \frac{\partial M(T,\lambda)}{\partial T} D*(\lambda)d\lambda} \qquad (11.8)$$

(b) Normalization of $D^*(\lambda)$ by the peak detectivity at wavelength λ_p, $D^*(\lambda_p)$ and the definition of an *effective* change in object radiant emittance with temperature is

$$\frac{\Delta M}{\Delta T} \triangleq \int_{\lambda_1}^{\lambda_2} \frac{\partial M(T,\lambda)}{\partial T} \frac{D^*(\lambda)}{D^*(\lambda_p)} d\lambda \qquad (11.9)$$

Note that $D^*(\lambda_p)$ is a constant and must be multiplied by (11.9) to equal the integral in (11.7).

(c) We can find $\frac{\partial M(T,\lambda)}{\partial T}$ from Planck's equation (5.7) by

$$\frac{\partial M(T,\lambda)}{\partial T} = \frac{(2\pi hc^2)(hc/k)e^{hc/(\lambda kT)}}{\lambda^6 T^2 (e^{hc/(\lambda kT)}-1)^2} = M(T,\lambda)\frac{(hc/k)e^{hc/(\lambda kT)}}{\lambda T^2 (e^{hc/(\lambda kT)}-1)} \approx M(T,\lambda)\frac{(hc/k)}{\lambda T^2} \qquad (11.10)$$

for $e^{hc/(\lambda kT)} \gg 1$, which is reasonable for the imaging of terrestrial objects. The NETD equation is simplified further with the above approximations to

$$NETD = \frac{\pi\sqrt{ab\Delta f}}{\alpha\beta A_o \tau_{optics}D^*(\lambda_p)\frac{\Delta M}{\Delta T}} = \frac{\pi\sqrt{ab\Delta f}}{\alpha\beta A_o \tau_{optics}D^*(\lambda_p)\frac{(hc/k)}{T^2}\int_{\lambda_1}^{\lambda_2}\frac{M(T,\lambda)D^*(\lambda)}{\lambda D^*(\lambda_p)}d\lambda} \qquad (11.11)$$

Equation (11.11) is also a somewhat general expression for NETD. It can be simplified even further, however, if certain detector assumptions can be made. For a detector that operates at the theoretical limit of detectivity, the NETD can be extended for background-limited infrared photon (BLIP) detection systems. BLIP [5] occurs when the background photon flux collected by the detector is the dominant noise source in the system. Because the detectivity, or $D^*(\lambda)$, depends on the solid angle at which the detector collects the background radiation, a BLIP quantity called *dee-double-star* or *dee-star-star* $D^{**}_{BLIP}(\lambda)$ is related to the detectivity

$$D^*_{BLIP}(\lambda) = \sqrt{\frac{\pi}{\Omega_{cs}}}\eta_q \, D^{**}_{BLIP}(\lambda) \qquad (11.12)$$

$D^{**}_{BLIP}(\lambda)$ is normalized for unity quantum efficiency and an effective background collection angle of π. Consider the optical system and cold-shield solid angles shown in Figure 11.5.

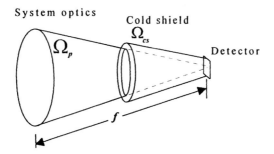

Figure 11.5 Cold-shield efficiency.

The purpose of the cold shield is to block background radiation from striking the detector if the sources are not within the cold-shield solid angle. However, not all cold shields are matched to the light input cone of the optics. The perfect cold-shield angle (for the small angle approximation) is

$$\Omega_p = \frac{\pi D^2}{4f^2}$$ (11.13)

where D is the input entrance pupil diameter and f is the system focal length. A cold-shield efficiency is taken to be

$$\eta_{cs} = \frac{\Omega_p}{\Omega_{cs}}$$ (11.14)

Substitution yields a detectivity of

$$D^*(\lambda) = 2(\frac{f}{D})(\eta_{cs}\eta_q)^{1/2} D_{BLIP}^{**}(\lambda)$$ (11.15)

This gives an NETD of

$$NETD = \frac{2\sqrt{\Delta f}}{\sqrt{\alpha\beta\eta_{cs}\eta_q} \, D\tau_{optics}D_{BLIP}^{**}(\lambda_p)\frac{\Delta M}{\Delta T}}$$ (11.16)

Finally, we have an NETD expression that can be used for gross sensitivity issues of an infrared sensor. There are a number of deficiencies that Lloyd points out in using the NETD described here. Some of these are that (1) NETD is usually measured at the electronics output and not at the display, so it may not include all of the noise sources; (2) NETD is a measure of total inband noise and the eye is not sensitive to all noise spatial frequencies in a uniform manner; and (3) NETD does not account for emissivities because blackbody radiation was assumed in the derivation. Recall that sensitivity is really a function of spatial frequency and NETD does not contain the spatial frequency dependence. It is well understood that MRT (discussed in Section 11.5) is a better measure of system performance. NETD is still used frequently, however, and as long as the limitations are understood, it can be a useful tool in system evaluation when used with other parameters. Typical values for system NETD range from around 0.02 to 0.20 deg C.

For a perfect cold-shield design, (11.16) can be simplified with a few substitutions and some algebra. The substitutions include $a/f = \alpha$, $b/f = \beta$, $A_d = ab$, and $\Delta L = \Delta M/\pi$. Band-averaged detectivity is usually specified by detector manufacturers so that a useful form of NETD is

$$NETD = \frac{4}{\pi}[\frac{(F/\#)^2 \sqrt{\Delta f}}{\tau_{optics}\sqrt{A_d} \, D^* \frac{\Delta L}{\Delta T}}]$$ (11.17)

where $F/\#$ is the f-number equal to f/D and ΔL is the differential radiance. Note that the radiance difference is taken with respect to temperature. D^* is the band averaged detectivity in $cm\sqrt{Hz}/W$. Finally, $\frac{\Delta L}{\Delta T}$ is the band radiance derivative of Planck's law and can be approximated (e.g., for 300 deg K optics paths, backgrounds), at 6.3 x 10^{-5} $W/(cm^2 - sr - K)$ for the 8- to 12-μm band and 6.7 x 10^{-6} $W/(cm^2 - sr - K)$ for the 3- to 5-μm band.

Example: Scanning System

An example provides the following longwave I^2R parameters for a parallel scanned system (Table 11.1).

Table 11.1
NETD scanning system example

Sensor parameters	
Entrance aperture diameter	20 cm
Focal length	35 cm
Horizontal FOV	4 deg
Vertical FOV	3 deg
Frame rate	30 Hz
Overscan ratio	1
Interlace	2:1
Number of detectors	180
Horizontal DAS	0.2 mrad
Vertical DAS	0.2 mrad
D*	5×10^{10} $cm \sqrt{Hz} /W$
Optics transmission	0.70
Scan efficiency	0.75

The solution is given by determining the parameters of (11.17). First, the $F/\#$ is 1.75. The detector dimensions can be determined from the DASs and the focal length to give 70 μm by 70 μm. The detector area is 49 x 10^{-6} square cm^2. If the bandwidth is matched to the system, the line scan time must be determined. With a 2:1 interlace, the detectors are scanned horizontally at a rate of 60 times per second. This means that a detector line is taken in 16.7 msec. With a scan efficiency of 0.75, the line time is 12.5 msec. There are 350 horizontal DASs across a line. Two samples or two integration times occur during the detector dwell so that effectively 700 independent signals are required from one line. Therefore, 700 signals per 12.5 msec are required for a sufficient bandwidth, or 55.9 kHz. The NETD is desired in the 8- to 12-μm waveband. Using (11.17), an NETD of 0.06 deg K is obtained. (11.17) does not take into account any improvement in NETD from the TDI process. For I^2R sensors with more than one row of scanning detectors that are summed in a TDI fashion, Shumaker [6] provides a NETC or a chain NETD that shows the improvement of the TDI chain:

$$NETC = \frac{NETD}{\sqrt{N_{TDI}}}$$

where N_{TDI} is the number of TDI detectors in a chain. An example of this is the second generation FLIRs, with a four detector TDI chain. The improvement here for the example above would be a factor of 2, or an NETC of 0.03 degree Kelvin.

Example: Staring System

An example provides the following midwave (3 to 5 micrometer) I^2R parameters for a staring system (Table 11.2).

Table 11.2
NETD staring system example

Sensor parameters	
Entrance aperture diameter	17 cm
Focal length	53 cm
Horizontal FOV	2.0 deg
Vertical FOV	2.0 deg
Array size	1,024 by 1,024
Frame rate	60 Hz
Fields per frame	1:1
Horizontal detector size	18 μm
Vertical detector size	18 μm
Horizontal pitch	18 μm
Vertical pitch	18 μm
D*	$50 \times 10^{10}\ cm\sqrt{Hz}/W$
Optics transmission	0.8
Scan efficiency	1.0

Again, the parameters in (11.17) must be determined. First, the $F/\#$ is calculated to be 3.1. The bandwidth can be approximated by $1/2t_{int}$, where t_{int} is the detector integration time. The integration time here is very similar to the detector dwell time in a scanning system. The bandwidth is then calculated to be 37.5 Hz. The area of a single detector is 18 μm by 18 μm, or $3.24 \times 10^{-6}\ cm^2$. The detectivity is given and the change in radiance with temperature is $6.7 \times 10^{-6}\ W/(cm^2 - sr - K)$ for the 3- to 5-μm band. Using these parameters gives the NETD at the output of a single detector. The NETD is calculated to be 0.015 deg C.

Note that the example of the staring sensor gives a smaller but comparable NETD to that of the scanning sensor. This should not be taken as a direct comparison because the first system is a longwave system and the second is a midwave system. The change in radiance with temperature is much less in this band for terrestrial temperatures. The staring array is desirable because the integration time is larger, thus reducing the NETD values. If a system similar to the longwave example system were constructed in a staring array configuration, the NETD would be much smaller. Finally, the NETD value given for the staring array may not be a good indicator of system noise, because we have described the NETD for a single-detector output. Fixed-pattern noise causes the NETD to appear at larger values, so three-dimensional noise may be a better system noise description.

11.3 THREE-DIMENSIONAL NOISE

Three-dimensional noise [7-9] is becoming a more common method of characterizing infrared system noise. NETD is limited in that it only characterizes temporal detector noise, where three-dimensional noise characterizes both spatial and temporal noises that are attributed to a wide variety of sources. In fact, three-dimensional noise has been successfully integrated into the U.S. Army's Night Vision and Electronic Sensor Directorate's (NVESD) FLIR92 MRTD sensor model. Consider the successive frames of acquired noise given in Figure 11.6.

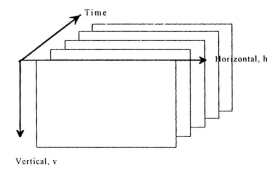

Figure 11.6 Three-dimensional noise coordinates.

A directional average is taken within the coordinate system shown in order to obtain eight parameters that describe the noise at the system's output. The noise is then calculated as the standard deviation of the noise values in the directions that were not averaged. The parameters are given in Table 11.3, where the subscript that is *missing* gives the directions that were averaged. The directional averages are converted to equivalent temperatures in a manner similar to NETD. The result is a set of eight noise parameters that can be used as analytical tools in sensor design, analyses, testing, and evaluation. The majority of these parameters cannot be calculated like NETD with the exception of σ_{tvh}, which is similar to NETD. σ_{tvh} is actually identical to NETD with the exception that the actual system noise bandwidth is used instead of the reference filter bandwidth. The other noise parameters can only be measured to determine the infrared sensor artifacts. In the FLIR92 infrared sensor model, reasonable estimates are made for these parameters based on a large database of historical measurements. The measurements were conducted on both scanning and staring-system noise parameters.

Table 11.3
Three-dimensional noise components from Scott, et al. [7]

Noise	Description	Source
σ_{tvh}	Random spatio-temporal noise	Detector temporal noise
σ_{tv}	Temporal row noise, line bounce	Line processing, 1/f, readout
σ_{th}	Temporal column noise, column bounce	Scan effects
σ_{vh}	Random spatial noise, bidirectional fixed-pattern noise	Pixel processing, detector-to-detector nonuniformity, 1/f
σ_v	Fixed row noise, line-to-line nonuniformity	Detector-to-detector nonuniformity
σ_h	Fixed-column noise, column-to-column nonuniformity	Scan effects, detector-to-detector nonuniformity
σ_t	Frame-to-frame noise, frame bounce	Frame processing
S	Mean of all noise components	

If all the noise components are considered statistically independent, an overall noise parameter can be given at the system output as

$$\Omega = \sqrt{\sigma_{tvh}^2 + \sigma_{th}^2 + \sigma_{tv}^2 + \sigma_{vh}^2 + \sigma_h^2 + \sigma_v^2 + \sigma_t^2} \qquad (11.18)$$

The frame-to-frame noise is typically negligible, so it is not included in most noise estimates.

The three-dimensional noise can be expanded further to include the perceived noise with eye and brain effects in the horizontal and vertical directions. Composite system noise (perceived) in the horizontal direction can be given by

$$\Omega_h = [\sigma_{tvh}^2 E_t E_v(\xi) E_h(\xi) + \sigma_{vh}^2 E_v(\xi) E_h(\xi) + \sigma_{th}^2 E_t E_h(\xi) + \sigma_h^2 E_h^2(\xi)]^{1/2} \qquad (11.19)$$

where E_t, $E_v(\xi)$, and $E_h(\xi)$ are the eye and brain temporal integration, vertical spatial integration, and horizontal spatial integration, respectively. In the vertical direction, the composite noise is given by

$$\Omega_v = [\sigma_{tvh}^2 E_t E_v(\eta) E_h(\eta) + \sigma_{vh}^2 E_v(\eta) E_h(\eta) + \sigma_{tv}^2 E_t E_v(\eta) + \sigma_v^2 E_v^2(\eta)]^{1/2} \quad (11.20)$$

Note that the noise terms included in each perceived composite signal correspond to only those terms that contribute in that particular direction.

Scanning systems show a wide variety of noise values. Three different estimates of three-dimensional noise values corresponding to low, moderate, and high noise systems are provided in Table 11.4. Staring arrays have been dominated by random spatial noise, so a single noise model is used. These model estimates are based on the construction of a measurement database at the U.S. Army's NVESD for infrared system characterizations. These estimates are given in Table 11.4 in terms of a percentage of the random spatio-temporal noise.

Table 11.4
3-D noise estimates based on historical measurements

Noise term	Scanning low noise	Scanning moderate noise	Scanning high noise	Staring noise
σ_{vh}	0	0	0	$0.40\sigma_{tvh}$
σ_{tv}	$0.25\sigma_{tvh}$	$0.75\sigma_{tvh}$	$1.0\sigma_{tvh}$	0
σ_v	$0.25\sigma_{tvh}$	$0.75\sigma_{tvh}$	$1.0\sigma_{tvh}$	0
σ_{th}	0	0	0	0
σ_h	0	0	0	0

11.4 MODULATION TRANSFER FUNCTION

The MTF of a system is a primary measure of the overall system resolution. The system MTF gives the transfer of input spatial frequencies in a manner similar to the transfer function in electronic systems for temporal frequencies. Usually, the MTF can be considered separable in the horizontal and vertical directions. For example, the horizontal MTF of a system includes all of the system horizontal components

$$MTF_{Sys}(\xi) = MTF_{optics}(\xi)MTF_{detector}(\xi)MTF_{electronics}(\xi)MTF_{display}(\xi)MTF_{eye}(\xi)$$

$$(11.21)$$

Note that the atmospheric MTF of the turbulence is not included in the system MTF, but it can be cascaded with the system MTF if the overall transfer of an imaging system within a particular scenario is desired. The addition of atmospheric MTF would allow the output image spectrum (and resulting image) to be determined from an input object spectrum (or object scene). The atmospheric MTF is usually left out, however, as the sensor characteristics may be desired as scene independent or a relative performance between two sensors is needed. Any atmospheric MTF that is selected would limit the sensor characterization to that scenario. The horizontal sensor MTF given is only for the part of the system within the dashed box in Figure 11.2.

The form of the vertical MTF is identical to (11.21), with η substituted for ξ, and the vertical MTF components may be different from those in the horizontal directions. Therefore, two MTFs are calculated for the sensor. Those MTFs that are circularly symmetric, such as the diffraction component of the optics MTF, may not be separable in Cartesian coordinates. A slice through the circular function in the horizontal direction, however, can give a reasonable estimate for how the component MTF behaves in that direction. This one-dimensional slice function can be used as horizontal and vertical MTF estimates.

At each spatial frequency, the MTF value for each component in the system is multiplied to determine system MTF at that particular spatial frequency. Figure 11.7 shows an example, where the component MTFs are shown. They are point-by-point multiplied to determine the overall system MTF. Also, one should not assume that the system cutoff frequency is where the MTF approaches zero. The system noise level provides a noise floor that limits the usefulness of small MTF values. For example, a high spatial frequency signal may propagate through the system MTF with a transfer of 10% (compared with dc light levels), but the noise may drown out signals that have been reduced to this output level.

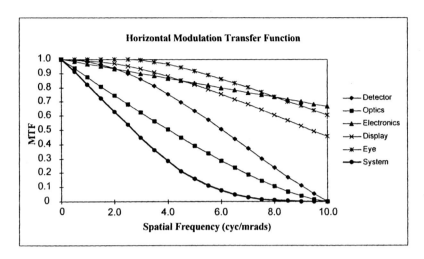

Figure 11.7 Modulation transfer function.

To illustrate the actions of the system MTF on the resolution of an image, consider Figure 11.8. An input scene is shown with variable frequency, where the frequency increases linearly from left to right. The amplitude of the signal in the horizontal direction is constant for all the frequencies shown so the spectrum is uniform over the frequency range. The spectrum is multiplied by the sensor MTF to determine the sensor's output image spectrum. The corresponding output spectrum is shown. Note that while the amplitude for all frequencies on the input is uniform, the high-frequency amplitudes suffer on the output image of the sensor. Reduced signal amplitudes on the output correspond to smaller modulation at the output of the sensor. Recall that the same effect can be seen on the output image by convolving the input scene with the sensor psf.

This text does not cover a number of MTF parameters. An example is the motion parameters associated with the device that directs the sensor's FOV to the target. Vibrations can cause a blurring that, in effect, produces an MTF that must be accounted for when the sensor is employed on a particular platform.

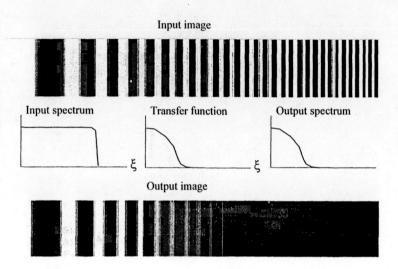

Figure 11.8 MTF response.

11.5 MINIMUM RESOLVABLE TEMPERATURE DIFFERENCE

Minimum resolvable temperature difference [10-12] (MRTD or just MRT) is defined [12] as the differential temperature of a four-bar target that makes the target just resolvable by a particular sensor. MRT is a sensor parameter that is a function and not just a value. It provides sensor sensitivity as a function of four-bar target frequency (i.e., resolution). The idea here is that the detection, recognition, and identification criteria of a target can be given in terms of a four-bar target spatial frequency. The response of the sensor is also given as a function of four-bar frequency response. The sensor performance is then determined using the combination of sensor response and the target characteristics.

The MRT is measured using 7:1 aspect ratio targets as shown in Figure 11.9. The target-to-background differential temperature is varied until the four bars are just resolvable to a trained observer. Sometimes the differential temperature is increased from a small value until the target is just resolved and then decreased from a large value until the target is just resolved. The average of the two differential temperatures is then taken as the MRT for the particular target's frequency. The same procedure is performed using negative contrast targets (the temperature of the target is cooler than the temperature of the background) to nullify test offsets. The average of the positive and negative magnitudes is then taken as the MRT. The differential temperature is plotted for each target frequency, where the collection of data points is the MRT. Note that the MRT curve appears to be related to the MTF curve in an inverted manner. This is indeed the case, as the subsequent discussion shows.

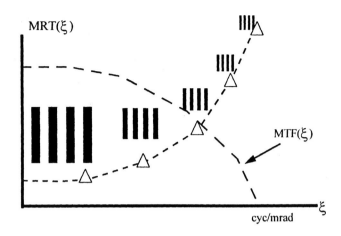

Figure 11.9 MRT curve.

Lloyd [3] describes the four most important elements of image quality as sharpness, graininess, contrast rendition, and interferences by artifacts. MRT became a widely accepted method for describing these characteristics in I^2R sensor performance because they are dominated by spatial resolution and thermal sensitivity. The derivation of MRT requires a number of assumptions. Those included in the NETD derivation are still considered applicable along with the following:

1. The eye integration time can be approximated between 0.1 and 0.2 sec.
2. The effect of spatial filtering in the eye for the display of a periodic square bar target of frequency f_T can be approximated by a matched filter for a single bar at $H(\xi) = sinc(\frac{\xi}{2f_T})$.
3. The electronic processing and monitor are assumed noiseless.
4. The system can be considered an LSI system, where the spatial frequency transfer can be described by the system MTF.

The detailed derivation of MRT is found in Lloyd [3], where it is developed using a perceived SNR for human vision of a four-bar target. The model assumes the matched filter listed in the above assumptions and also that the first harmonic of the four-bar target frequency is passed by the system (i.e., the square wave response is converted to a sine wave response). The perceived SNR is also found to improve with the number of time samples per eye integration time.

The MRT equation has undergone numerous changes and has been approximated in many forms. A particular version of the MRT model used frequently is the FLIR92 model by the U.S. Army's NVESD. The horizontal MRT of an I^2R sensor is given by

$$MRT_z(\xi) = \frac{\pi^2}{8} \frac{SNRT\sigma_{tvh}k_z(\xi)}{MTF(\xi)}[E_t E_{h_z}(\xi)E_{v_z}(\xi)]^{1/2} \qquad (11.22)$$

where z is the direction of the MRT (h for horizontal and v for vertical). *SNRT* is the eye signal-to-noise threshold required to resolve an MRT target and is usually set to around 2.5. The random spatio-temporal noise σ_{tvh} is similar to the NETD with the exception of the bandwidth reference filter (the actual noise bandwidth of the electronics is used). Therefore, the random spatio-temporal noise is given by

$$\sigma_{tvh} = \frac{4f^2 \sqrt{\Delta f}}{\pi \tau_{optics}D^2 \sqrt{ab} \, [\int_0^\infty D*(300, \lambda)\frac{\partial M(\lambda)}{\partial T}d\lambda]} \qquad (11.23)$$

Note that the random spatio-temporal noise is related to NETD only by the reference filter bandwidth used to measure NETD and the infrared sensor electronics bandwidth:

$$\sigma_{tvh} = \frac{\sqrt{\Delta f}}{\sqrt{\Delta f_r}} \qquad (11.24)$$

If a reference filter is not used on the output of the system during the NETD measurement, which is a common practice in many laboratories, the two noise parameters are identical.

The eye-brain temporal and spatial integration effects are given by E_t, $E_h(\xi)$, and $E_v(\xi)$. The temporal eye and brain integral is approximated by

$$E_t = \frac{\alpha_t}{F_R t_{eye}} \qquad (11.25)$$

where F_R is the frame rate and t_{eye} is the integration time of the eye. Frame rates are typically 30 Hz and eye integration times are around 0.1 sec for an observer viewing a display brightness of 0.15 mL. Smaller eye integration times are appropriate for higher display brightness. The temporal sample correlation factor α_t can usually be set to 1.

The eye-brain spatial integrations describe the human visual filtering of the noisy bar targets. These integrals are a little different for a scanning system and a staring system. For the scanning-system horizontal MRT, the horizontal and vertical integrations are given by

$$E_{h_h}(\xi) = \frac{v}{\Delta f} \int_0^\infty S(\alpha)H_{NF_h}^2(\alpha)sinc^2(\frac{\alpha}{2\xi})d\alpha \qquad (11.26)$$

and

$$E_{v_h}(\eta) = \frac{DAS_v}{N_{os}} \int_{-\infty}^{\infty} H_{NF_v}^2(\alpha) sinc^2(\frac{7\alpha}{2\eta}) d\alpha \qquad (11.27)$$

The scan velocity v in (11.26) can be estimated by first calculating the detector dwell time (the average time it takes a detector to scan across a point in the sensor's FOV)

$$t_D = \frac{N_v DAS_h DAS_v \eta_{sc}}{FOV_h FOV_v F_R N_{os}} \qquad [sec] \qquad (11.28)$$

where N_v is the number of detectors in the vertical direction, the detector angular subtenses and the sensor field-of-views are given in milliradians, and the scan efficiency η_{sc} is unitless. N_{os} is the overscan ratio (or the number of samples per detector angular subtense in the vertical direction). The scan velocity is simply

$$v = \frac{DAS_h}{t_D} \qquad [mrad/s] \qquad (11.29)$$

The system noise bandwidth for scanning systems is considered the bandwidth at the output port of the electronics (does not include the display monitor):

$$\Delta f = \int_0^{\infty} S(\alpha) H_{TPF}^2(\alpha) sinc^2(\alpha t_i) d\alpha \quad [Hz] \qquad (11.30)$$

where $S(\alpha)$ is the noise power spectrum, $H_{TPF}(\alpha)$ is the temporal post-filter transfer function, and t_i is the integration time of the detector. The dummy variable α in (11.30) has units in Hertz. The noise power spectrum can be estimated as a combination of white noise and $1/f$ noise

$$S(f_e) = 1 + \frac{f_k}{f_e} \qquad (11.31)$$

where f_k is the $1/f$ noise knee frequency. The temporal post-filter transfer function, $H_{TPF}(f_e)$ is a combination of all transfer functions between the detector output and the electronics output. This transfer function includes the finite response of the detector, the electronics low-pass filter, the electronics high-pass filter, and any electronics boost:

$$H_{TPF}(f_e) = H_{dt}(f_e) H_{elp}(f_e) H_{ehp}(f_e) H_{eb}(f_e) \qquad (11.32)$$

The effect of the electronics high-pass filter (9.22) is typically minimal. $H_{dt}(f_e)$ and $H_{elp}(f_e)$ are both low-pass filters given by (9.18), but with the detector 3-dB cutoff and the electronics 3-dB cutoff, respectively. The electronics boost transfer function, if any, is given by (9.34). Note that H_{TPF} only applies in the horizontal, or scan, direction. Both (11.31) and (11.32) can be written as a function of temporal frequency (as shown) or spatial frequency with the conversion from Chapter 9, $f_e = v\xi$. The conversion is necessary in (11.26) and (11.27). Usually, the transfer functions of the filters in H_{TPF} are not as limiting as the *sinc* in (11.30) because of the detector integration time. However, the *sinc* term should only be present in (11.30) for detectors that have integration circuits. For example, all second-generation FLIRs would have the *sinc* term; however, most first-generation FLIRs that include the EO mux would not include this term. For detectors that do not integrate, the system noise bandwidth is determined primarily from the electronics low-pass filter.

Now that we have developed the lower level parameters, we can evaluate the eye-brain spatial integrals for the scanning system horizontal MRT. These spatial integrals are the response of the eye-brain to a noisy bar target at the display. The integral is one of a matched filter where the eye integrates the noise over a bar that is matched to that of the four-bar target. The bar height is 7 times larger in the vertical direction than in the horizontal direction, thus, the 7 is in the frequency response of the vertical *sinc* term.

Equation (11.27) is a two-sided (both sides of the origin) integral and (11.26) is a one-sided integral. Equation (11.26) is given in frequency terms and (11.27) is given in sample rate terms so there is a factor of 2 difference. Equation (11.27) can be evaluated as a one-sided integral, but the result must be multiplied by a factor of 2. Finally, the noise filter H_{NF} is the detector-to-eye filter that includes all transfer functions from the detector to the observer's eye. In the horizontal direction:

$$H_{NF_h}(\xi) = H_{TPF}(\xi)H_{SPF_h}(\xi)\, sinc(\xi v t_i) \qquad (11.33)$$

where $H_{SPF}(\xi)$ is the spatial post-filter that includes any spatial processing between the detector output and the human eye. It usually includes the monitor MTF (typically a CRT with accounting for the spot-size and sample-and-hold), the human eye MTF, and any digital electronics spatial processing. In the vertical direction, the noise filter is simply

$$H_{NF_v}(\eta) = H_{SPF_v}(\eta) \qquad (11.34)$$

Where the spatial post-filter in the vertical direction includes the monitor (sample-and-hold does not apply to the vertical direction), the human eye, and any digital electronics processing.

As shown, there are many parameters that affect the spatial integrals described by (11.26) and (11.27). The scanning system vertical MRT spatial integrals are similar:

$$E_{h_v}(\xi) = \frac{v}{\Delta f} \int_0^\infty S(\alpha) H_{NF_h}^2(\alpha) sinc^2(\tfrac{7\alpha}{2\xi}) d\alpha \qquad (11.35)$$

and

$$E_{v_v}(\eta) = \frac{DAS_v}{N_{as}} \int_{-\infty}^\infty H_{NF_v}^2(\alpha) sinc^2(\tfrac{\alpha}{2\eta}) d\alpha \qquad (11.36)$$

The only difference here is that the MRT bars are rotated to the vertical direction. That is, the bars are longer in the horizontal direction by a factor of 7.

The last MRT parameter is $k_z(\xi)$, the noise correction factor. The horizontal noise correction factor can be calculated using the three-dimensional noise parameters given in the previous section. This parameter provides the effects of the other-than-random spatial noise. For a rough estimate of a sensor design MRT, this parameter can be set to 1. However, the previous section gave estimates for the various types of sensors based on real data. These estimates should be considered for a detailed design of a sensor. The horizontal correction factor is

$$k_h(\xi) = [1 + \tfrac{1}{E_t}(\tfrac{\sigma_{vh}}{\sigma_{tvh}})^2 + \tfrac{1}{E_{v_h}(\xi)}(\tfrac{\sigma_{th}}{\sigma_{tvh}})^2 + \tfrac{1}{E_t E_{v_h}(\xi)}(\tfrac{\sigma_h}{\sigma_{tvh}})^2]^{1/2} \qquad (11.37)$$

and the vertical correction factor is

$$k_v(\eta) = [1 + \tfrac{1}{E_t}(\tfrac{\sigma_{vh}}{\sigma_{tvh}})^2 + \tfrac{1}{E_{h_v}(\eta)}(\tfrac{\sigma_{tv}}{\sigma_{tvh}})^2 + \tfrac{1}{E_t E_{h_v}(\eta)}(\tfrac{\sigma_v}{\sigma_{tvh}})^2]^{1/2} \qquad (11.38)$$

The estimates for these values can be found for scanning and staring systems in the previous section.

Example: Second-Generation FLIR

A longwave second generation, parallel scan I²R sensor has the parameters stated in Table 11.5. Determine the horizontal MRT.

The MRT for the second-generation FLIR is given in (11.22). The first step in evaluating this equation is to determine the system MTF. The system MTF comprises the pre-filter rollup transfer functions, the temporal post-filter transfer functions, and the spatial post-filter transfer functions. The pre-filter rollup transfer functions are shown in Figure 11.10. The optics transfer function is the incoherent transfer function corresponding to diffraction. We are assuming (since the specifications did not state aberrations) that the system is diffraction limited. Next, the detector shape transfer function corresponds to the shape and size of the individual detectors.

Table 11.5
Second-generation MRT parameters

Second-generation MRT parameters	
Spectral band	7.5 to 10.0 μm
Focal length	25 cm
Aperture diameter	12.5 cm
Average optical transmission	0.7
Horizontal/vertical aspect	1.33
Frame rate	30 Hz
Fields per frame	1
Horizontal detector dimension	40 μm
Vertical detector dimension	40 μm
Peak D*	10E10 Jones
Dstar wavelength	[7.50 8.00 8.5 9.0 9.50 10.0]
Normalized D*	[0.75 0.80 0.85 0.9 0.95 1.0]
Detector integration time	10 μsec
1/f knee frequency	100 Hz
Detectors in TDI	4
Number of vertical detectors	480
Samples per DASv	2
Samples per DASh	2
Detector 3-dB response freq.	500,000 Hz
Scan efficiency	0.75
Electronics high-pass 3-dB freq.	1 Hz
Electronics high-pass filter order	1
Electronics low-pass 3-dB freq.	100,000 Hz
Electronics low-pass filter order	1
No boost filter	
Number of display lines	480
Display brightness	10 mL
Display height	15.24 cm
Display viewing distance	30.0
Eye model	Kornfeld-Lawson
Threshold SNR	2.5
Eye integration time	0.1 sec

Finally, the detector sample-and-hold transfer function is one that accounts for an integration of the detector output as it scans through space between two sample points. It is a *sinc* function corresponding to the spatial width between two samples. In the horizontal direction, the sample spacing is 0.08 mrad.

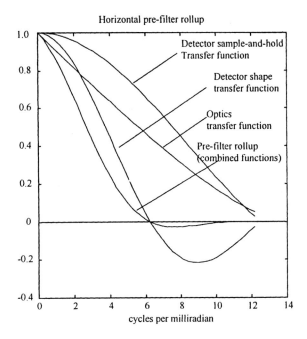

Figure 11.10 Second-generation spatial pre-filter rollup MTF.

The second set of transfer functions combine to give the temporal post-filter MTFs. The temporal post-filter MTF comprises the detector temporal transfer function, the electronics low-pass filter, the electronics high-pass filter, and the boosting filter (there is no boost in this example). Because high-performance electronics are inexpensive relative to the other infrared sensor components, these transfer functions usually outperform the spatial pre-filter and spatial post-filter transfer functions. Because the detector and electronics 3-dB frequencies are given, the temporal post-filter transfer functions can be calculated and are shown in Figure 11.11. The response of the temporal filters can be plotted as a function of temporal frequency (Hz) or in spatial frequency (cycles per milliradian). The temporal frequency is simply the spatial frequency times the scan velocity. The scan velocity was calculated using (11.28) and (11.29) to be 2,043 mrad/s (the detector dwell time was calculated to be 0.78 μsec).

The spatial post-filter transfer function includes the display spot-size (CRT) transfer function, the display sample-and-hold transfer function, and the eye transfer function. These functions, along with the combined spatial post-filter transfer function, are shown in Figure 11.12.

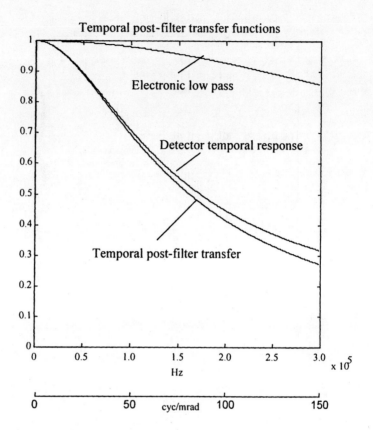

Figure 11.11 Temporal post-filter transfer.

These transfer functions are described in Chapter 10. For the eye and display transfer calculations, the magnification of the system is calculated to be 12.9 (10.2). The total MTF of the system is the combined pre-filter rollup, the temporal post-filter rollup, and the spatial post-filter rollup. These rollups, or combinations of transfer functions, and the system MTF are shown in Figure 11.13.

Now that the system horizontal MTF is calculated, the spatio-temporal noise is next. We require a system noise bandwidth that is given by (11.30). Because this is a second-generation FLIR, the integration time of the detector is included in the calculation. In this case, this *sinc* term dominates the calculation. The integration time is given at 10 μsec, so the system noise bandwidth is calculated at 4,190 Hz. The spectral detectivity is the peak detectivity times the normalized detectivity at each of the detectivity wavelengths. This detectivity is used in the denominator integration of (11.23) to give a spatio-temporal noise of 0.062 deg Kelvin.

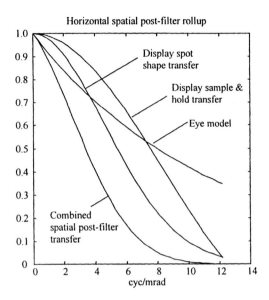

Figure 11.12 Spatial post-filter transfer.

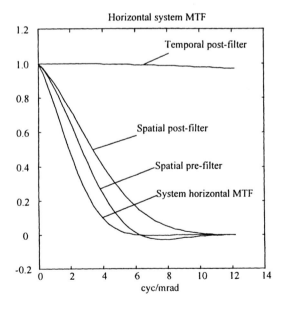

Figure 11.13 System horizontal MTF.

The rest of the MRT parameters are the threshold SNR (given at 2.5), $k_h(\xi)$, and the eye integrals. We set $k_h(\xi)$ to 1 because the three-dimensional noise parameters are not given. Therefore, the system is assumed to be limited only by random spatio-temporal noise and not pattern noise. Alternatively, the estimates in Table 11.4 for typical systems may be used. Finally, the eye integrals are estimated. The temporal integral E_t is simple at 0.333. The two spatial integrals given by (11.26) and (11.27) are provided in Figure 11.14. We now have all the parameters and functions necessary to calculate the horizontal MRT. The result is typically plotted on a semilog scale and is shown in Figure 11.15.

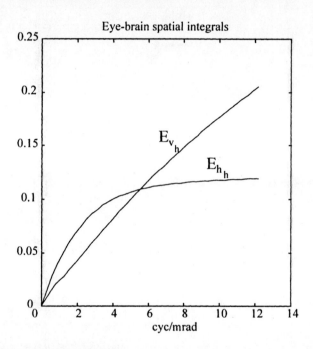

Figure 11.14 Spatial eye integrals.

The sample rate in both the vertical and horizontal direction was 12.5 cycles per milliradian and the half-sample rate (sometimes called the *Nyquist rate*) is 6.25 cycles per milliradian. The above MRT plot matches up high-temperature values very well to a spatial frequency near this "Nyquist Limit." Therefore, the MRT shown is ready to use in acquisition modeling (presented later in this chapter). This is not the case for staring sensors. They are sometimes undersampled significantly.

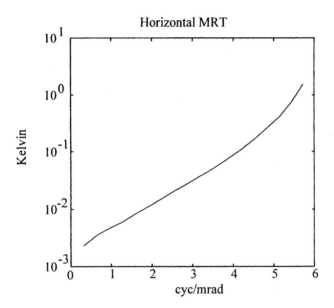

Figure 11.15 Second-generation FLIR example MRT.

Example: Third-Generation FLIR (Staring Sensor)

There are a few small differences in the modeling of second-generation FLIRs and staring sensors. The first difference is the $H_{TPF}(\xi)$ is set to 1 and $S(\xi)$ is set to 1 as their effect in the readout electronics of the detector chip is typically negligible compared with the other effects. This means that the noise bandwidth of (11.30) is primarily driven by the integration time of the detector. A second difference is the horizontal spatial eye integrals. They are no longer tied to the scan mirror velocity. They are

$$E_{h_h}(\xi) = \delta_h \int_0^\infty H_{NF_h}^2(\alpha) \ sinc^2(\tfrac{\alpha}{2\xi})d\alpha \qquad (11.39)$$

and

$$E_{h_v}(\xi) = \delta_h \int_0^\infty H_{NF_h}^2(\alpha) \ sinc^2(\tfrac{7\alpha}{2\xi})d\alpha \qquad (11.40)$$

where δ_h is the distance between samples, in milliradians, in the horizontal direction (this is the detector pitch divided by the sensor focal length). In fact, $\frac{DAS_v}{N_{os}}$ in (11.27) and (11.36) can be replaced with δ_v as they both describe the distance between vertical samples in milliradians. With these few modifications, we are prepared to perform a staring sensor analysis. Consider the following parameters (Table 11.6).

Table 11.6
Staring-sensor MRT parameters

Staring FLIR MRT parameters	
Spectral band	7.0 to 8.8 μm
Focal length	5 cm
Aperture diameter	3.85 cm
Average optical transmission	0.8
Horizontal/vertical aspect	1.0
Frame rate	30 Hz
Fields per frame	2
Horizontal detector dimension	25 μm
Vertical detector dimension	25 μm
Peak D*	5E10 Jones
Dstar wavelength	[7.0 7.2 7.4 7.6 7.8 8.0 8.2 8.4 8.6 8.8]
Normalized D*	[1.0 1.0 1.0 1.0 1.0 1.0 1.0 1.0 1.0 1.0]
Detector integration time	1333 μsec
Number of horizontal detectors	256
Number of vertical detectors	256
Horizontal detector pitch	30 μm
Vertical detector pitch	30 μm
Number of display lines	480
Display brightness	10 mL
Display height	15.24 cm
Display viewing distance	30.0
Eye model	Kornfeld-Lawson
Threshold SNR	2.5
Eye integration time	0.1 sec

This sensor is a wide FOV sensor at 8.8 by 8.8 deg. The half-sample, or Nyquist frequency, is 0.83 cycles per milliradian. The magnification is calculated to be 3.24. The system noise bandwidth is 38 Hz and the spatio-temporal noise is 0.005 Kelvin (or 5 mK). The horizontal and vertical system transfer functions are shown in Figure 11.16. The corresponding MRTs are shown in Figure 11.17. The flat part of the MRTs in the upper right corner represent infinite differential temperatures.

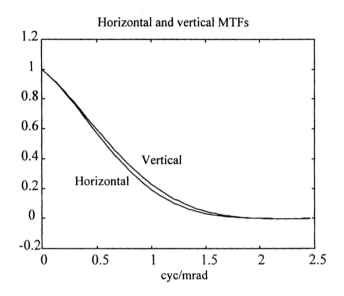

Figure 11.16 Staring-sensor MTFs.

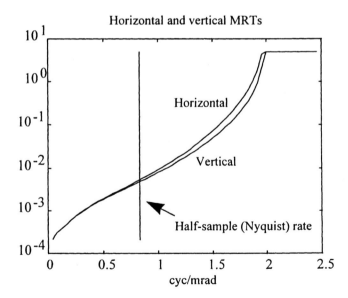

Figure 11.17 Staring-sensor MTFs.

The MRTs are usually smaller across the lower spatial frequencies than scanning sensors because the detector has a longer time to integrate light at a particular image position. Therefore, the sensors are more sensitive than their equivalent scanning counterpart sensors. In terms of resolution, there is the sampling effects to consider. Notice the half-sample rate limit shown in the MRT plot of Figure 11.17. Many scientists and engineers believe that this is the absolute resolution limit of the staring system and that no MRT can be obtained beyond this frequency. With this reasoning, the MRT is set to infinity, or some sufficiently large value, at (and beyond) this frequency. Other scientists believe that the MRT extends beyond the half-sample rate and, in fact, the MRT has been measured beyond this frequency. Currently, models of sampling effects are under way and a means for addressing the MRT of sampled systems beyond the half-sample rate will be available. A final note is with regard to microscanning. If a microscan mirror were to accompany this particular sensor that increased the sampling rate by a factor of 2, the half-sample rate would shift to 1.66 cycles per milliradian. This increased half-sample frequency would allow for the use of the MRT curve up to this new frequency. For this type of sensor, the benefits in increased resolution are apparent from the MRT plot.

11.6 TWO-DIMENSIONAL MRT

A two-dimensional MRT is determined using the vertical and horizontal MRTs found in the previous section. Consider the horizontal and vertical MRTs shown in Figure 11.18. The spatial frequencies of the horizontal and vertical MRTs are noted when both of the MRTs are matched. The geometric mean of the horizontal and vertical spatial frequencies gives the two-dimensional MRT spatial frequency

$$\rho_{2d} = \sqrt{\xi \eta} \qquad (11.41)$$

The matching MRT is then plotted as a function of the two-dimensional spatial frequency. This new function is the two-dimensional MRT. Note that the conversion is a spatial frequency conversion and no manipulation is performed on the two-differential temperatures.

11.7 PROBABILITIES OF DISCRIMINATION

One of the primary system level tactical I^2R sensor performance measures is the probability of performing a visual discrimination task (detection, recognition, and identification) where the sensor is at a given range from a target. Over the years, a variety of researchers [13,14] have demonstrated that the level of target discrimination possible with a system is related to the resolvability of bar chart equivalents of the target. Here, we focus on static performance, which refers to the ability of the observer to perform a discrimination task while having prior knowledge that a target is within the FOV and given an infinite amount of time. The target, scene, and sensor are stationary.

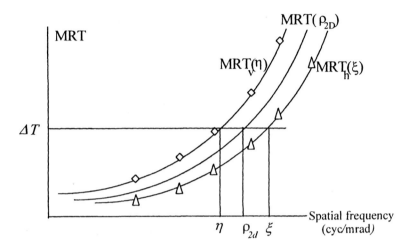

Figure 11.18 Two-dimensional MRT.

The performance measures of discrimination were first quantified by Johnson [13] in 1958 and have been modified slightly over the years for I²R sensors since the work was based on image intensifier imagery. As a result of Johnson's original performance measures, the current discrimination criteria (with 50% probabilities) are shown in Table 11.7. Johnson's development was based on using an image intensifier and the Air Force's tri-bar chart, where he sought a way to relate in-the-field performance of image intensifiers to objective laboratory measures.

The initial discrimination criteria developed by Johnson were modified to be relevant for FLIR performance prediction by Ratches, et al. [14] in 1975. This performance prediction as a function of range was based on a one-dimensional model using only the horizontal MRT. The technique was acceptable because most FLIRs at the time included a fixed relationship between the vertical and horizontal resolution (approximately 2:1). The work has been further modified to reflect the two-dimensional model that is derived using both the horizontal and vertical MRTs. The 50% probability cycle criteria for the one- and two-dimensional MRTs are shown in Table 11.7.

Table 11.7
Discrimination criteria

Discrimination level	Meaning	One-dimensional cycles across minimum dimension	Two-dimensional cycles across critical dimension, N_{50}
Detection	An object is present	1	0.75
Recognition	Class to which an object belongs (e.g., human, tank, truck)	4.0	3.0
Identification	Object is discerned with enough clarity to specify type (M1A, T-62, T-72 Tank)	8.0	6.0

There are a number of assumptions that have been made over the years in the development of the discrimination performance measure. The first is that the majority of targets that were used in field tests for the validation of the models were either high contrast or high differential temperature targets. Probability of discrimination increases (within limits) as target viewing time, angular subtense, and contrast increase. The work performed to date was mostly based on targets with a maximal height-to-width-ratio of 2:1. The only other significant work was performed by Moser [15], which dealt with targets that had a larger width-to-height ratio (e.g., ships). It is unclear exactly how medium-size targets, such as rocket launcher platforms should be modeled. In recent years, there has been much work to overcome the inherent limitations of the NVESD performance model and to incorporate the aspects and issues of the second-generation FLIR. These features include sampling, sample-scene phase effect, noise considerations, and detector nonuniformity.

The procedure for producing a probability of detection, recognition, or identification curve is quite simple. Consider the process flow given in Figure 11.19. There are four parameters that are needed to generate a static probability of discrimination curve as a function of range: the estimated target-to-background temperature differential, an estimated height and width of a target, an estimate for the atmospheric transmission of the band of interest for a number of ranges around the ranges of interest, and the sensor two-dimensional MRT (either modeled or measured on a real system).

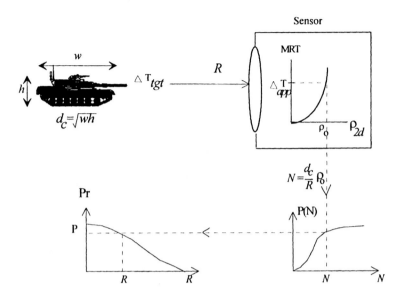

Figure 11.19 Probability of discrimination process.

The target parameters are determined first. The critical dimension of the target is taken as the geometric mean of the target height and width:

$$d_c = \sqrt{wh} \tag{11.42}$$

The target-to-background temperature difference is then estimated based on target and background characteristics. For ground targets, these differential temperatures are usually between 1.25 and 4.0 deg C. The apparent differential temperature is then determined. There are numerous techniques for determining the apparent differential temperature that were covered in Chapter 5.

Once an apparent differential temperature is obtained, the highest corresponding spatial frequency that can be resolved by the sensor is determined. This is accomplished by finding the spatial frequency ρ_o that matches the target apparent differential temperature on the MRT curve. The number of cycles across the critical target dimension that can actually be resolved by the sensor is

$$N = \rho_o \frac{d_c}{R} \tag{11.43}$$

where d_c is the critical target dimension in meters, and R is the range from the sensor to the target in kilometers.

The probability of discrimination is determined using the target transfer probability function (TTPF). The level of discrimination (detection, recognition, or identification) is selected from Table 11.7 and the corresponding 50% cycle criteria, N_{50}, is taken from the table. The probability of detection, recognition, or identification is then determined with the TTPF as

$$P(N) = \frac{(\frac{N}{N_{50}})^{2.7+0.7[\frac{N}{N_{50}}]}}{1+(\frac{N}{N_{50}})^{2.7+0.7[\frac{N}{N_{50}}]}}$$

(11.44)

This function is shown in Figure 11.20. The probability of discrimination task is then assigned to the particular range. A typical probability of discrimination curve has the probability plotted as a function of range. Therefore, the above procedure would be repeated for a number of different ranges.

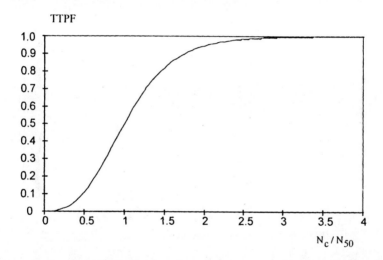

Figure 11.20 TTPF function.

While the following may be obvious, there are a number of characteristics that improve probability of detection, recognition, and identification in I²R systems. Improvements are seen with larger targets, larger target-to-background differential temperatures, larger target emissivities, larger atmospheric transmission, smaller MRT values (as a function of spatial frequency), and usually smaller FOVs (if the target does not have an extremely small differential temperature).

An example of the probability of discrimination is worthwhile as this procedure is one of the more useful ones in sensor analysis. This procedure provides the conversion of the sensor performance MRT specification to an operation performance specification. In fact, it is used frequently to give the probability of discrimination regardless of the sensor MRT source. The output of a sensor model such as FLIR92 or an actual measured (laboratory) sensor MRT can be used. Consider the two-dimensional longwave sensor MRT given in Table 11.8.

Table 11.8
2D MRT for discrimination example

ρ_{2D} [*cyc/mrad*]	MRT_{2D} [deg K]
0.297	0.010
0.599	0.021
1.091	0.043
1.692	0.090
2.265	0.185
2.754	0.382
3.148	0.790
3.440	1.631
3.649	3.369
3.778	6.958

It is desired to determine the sensor probability functions of detection, recognition, and identification of a standard NATO target at a range of up to 20 km. A standard NATO target, which is representative of a front aspect view of a tank, has a width of 2.3m, a height of 2.3m, and a target-to-background differential temperature (blackbody equivalent assuming a 300 deg C background) of 1.25 deg C. The conditions are clear, the standard U.S. atmosphere, and an altitude of 0.5 km above sea level. ModTran has been run for this condition with each of the ranges desired and the longwave transmission (8 to 12 μm) is given in the second column of Table 11.9.

The calculation begins by determining an apparent target-to-background differential temperature as seen by the sensor. In the longwave, it is common to multiply the actual differential temperature by the atmospheric transmission. This procedure is accompanied by an error of a few percent. If this had been a midwave (3- to 5-μm) sensor, the target-to-background temperature must first be converted to a differential radiance and then reduced by the atmospheric transmission to get an apparent target-to-background differential radiance. By trial and error, an equivalent blackbody temperature would be determined for the target and background corresponding to the differential radiance yielding the apparent target differential temperature.

Here, because we are working in the longwave, we multiply the target-to-background differential temperature by the atmospheric transmission to determine the apparent differential temperature:

$$\Delta T_{app}(R) = \Delta T_{tgt}\tau_{atm}(R) \qquad (11.45)$$

The apparent differential temperature is given in the third column of Table 11.9. For each $\Delta T_{app}(R)$, a frequency ρ_o must be determined using the sensor two-dimensional MRT. Recall that ρ_o is the highest spatial frequency that can be resolved by the sensor at a given $\Delta T_{app}(R)$. Interpolation is usually required to give an accurate ρ_o.

Table 11.9
Probability of discrimination example

Range, R	$\tau_{atm}(R)$	$\Delta T_{app}(R)$	ρ_o	N	P_{ID}	P_R	P_D
km	unitless	Celsius	cyc/mrad	number	unitless	unitless	unitless
1	0.900	1.125	3.26	7.50	0.69	0.98	1.00
2	0.832	1.040	3.23	3.70	0.18	0.68	1.00
3	0.775	0.969	3.21	2.46	0.07	0.34	1.00
4	0.725	0.906	3.19	1.83	0.03	0.17	0.98
6	0.638	0.799	3.15	1.20	0.01	0.06	0.86
8	0.566	0.707	3.07	0.88	0	0.03	0.64
10	0.504	0.630	2.99	0.69	0	0.02	0.43
12	0.450	0.562	2.92	0.56	0	0.01	0.28
14	0.403	0.504	2.87	0.47	0	0	0.19
16	0.362	0.452	2.82	0.40	0	0	0.13
18	0.325	0.406	2.77	0.35	0	0	0.09
20	0.292	0.365	2.71	0.31	0	0	0.07

Take, for example, R equal to 6 km in the table. The apparent target-to-background temperature is 0.80 deg C, which lies between the 0.790 and 1.631 MRT points in Table 11.8. The corresponding spatial frequencies are 3.148 and 3.440 cyc/mrad, respectively. Interpolating, the spatial frequency corresponding to 6 km is

$$\rho_o = 3.148 + (3.440 - 3.148)[\tfrac{0.799-0.790}{1.631-0.790}] = 3.1 \qquad [\text{cyc/mrad}] \qquad (11.46)$$

Interpolations are calculated for each of the apparent differential temperatures to give the critical frequency as a function of range. These are given in the fourth column of Table 11.9. The critical number of cycles are then calculated using the critical frequency, the range, and the critical target dimension using (11.43). The geometric mean of the height and width gives a critical dimension of 2.3 meters. The number of resolvable cycles across the target are given in the fifth column of Table 11.9. Finally, the probabilities of identification, recognition, and detection are given in the sixth, seventh, and eighth columns, respectively using (11.44). The 50% number of cycles across target N_{50} for identification, recognition, and detection were taken as 0.75, 3.0, and 6.0, respectively. A graphical representation is given in Figure 11.21.

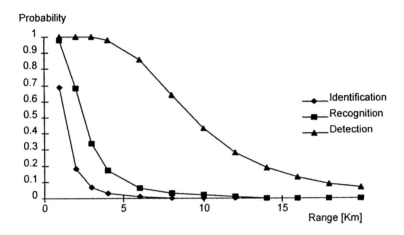

Figure 11.21 Probability of discrimination example.

Sometimes it is convenient to represent the acquisition process with the sensor two-dimensional MRT and the target "load line" on the same graph. Take, for example, the second-generation FLIR example in the MRT section of this chapter. Apply the FLIR to a 2.3m by 2.3m target with a target-to-background contrast of 2.0 deg K. Using the broadband Beer's law with a 1-km atmospheric transmission of 0.85/km, the target load line and the sensor MRT are plotted in Figure 11.22. The target begins at 2.0 deg K contrast at a range of 0.0 and decreases by a factor of 0.85 for each kilometer. Therefore, the apparent differential temperature of the target can be plotted as a function of range. Because it takes an N_{50} of three cycles across the target to obtain a 50 percent probability of recognition, we can convert the range axis to a target load line spatial frequency:

$$\rho_{2D} = \frac{N_{50}}{d_c} R \qquad [\text{cyc/mrad}] \qquad (11.47)$$

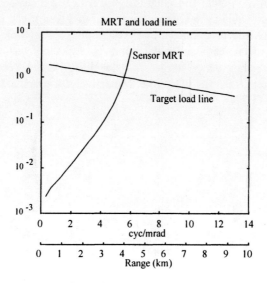

Figure 11.22 Target load line and sensor MRT.

so that the target load line can be plotted on the same spatial frequency axis as the sensor MRT. The two lines cross at the point where the sensor provides the number of cycles necessary for a 50% probability of discrimination (in this case, recognition). The probability of recognition for this example is shown in Figure 11.23.

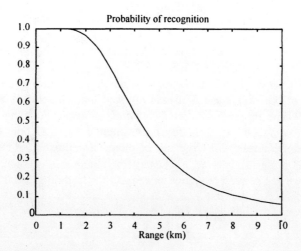

Figure 11.23 Probability of recognition.

11.8 INFRARED SEARCH AND TRACK (IRST)

The concept of InfraRed Search and Track (IRST) [16, 17] systems is similar to that of the I^2R system with a few modifications. An IRST covers an extremely large horizontal field-of-regard (FOR) to detect and locate incoming threats (Figure 11.24). The FOR is the area that a sensor's FOV can pan, or scan, through. For example, a naval IRST may be designed to detect and locate sea-skimming, antiship missiles. The idea is for a line scanner or staring array to pan around the ship in a 360 deg (or some large angle) FOR to detect incoming threats. High sensitivity and high revisit rates are desired. Some aircraft are also fitted with sensors that are wide angle area IRSTs that search only the forward area for incoming threats.

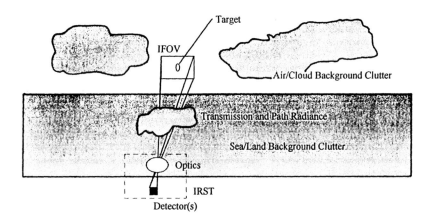

Figure 11.24 IRST nomenclature.

An IRST comprises a set of optics and infrared detectors. The processing electronics are not typically the major contributor of noise (i.e., Johnson noise and read-out noise are small compared with the BLIP limitations). Small incoming targets are characterized by some target intensity $I_{tgt}(\lambda)$ with units of Watts per steradian per micrometer (wavelength dependent). The target intensity competes with clutter radiance signals from air/clouds and the sea/land. The target intensity is also decreased by the atmospheric transmission between the target and the IRST. Finally, the path radiance provides an additive signal to the target flux on the detector of the IRST.

The relationship between the target intensity and the target irradiance involves the target-to-IRST range R and the atmospheric transmission $\tau_{atm}(\lambda)$. The actual target intensity is provided over a large solid angle and the atmospheric transmission degrades the signal. The apparent irradiance of the target at the IRST entrance aperture is

$$E_{tgt}(\lambda) = \frac{I_{tgt}(\lambda)}{R^2}\tau_{atm}(\lambda) \quad [\text{W/m}^2\text{-}\mu\text{m}] \tag{11.48}$$

Note that the irradiance falls off geometrically with the square of the range and also by the transmission of the atmosphere.

The background can be ocean, sky, clouds, or land. The background radiance, specified because it fills the instantaneous field-of-view (*IFOV*), provides additive flux on the detector. In this case, the IFOV is described in the same manner as the detector angular subtense. The irradiance at the sensor entrance aperture because the background is

$$E_{BG}(\lambda) = \frac{\alpha\beta}{\pi}L_{BG}(T_{BG},\lambda)\tau_{atm}(\lambda) \quad [\text{W/m}^2\text{-}\mu\text{m}] \tag{11.49}$$

where α is the horizontal DAS and β is the vertical DAS. $L_{BG}(\lambda)$ is the radiance of the background and T_{BG} is the temperature of the background. Finally, the last additive irradiance is due to the path radiance in the atmosphere between the target and the sensor. The path irradiance includes the radiation emission of the water and aerosol particles along with the scattered light of external sources. The irradiance from the path radiance (from emission) is

$$E_P(\lambda) = \frac{\alpha\beta}{\pi}L_P(T_A,\lambda)[1 - \tau_{atm}(\lambda)] \quad [\text{W/m}^2\text{-}\mu\text{m}] \tag{11.50}$$

where T_A is the temperature of the air.

Any irradiance contributor at the entrance aperture of the sensor provides an additive voltage at the output of the detector. The irradiance that enters the aperture falls on the detector because only radiance quantities within the sensor IFOV were considered. Therefore, the flux at the detector of the IRST is

$$\Phi(\lambda) = A_o E_{Total}(\lambda)\tau_{optics}(\lambda) \quad [\text{W/}\mu\text{m}] \tag{11.51}$$

where $E_{Total}(\lambda)$ includes the target, background, and path irradiances. The IRST voltage is the band integrated flux over the detector responsivity. Therefore:

$$V_s = \int_{\lambda_1}^{\lambda_2} A_o E_{Total}(\lambda)\tau_{optics}(\lambda)R(\lambda)d\lambda \quad [\text{V}] \tag{11.52}$$

Equation (11.52) gives the expression for the detector voltage. However, the signal of interest is the differential voltage between the case when the target is present and when the target is not present. The path radiance and the background radiance is present in both cases. The only differential flux is provided by the target irradiance. The corresponding differential voltage is

$$\Delta V_s = \int_{\lambda_1}^{\lambda_2} A_o E_{tgt}(\lambda) \tau_{optics}(\lambda) R(\lambda) d\lambda \quad \text{[V]} \quad (11.53)$$

Solving for the target intensity gives a differential voltage of

$$\Delta V_s = \int_{\lambda_1}^{\lambda_2} A_o \frac{I_{tgt}(\lambda)}{R^2} \tau_{atm}(\lambda) \tau_{optics}(\lambda) R(\lambda) d\lambda \quad \text{[V]} \quad (11.54)$$

The noise at the output of the detector can be characterized in terms of its detectivity, where the detectivity describes the physical limitations of the detector. The noise voltage at the output of the detector is

$$V_n = \int_{\lambda_1}^{\lambda_2} \frac{(A_d \Delta f)^{1/2} R(\lambda)}{D*(\lambda)} d\lambda \quad \text{[V]} \quad (11.55)$$

where A_d is the detector area, Δf is the system bandwidth, $R(\lambda)$ is the detector responsivity in volts per watt, and $D*(\lambda)$ is the detectivity of the detector.

The contributions of clutter can also be considered noise. We use a clutter radiance that is considered the standard deviation of the background radiance $\sigma_{BG}(T_{BG}, \lambda)$. The noise can then be considered the signal corresponding to the clutter:

$$V_c = \int_{\lambda_1}^{\lambda_2} A_o \frac{\alpha\beta}{\pi} \sigma_{BG}(T_{BG}, \lambda) \tau_{atm}(\lambda) \tau_{optics}(\lambda) R(\lambda) d\lambda \quad \text{[V]} \quad (11.56)$$

The overall noise total is the rss of the noise contributors such that

$$V_{nt} = \sqrt{V_n^2 + V_c^2} \quad \text{[V]} \quad (11.57)$$

One should note that noise can be dominated by the background clutter such that an improvement in detectivity would not provide an improved SNR. Also note that $\sigma_{BG}(T_{BG}, \lambda)$ is measured with a particular size detector (i.e., IFOV). Larger detectors tend to reduce the variance in the background radiance, so the background radiance standard deviation must be specified for a given IFOV.

Using the noise terms, the signal to noise expression for the output of the IRST is

$$SNR = \frac{\int_{\lambda_1}^{\lambda_2} A_o \frac{I_{tgt}(\lambda)}{R^2} \tau_{atm}(\lambda) \tau_{optics}(\lambda) R(\lambda) d\lambda}{\sqrt{[\int_{\lambda_1}^{\lambda_2} \frac{(A_d \Delta f)^{1/2} R(\lambda)}{D*(\lambda)} d\lambda]^2 + [\int_{\lambda_1}^{\lambda_2} A_o \frac{\alpha\beta}{\pi} \sigma_{BG}(T_{BG}, \lambda) \tau_{atm}(\lambda) \tau_{optics}(\lambda) R(\lambda) d\lambda]^2}} \quad (11.58)$$

This is the guiding equation for the IRST calculations that include clutter. It has little to no assumptions and various cases can be derived from it. As an exercise, we take the simplest example: the band-averaged case of negligible clutter. If the background clutter is negligible, the SNR becomes

$$SNR = \frac{\int_{\lambda_1}^{\lambda_2} A_o \frac{I_{tgt}(\lambda)}{R^2} \tau_{atm}(\lambda)\tau_{optics}(\lambda)R(\lambda)d\lambda}{\int_{\lambda_1}^{\lambda_2} \frac{(A_d\Delta f)^{1/2}R(\lambda)}{D*(\lambda)}d\lambda} \qquad (11.59)$$

where further simplification gives

$$SNR = \frac{A_o}{R^2(A_d\Delta f)^{1/2}} \frac{\int_{\lambda_1}^{\lambda_2} I_{tgt}(\lambda)\tau_{atm}(\lambda)\tau_{optics}(\lambda)R(\lambda)d\lambda}{\int_{\lambda_1}^{\lambda_2} \frac{R(\lambda)}{D*(\lambda)}d\lambda} \qquad (11.60)$$

It is not suggested that band-averaging quantities is a solution to IRST modeling. It is done quite frequently and, while errors may be acceptable in the longwave, significant errors are seen in the midwave. For some applications, it is convenient for back-of-the-envelope analysis. Band-averaged quantities yield

$$SNR = \frac{A_o I_{tgt}\tau_{atm}\tau_{optics}D*}{R^2(A_d\Delta f)^{1/2}} \qquad (11.61)$$

The missing fundamental parameters are those that provide the system bandwidth. Here:

$$\Delta f = \frac{1}{2t_{int}} \qquad (11.62)$$

where t_{int} is the detector integration time. To determine the detector integration time estimate, the scanning geometry must be considered.

The integration time of the detector is usually driven by the average dwell time of detector on any given point on the FOR. Consider the IRST geometry given in Figure 11.25.

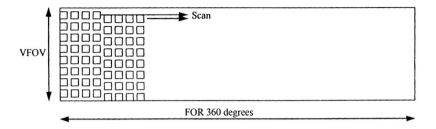

Figure 11.25 IRST scan geometry.

Using Figure 11.25, we consider a few definitions. The overscan ratio is the amount of overlap by the detectors in the vertical direction

$$N_{os} = \frac{ss_v}{\beta} \qquad (11.63)$$

where ss_v is the vertical sample spacing (center-to-center) of the detectors in milliradians and β is the vertical detector angular subtense. This is an important parameter in that more overlap increases the overall average dwell time for any given detector. The field-of-regard sweep time is t_{fov} and the number of TDI detectors is N_{tdi}. The effective dwell time is then

$$t_{int} = \frac{\alpha t_{fov} N_{os} N_{tdi}}{FOR} = \frac{\alpha t_{fov} N_{os} N_{tdi}}{2\pi(1000)} \qquad [sec] \qquad (11.64)$$

where the horizontal FOR is assumed to be 2π radians (the 1,000 is to convert the units to milliradians). Therefore, for the band-averaged, no-clutter, detector-limited IRST case, an SNR found using (11.61) to be

$$SNR = \frac{A_o I_{tgt} \tau_{atm} \tau_{optics} D*}{\pi R^2 \sqrt{bf}} \sqrt{t_{fov} N_{os} N_{tdi}} \qquad (11.65)$$

where b is the vertical size of the detector (meters) and f is the focal length of the sensor. It is surprising, at first, to find that the SNR is not a function of horizontal detector size. An increase in detector size increases the noise; however, it also increases the integration time by the same rate. Finally, IRSTs are similar to missiles in that an SNR of between 5 and 10 is required for successful tracking to occur.

IRST Example

Equation (11.61) can be written in terms of the target irradiance, E_{IRST}, at the entrance aperture of the IRST where $I_{tgt} = E_{IRST}/[R^2\tau_{atm}]$ so that

$$SNR = \frac{A_o E_{IRST} \tau_{optics} D*}{\sqrt{A_d \Delta f}} \quad \text{[unitless]} \quad (11.66)$$

The target irradiance that results in a SNR of 1 is called the noise equivalent irradiance (NEI). Setting the SNR = 1 and rewriting (11.66) gives

$$NEI = \frac{\sqrt{A_d \Delta f}}{A_o D* \tau_{optics}} \quad \text{[W/cm}^2\text{]} \quad (11.67)$$

The U.S. Navy's IRST testbed has the following characteristics in the high-resolution mode (Table 11.10). Determine the NEI of the system.

Table 11.10
IRST parameters

IRST parameters	
Focal plane	480 by 6 TDI (second-gen)
Waveband	3 - 5 μm
Detector width (a)	38 μm
Detector height (b)	43.5 μm
Optics diameter	20 cm
Detectivity	8×10^{11} Jones
Optical transmission	0.69
Bandwidth	36 kHz

The area of the detector is 1.65×10^{-5} cm^2 and the area of the optical aperture is 314 cm^2. Using (11.67), the NEI is calculated to be 4.4×10^{-15} W/cm^2. The Navy uses two efficiency factors to account for the analog-to-digital process of the electronics and a target pulse coupling efficiency. Both of these combined efficiency factors give an overall efficiency factor of 0.74, yielding a practical NEI of 6.0×10^{-15} W/cm^2. Finally, we consider the TDI improvement of $\sqrt{6} = 2.45$ to give a final NEI of 1.34×10^{-15} W/cm^2.

EXERCISES

11.1 Calculate the NETD of a longwave (8- to 12-μm) scanning I^{2}R sensor with the following parameters in Table 11.11:

Table 11.11

Sensor parameters

Sensor parameters	
Entrance aperture diameter	0.2m
Focal length	0.7m
Horizontal FOV	4 deg
Vertical FOV	3 deg
Frame rate	30 Hz
Overscan	1
Scan efficiency	0.75
Horizontal DAS	0.1 mrad
Vertical DAS	0.1 mrad
D*	5E10 $(cm\text{-}Hz)^{1/2}/W$
Optics transmission	0.7
Number of detectors	180

11.2 Suppose the I^2R imager in Exercise 11.1 were designed with four linear TDI detectors (i.e., in the serial scan direction). Determine the effective NETC for the sensor.

11.3 The random spatio-temporal noise of a system is estimated at 0.037 deg C. Determine a reasonable estimate of the fixed-row noise for a low-noise scanned system.

11.4 Plot the component and front-end system horizontal MTFs for the second-generation FLIR system data given in Table 11.12. Neglect the display and visual perception MTFs. Determine the spatial frequency where the system MTF is 0.5.

11.5 The NETD of a sensor is measured to be 0.012 deg C, measured with a reference filter of bandwidth 25 kHz. The system bandwidth is 35 kHz. Determine the random spatio-temporal noise of the system.

11.6 A second-generation I^2R sensor has the following characteristics. Note that the horizontal and vertical MTFs are given in Table 11.13. Calculate the horizontal and vertical detector angular subtenses. Calculate the system noise equivalent temperature difference (use NETC). Determine and plot the horizontal and vertical MRT. Finally, plot the two-dimensional MRT.

Table 11.12
Horizontal MTF components

cyc/mrad	$MTF_{diffraction}$	$MTF_{aberration}$	$MTF_{detector}$	MTF_{elect}
0	1	1	1	1
0.62	0.94	1	1	1
1.25	0.89	1	0.98	0.99
1.87	0.83	1	0.96	0.99
2.5	0.77	1	0.94	0.97
3.12	0.72	1	0.9	0.96
3.74	0.66	1	0.86	0.94
4.37	0.61	1	0.81	0.92
4.99	0.56	1	0.76	0.9
5.61	0.5	1	0.7	0.88
6.24	0.45	1	0.64	0.86
6.86	0.4	1	0.57	0.84
7.48	0.35	1	0.51	0.82
8.11	0.31	1	0.44	0.79
8.73	0.26	1	0.37	0.77
9.36	0.22	1	0.3	0.75
9.98	0.18	1	0.23	0.73
10.6	0.14	1	0.17	0.71
11.23	0.1	1	0.11	0.69
11.85	0.07	1	0.05	0.67
12.47	0.04	1	0	0.65

Table 11.13

Sensor parameters

IRST parameters	
Focal length	35 cm
Entrance aperture diameter	12 cm
Optical transmission	0.60
Frame rate	30 Hz
Interlace fields per frame	2
Vertical FOV	2 deg
Horizontal FOV	2.5 deg
Detector width	28 μm
Detector height	38 μm
D*	12×10^{10} $cm\sqrt{Hz}/W$
Number of detectors	480
Number of detectors in TDI chain	4
Overscan ratio	1.5
Serial scan ratio	1.7
Scan efficiency	0.90

ξ [cyc/mrad]	Horizontal MTF	η [cyc/mrad]	Vertical MTF
0	1	0	1
0.633	0.868	0.458	0.907
1.25	0.718	1.37	0.700
2.50	0.425	2.29	0.494
3.70	0.206	3.20	0.317
4.90	0.081	4.58	0.135
6.20	0.025	5.96	0.044
7.40	0.006	7.33	0.010

11.7 Using the sensor and atmospheric transmission data given in the probability of discrimination example, calculated the probability of detection, recognition, and identification curves for a 4m by 3m target. Assume that the target has a target-to-background equivalent blackbody temperature differential of 4 deg C.

REFERENCES

[1] Waldman, G., and J. Wootton, *EO System Performance Modeling*, Boston, MA: Artech House, 1993.

[2] Lloyd, J. M., "Fundamentals of Electro-Optical Imaging System Analysis" in the *Infrared and Electro-Optical Systems Handbook*, ERIM and SPIE Press, 1993.

[3] Lloyd, J. M., *Thermal Imaging Systems*, New York: Plenum Press, 1975.

[4] Driggers, R., C. Halford, G. Boreman, and M. Wellfare, "Comparison of Two Frame Noise Calculations for Infrared Line Scanners," *Optical Engineering*, Vol. 29, July 1990.

[5] Dereniak, E., and G. Boreman, *Infrared Detectors and Systems*, New York: Wiley, 1996.

[6] Shumaker, D., J. Wood, and C. Thacker, *FLIR Performance Handbook*, DCS Corporation, 1988.

[7] Scott, L., and J. D'Agostino, *Application of 3-D Noise to MRTD Prediction*, Appendix C of FLIR92 Thermal Imaging Systems Performance Model, U.S. Army Night Vision and Electronic Sensors Directorate, 1993.

[8] D'Agostino, J., *A 3-D Noise Analysis Methodology*, Appendix A of FLIR92 Thermal Imaging Systems Performance Model, U.S. Army Night Vision and Electronic Sensors Directorate, 1993.

[9] Webb, C., P. Bell, and G. Mayott, "Laboratory Procedure for the Characterization of 3-D Noise in Thermal Imaging Systems," *Proceedings of the IRIS Passive Sensors Symposium*, Mar. 1991.

[10] Ratches, J. A., W. R. Lawson, L. P. Obert, R. J. Bergemann, T. W. Cassidy, and J. M. Swenson, "Night Vision Static Performance Model for Thermal Viewing Systems," ECOM Report ECOM-7043, Fort Monmouth, NJ (1975).

[11] Scott, L., and J. D'Agostino, "NVEOD FLIR92 Thermal Imaging Systems Performance Model," in *Infrared Imaging Systems: Design, Analysis, Modeling and Testing III*, *SPIE Proceedings* Vol. 1689, 1992.

[12] *FLIR92 Thermal Imaging Systems Performance Model*, Report 5008993, U.S. Army Night Vision and Electronic Sensors Directorate, Jan. 1993.

[13] Johnson, J., "Analysis of Image Forming Systems," *Image Intensifier Symposium*, Warfare Vision Branch, Warfare Electrical Engineering Dept., U.S. Army Engineering Research and Development Laboratories, Ft. Belvoir, VA, 1958.

[14] Ratches, J., "Static Performance Model for Thermal Imaging Systems," *Optical Engineering*, Vol. 15, No. 6, pp. 525 - 530, 1976.

[15] Moser, P., "Mathematical Model of FLIR Performance," NAVAIRDEVCEN Technical Memorandum NADC-20203:PMM, U.S. Naval Air Development Center, Warminster, PA, 1972.

[16] George, P., and J. Buss, "Navy EO Sensor Testbed Development for Infrared Search and Track," *SPIE Proceedings*, Vol. 2552, July 1995.

[17] Headley, R., K. Hepfer, and P. Dezeeuw, "Horizontal Infrared Surveillance Sensor, (HISS): A Review of the HISS Project and Measured Performance During Multi-Sensor Integration Testing," *SPIE Proceedings*, Vol. 2552, July 1995.

Chapter 12

Electro-Optical Systems

All electronic imaging sensors are systems that convert photons into electrical signals. These electrical signals provide input to digital image processors or are presented to the human eye by a visible display. EO systems are sometimes called television (TV) systems, where the spectral band of interest is very close to that of the human eye. Therefore, the image that is generated by an EO system appears very similar to an image that would be perceived by the human visual system. Recall that human visual receptors respond to the 0.4- to 0.7-μm waveband. Common video cameras cover this range and extend out to approximately 1 μm. Military EO systems are typically sensitive from 0.65 to 1.1 μm. Over this band, the eye has little to no sensitivity; however, the imagery still looks very similar to visible band imagery.

As a point of terminology clarification, radiometry describes the electromagnetic radiation at all wavelengths and frequencies, while photometry describes only visible light (that which can be seen with the human eye). In this chapter, we use photometric units when describing variables that are applicable to the visible spectrum and radiometric units for all other variables. (Refer to Chapter 5 for the specific definitions of radiometric and photometric units.)

EO systems are categorized in many ways. One particular method [1] is by the amount of light in which the systems operate. This method discriminates *Low-light level TV* (LLLTV) and *daylight TV* (DTV). LLLTV usually includes an image intensifier with gains of 30 to 12,000. The image intensifier tubes amplify the light field before the conversion of photons to electrons by a camera tube or solid-state CCD array. This amplification of light is called *pre-storage gain*. The image intensifiers are characterized with a transfer function for inclusion in the system modulation transfer function (MTF). We are primarily concerned here with the DTV, where the limiting performance is sensitivity from photon noise or read-out noise.

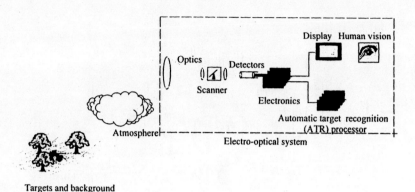

Targets and background

Figure 12.1 EO sensor system.

The conversion of photons to electrons in an EO system is performed either by photocathode tubes or CCD arrays. CCD arrays are becoming more common in EO systems and we limit our discussion to the standard CCD camera that is monochrome (noncolor) and whose output has been formatted into a standard video signal. The system is identical to the staring array case of the I^2R sensor and is shown in Figure 12.1. The scanner remains for completeness as staring arrays may be scanned over a FOR.

The performance of EO systems is similar to I^2R systems in that it is also a function of sensitivity and resolution. The performance parameters are not specified in equivalent blackbody temperature differentials but in terms of contrast resulting from reflected light. The resolution is again specified by the system MTF. The sensitivity, unlike I^2R systems, is specified in terms of noise equivalent input (NEI), minimum photometric signal, or specific sensitivity. Finally, the most important performance parameter, defined as the minimum resolvable contrast (MRC), specifies the sensitivity as a function of system resolution. This parameter, along with target size, target-to-background contrast, and atmospheric transmission, yields the performance curves for the probabilities of discrimination.

A large number of EO sensors are used on military platforms such as ground vehicles, low-altitude air vehicles (rotary and fixed-wing aircraft), high-altitude air vehicles, and satellite systems. Tactical users of ground vehicle and low-altitude air vehicle sensors typically use the probabilities of discrimination (detection, recognition, and identification) as design requirements and system performance indicators. Intelligence, surveillance, and reconnaissance [ISR] users of high-altitude air vehicles and satellite sensors have traditionally used the National Imagery Interpretation Rating System (NIIRS) [2] performance measures for guidance in design and measures of system performance. The NIIRS technique has been applied to EO sensors for some time and has recently been applied to high-altitude midwave infrared sensors. Figure 12.2 shows a number of military imaging platforms and the sensor performance description (NIIRS or probability of recognition [Pr]) for each sensor.

While there has been extensive publications regarding the modeling of infrared sensors (primarily tactical sensors), there are few publications describing EO system performance. In addition, there are no validated models or formal approaches for EO systems. This has resulted in numerous models used in various parts of the community. Excellent industry models were developed by Frame [3, 4] and Van Meeteren [5] and are available in the open literature. The authors focus here on the three primary U.S. Government (and diverse) approaches for modeling EO sensors. These are the Rosell [6, 7] model, the Vollmerhausen model [8], and the general image quality equation (GIQE) [9] model. The Rosell model is a band-integrated model that includes a band-averaged photometric responsivity. This model provides the probabilities of discrimination and was developed primarily for tactical sensors. The Vollmerhausen model is a more accurate, spectral radiometric model that also accounts for the contrast threshold function of the eye. This is also a tactical model that results in the MRC of the system. Finally, the GIQE model provides the NIIRS rating of a sensor and was developed by the intelligence community for high-flying and space-borne sensors. This chapter begins with some basic parameters for EO systems and then describes the three modeling approaches.

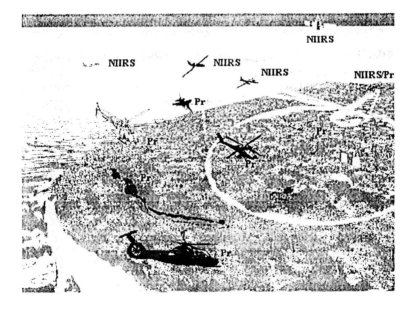

Figure 12.2 Military platforms and sensor performance descriptions (Courtesy of Joint Precision Strike Demonstration Project Office).

12.1 RESOLUTION

The resolution of an EO system is characterized in the same fashion as an I^{2}R system. Each component of the EO system has an MTF that must be considered. The techniques for determining these MTFs are the same as those for I^{2}R systems and are given in the component chapters of this text. Differences occur only for those components that have MTFs that change with wavelength. An example of such an MTF is the diffraction MTF of the optics. EO systems operate on much shorter wavelengths. The diffraction cutoff frequency D/λ, in cycles per milliradian for a 10-cm aperture diameter $D,$ is shown in Figure 12.3. In some systems, the diffraction spot is smaller than the spot caused by the aberrations of the optical system. Even with the larger aberration-limited spot, the typical spot size of EO systems is significantly smaller than that of an I^{2}R with the same diameter optics.

Like I^{2}R systems, the system horizontal MTF is determined from the component MTFs:

$$MTF_{Sys}(\xi) = MTF_{optics}(\xi)MTF_{detector}(\xi)MTF_{electronics}(\xi)MTF_{display}(\xi)MTF_{eye}(\xi) \qquad (12.1)$$

The vertical MTF is found in the same manner.

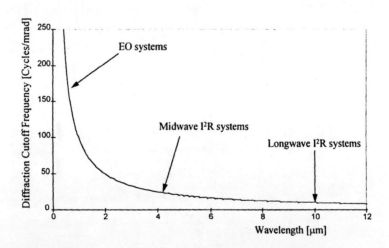

Figure 12.3 Diffraction cutoff frequency for a 10-cm diameter lens.

It is common for EO systems to provide higher resolution than I^{2}R systems. This is not just because of the diffraction MTF, but also because of detector characteristics. EO detector technology is far more mature than that of I^{2}R detectors since the commercial world has boosted detector development. Visible CCD arrays of 1,000 by 1,000 detectors are not uncommon and are becoming more cost effective. There are currently large-density arrays of 3,000 by 3,000 detector CCDs that are used as expensive specialty items. The introduction of High-Definition Television (HDTV) effectively doubles the number of active video lines from 480 to 960, providing a common means for displaying high-resolution images. HDTV is predicted to be widespread in the near future and will drive down the cost of large array CCDs even further.

In addition to the commercial support for EO system development, the strategic military world of ISR often uses EO systems because of their improved resolution. The need for higher resolution is driven by the range of systems on high-altitude aircraft and satellites. Unfortunately, many of these systems collect useful imagery only during daylight and cloud-free hours.

12.2 SENSITIVITY AND EO NOISE

The sensitivity of EO systems is limited by various noise contributors [10]. Some of the primary noise sources are:

Shot noise. Caused by the discrete nature of photon to electron transitions, it occurs when photoelectrons are generated in the detection process and when dark current electrons are present.

Pattern noise. Noise that does not change significantly from frame to frame. This noise can be caused by detector construction nonuniformities.

Reset noise. Caused during the resetting of the sensing capacitor. This is the Johnson noise associated with the resistance in the resetting field effect transistor.

On-chip and off-chip amplifiers. Contributes both 1/f ("one over f") noise and white noise to the output signal. These noises are caused by the contacts and resistance in the amplifiers.

Quantization noise. The noise associated with the analog-to-digital converter's discrete output levels. These levels contribute an error (or noise) to the output signal.

Both the photon noise and the pattern noise are associated with the arrival of discrete light packets and the conversion of these packets to electrons. These noise contributors are small for low-light levels and increase with the amount of light received by the sensor. The other components listed are associated with the electronic readout of the CCD electron "wells." Over some integration time, a CCD detector will collect photoelectrons in a well that will be "read out" by the electronics. If the light level is high and the integration time is too long, the well can become filled, or saturated.

For low light levels (even for DTV systems), the noise is dominated by the electronic readout noise components. This includes reset noise, white noise, 1/f noise, and quantization noise. The readout noise is sometimes called the *noise floor* or *noise equivalent electrons*, referring to the number of equivalent electrons collected in a well over the integration time.

Holst [11] provides a simplification of system noise as the root-sum-square of the shot noise, readout noise, and the pattern noise:

$$< n_{sys} >= \sqrt{< n_{shot}^2 > + < n_{readout}^2 > + < n_{pattern}^2 >} \text{ [electrons]} \qquad (12.2)$$

where the brackets, $<>$, correspond to the ensemble average. For low light levels, the shot noise and the pattern noise are small and the readout noise is dominant. For high light levels, the shot noise and pattern noise may be larger than the readout noise.

Noise manifests itself as currents that reduce the overall performance of the system. The noise electrons described above contribute to the noise currents. The following descriptions are for currents corresponding to photon-electron (shot) noise, fixed-pattern noise, and readout noise.

Photon-Electron Shot Noise

The photon-electron (p-e) shot noise is a function of the amount of light collected from the target and the background. The average current can be taken as the average of the target (i_t) and background (i_b) currents

$$i_{ave} = \frac{i_t + i_b}{2} \text{ [A]} \qquad (12.3)$$

Also, the apparent contrast seen by the EO sensor can be approximated by

$$C \cong \frac{|i_b - i_t|}{i_b} \text{ [unitless]} \qquad (12.4)$$

The p-e, or shot, noise is related to the average current such that the noise current is

$$i_{p-e}^2 = 2ei_{ave}\Delta f \text{ [A}^2\text{]} \qquad (12.5)$$

where e is the charge on an electron (1.6022×10^{-19} Coulombs) and Δf is the noise equivalent bandwidth. Equations (12.3) and (12.4) are used to simplify (12.5):

$$i_{p-e}^2 = (2 - C)ei_t\Delta f \text{ [A}^2\text{]} \qquad (12.6)$$

The current generated by the target flux is usually assumed to be of a larger value than that of the background current, but in practice, little difference between the delectability of objects is seen for positive or negative contrast. Therefore, we use i_b as the conversion factor because the background tends to encompass more the of sensor's FOV. Also, if a pre-storage gain G is present and if horizontal and vertical readout efficiencies (e_h and e_v) are provided, then

$$i_{p-e}^2 = \frac{(2-C)ei_b \Delta f\, G^2}{e_h e_v} \qquad [A^2] \qquad (12.7)$$

Finally, the noise current density is related to the noise current by

$$J_{p-e}^2 = \frac{i_{p-e}^2}{2\Delta f} \qquad [A^2/Hz] \qquad (12.8)$$

so that

$$J_{p-e}^2 = \frac{(2-C)ei_b G^2}{2e_h e_v} \qquad [A^2/Hz] \qquad (12.9)$$

Note that the p-e noise is a function of target-to-background contrast and background current.

Fixed-Pattern Noise

The sensitivity of individual elements within a detector array can vary significantly. Two common causes are *fabrication artifacts* and *material impurities*. Fixed-pattern noise is not temporal in nature (it can, however, change with scene brightness) and is fixed when viewing a static scene. However, it is converted to temporal noise in the readout process. Fixed-pattern noise is also a function of background current, with the current density identified as

$$J_{fp}^2 = \frac{[Mi_b]^2 t_f}{N_x N_y} \qquad [A^2/Hz] \qquad (12.10)$$

where M is the standard deviation of the fixed-pattern noise. It is sometimes called the *fixed-pattern noise modulation*. N_x and N_y are the number of pixels in the x and y directions and t_f is the frame integration time (inverse of the frame rate). The current density can be used to determine the fixed-pattern noise current given an "information bandwidth":

$$\Delta f_I = \frac{N_x N_y}{2t_f} \qquad [Hz] \qquad (12.11)$$

Using the noise current and current density relationship of (12.10), the noise current density is

$$i_{fp}^2 = (Mi_b)^2 \quad [\text{A}^2] \tag{12.12}$$

Note that the fixed-pattern noise current is a function of the fixed-pattern noise modulation and the background current.

Readout (Floor) Noise

The readout noise, or floor noise, is the "catch-all" term for all the other noise sources that are left over. It includes on-chip amplifier, Johnson, and off-chip amplifier noise. It is usually specified by some equivalent $n_{readout}$ noise electrons collected by a detector over some integration time. The mean-squared floor noise current is given by

$$i_{readout}^2 = \frac{4\Delta f_i^2 (n_{readout}e)^2}{(e_h e_v)^2} \quad [\text{A}^2] \tag{12.13}$$

and the noise current density is given by

$$J_{readout}^2 = \frac{2\Delta f_i (n_{readout}e)^2}{(e_h e_v)^2} \quad [\text{A}^2/\text{Hz}] \tag{12.14}$$

The readout noise is not usually a problem for a sensor when the scenario contains a high background current, but it can easily be the limiting factor for sensors in low light levels.

Total Noise Current

The combined noise in an EO system can be approximated with the simplified noise model

$$i_{noise} = \sqrt{i_{p-e}^2 + i_{fp}^2 + i_{readout}^2} \quad [\text{A}] \tag{12.15}$$

Recall that the p-e and fixed-pattern noises were functions of the background current such that a typical system noise is given as a function of the background light level as shown in Figure 12.4.

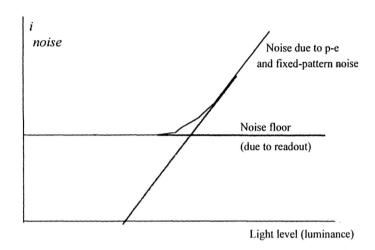

Figure 12.4 Total EO system noise current.

The system noise shown is limited by readout noise at low light levels and by p-e and fixed-pattern noise at higher levels. Also, even though the noise level increases at the higher light levels, the target-to-background signal is also increasing. Usually, the signal-to-noise ratio (SNR) increases until p-e and fixed-pattern noise become dominant. Then, the SNR approaches a constant value for higher light levels.

Example

Determine the total EO sensor noise current for a 480 by 640 CCD array with the following characteristics: a 6.4 µA background current, a target-to-background contrast of 0.33 (33%), a frame rate of 30 Hz, horizontal and vertical readout efficiencies of 0.9, and a fixed-pattern modulation of 0.0005. Assume that the readout noise is 120 electrons and the pre-storage gain is 1. Also, determine the limiting noise contributor (from readout noise, fixed-pattern noise, and shot noise). The solution is provided with the calculation of each noise contributor. First, Δf is assumed to be 30 Hz and $\Delta f_1 = (640)(480)/(2\frac{1}{30})$ or 4.61 MHz. The solution is found with (12.7), (12.12), and (12.13):

$$i_{p-e}^2 = \frac{(2-0.33)(1.6x10^{-19}C)(6.4x10^{-6})(1/30)}{(0.9)(0.9)} = 7.04x10^{-26} \ [A^2]$$

$$i_{fp}^2 = [(0.0005)(6.4x10^{-6})]^2 = 1.02x10^{-17} \ [A^2]$$

$$i^2_{readout} = \frac{2(4.6x10^6)^2[(n_{readout})(1.6x10^{-19})]^2}{(0.9)(0.9)^2} = 2.38x10^{-20} \quad [A^2]$$

From the values calculated above, the fixed-pattern noise provides the largest noise current. The total rms noise current can be determined by adding the above contributors and taking the root in an root-sum-squared fashion to give an i_{noise} of 3.19 rms nanoamperes.

12.3 SENSITIVITY PARAMETERS

The NEI of an EO system is similar to the NETD parameter for the I²R system. In a manner similar to NETD, we consider the exitance (recall exitance includes reflected flux) of a surface, $M_q(\lambda)$ in photons/sec-cm²-μm shown in Figure 12.5. Assuming a Lambertian surface, the radiance is

$$L_q(\lambda) = \frac{M_q(\lambda)}{\pi} \quad [\text{photons/sec-cm}^2\text{-sr-}\mu\text{m}] \tag{12.16}$$

The amount of area seen by the detector is

$$A_{src} = \frac{a}{f}R\frac{b}{f}R = \frac{ab}{f^2}R^2 \quad [\text{cm}^2] \tag{12.17}$$

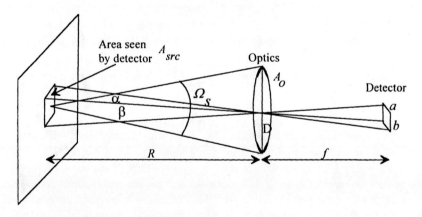

Figure 12.5 NEI nomenclature.

The intensity of the source area seen by the detector is

$$I_q(\lambda) = \frac{M_q(\lambda)}{\pi}\frac{ab}{f^2}R^2 \quad [\text{photons/sec-sr-}\mu\text{m}] \tag{12.18}$$

The total amount of the intensity that enters the aperture of the sensor corresponds to the amount of flux that falls on the detector:

$$\Phi_q = \int_{\lambda_1}^{\lambda_2} \Omega_s \tau_{optics}(\lambda) I_q(\lambda) d\lambda = \frac{D^2 ab}{4f^2} \int_{\lambda_1}^{\lambda_2} \tau_{optics}(\lambda) M_q(\lambda) d\lambda \quad [\text{photons/sec}] \quad (12.19)$$

where $\Omega_s = \frac{\pi D^2}{4f^2}$ is the solid angle of the sensor. Over an integration time t_{int} and a quantum efficiency η_q, the number of electrons collected is

$$N_q = \frac{D^2 ab \eta_q t_{int}}{4f^2} \int_{\lambda_1}^{\lambda_2} \tau_{optics}(\lambda) M_q(\lambda) d\lambda \quad [\text{photons}] \quad (12.20)$$

We know the number of noise electron, n_{sys}, so with the average optical transmission, τ_{optics}, we can rearrange (12.20) to determine the NEI:

$$NEI = \frac{4f^2 n_{sys}}{D^2 \eta_q ab \tau_{optics}} \quad [\text{photons/sec-cm}^2] \quad (12.21)$$

where the area of the detector, A_d, is the product of a and b. NEI corresponds to the exitance of the surface that gives a SNR of unity.

There is a similar quantity to *NEI* that gives an EO sensor's sensitivity in terms of the photometric irradiance (illuminance) at the entrance aperture of the sensor. Note that this is different than an exitance like *NEI*. The assumptions here are that the illuminance at the entrance aperture was caused by a distant point source. The derivation is very similar to the one described above (it begins at the entrance aperture of the sensor and is assumed to be a plane wave) and is reserved as an exercise at the end of this chapter.

The minimal photometric signal in terms of illuminance [11] is

$$E_v = \frac{n_{readout} hc}{\eta_q \Delta \lambda t_{optics} t_{int}} \frac{683}{A_o} \int_{0.38}^{0.75} \frac{V(\lambda)}{\lambda} d\lambda \quad [\text{lx}] \quad (12.22)$$

where $V(\lambda)$ is the photopic efficiency, h is Planck's constant, c is the speed of light, η_q is the detector quantum efficiency, $\Delta \lambda$ is the spectral band, and τ_{optics} is the band-averaged optical transmission. Finally, t_{int} is the integration time, $n_{readout}$ is the readout noise in electrons, and A_o is the entrance aperture area.

The sensitivity of most commercial camcorders is specified with the minimal photometric signal. A typical home-use camcorder will have a sensitivity of around 2 lx. The problem with the photometric specification is that it is applied to sensors that are not closely matched to the human eye. For a sensor with a different spectral response, a photometric specification can be meaningless.

Equivalent Radiant Responsivity and Photometric Responsivity

Two of the more important parameters that describe sensor responsivity is *radiant responsivity* and *photometric responsivity*. These parameters are sometimes called *equivalent radiant sensitivity* and *photometric sensitivity* even though their units are those of responsivity. They describe the amount of current seen on the output of the photon-to-current transducer. The current on the output of a detector is

$$i = \frac{A_e}{4f^2} \int_{\lambda_1}^{\lambda_2} \tau_o(\lambda) S_p(\lambda) \rho_r(\lambda) E_s(\lambda) d\lambda \quad [A] \qquad (12.23)$$

where A_e is the effective photosurface area in square meters, $S_p(\lambda)$ is the detector's responsivity in amps per watt or amps per lumen, $E_s(\lambda)$ is the scene irradiance in watts per square meter or lumen per square meter, and $\rho_r(\lambda)$ is the reflectivity of the scene. $\tau_o(\lambda)$ is the transmission of the optics and f is the focal length of the sensor. The spectral reflectivity is usually averaged over the spectral band due to the complexity of most scenes.

In the laboratory, the most common source is a tungsten bulb operated at a temperature of 2,854 deg K. The spectral distribution of the bulb can be determined by the blackbody equation:

$$E_s(\lambda, T) = \frac{c_1}{\lambda^5} \frac{1}{e^{c_2/\lambda T} - 1} \quad [W/cm^2\text{-}\mu m] \qquad (12.24)$$

where c_1 is 3.74 x 10^4 W-μm^4/cm^2, c_2 is 14.388 x 10^4 μm-K with λ given in micrometers and T given in Kelvin.

The use of equivalent photometric responsivity became more of a standard than radiant responsivity because the common light measurement device in commercial television systems was a photometer. This practice carried over into military applications and now the photometrically estimated current (using the 2,854 deg K tungsten source) gives results closer to those measured in the laboratory. Also, photometric units correspond more closely to actual field scenarios where the scene light has been measured with photometers. The equivalent luminous responsivity is given by

$$S_L = \frac{\int_{\lambda_1}^{\lambda_2} S(\lambda) E_s(\lambda) d\lambda}{680 \int_{0.40}^{0.76} V(\lambda) E_s(\lambda) d\lambda} \quad [A/Lumen] \qquad (12.25)$$

where $V(\lambda)$ is the relative spectral response of the human eye. The more accurate method of estimating the responsivity of a sensor is the equivalent radiant responsivity, which is given by

$$S_R = \frac{\int_{\lambda_1}^{\lambda_2} S(\lambda)E_s(\lambda)d\lambda}{\int_{\lambda_1}^{\lambda_2} E_s(\lambda)d\lambda} \quad [A/W] \tag{12.26}$$

This responsivity can give an estimate for current by

$$i = \frac{A_e \tau_o}{4f^2} S_R E_s \quad [A] \tag{12.27}$$

The estimate for current can also be given with S_L in (12.27) if the scene irradiance is given in terms of photometric units. In summary, equivalent radiant responsivity is a more accurate method for predicting the current if the scene radiometric characteristics are known. This is rarely the case, as typical scene brightness is measured in photometric units, so equivalent photometric responsivity is common.

12.4 ROSELL'S MINIMUM RESOLVABLE CONTRAST MODEL

EO systems are similar to I²R systems in that sensitivity and resolution are not independent. An EO parameter very similar to MRT is that of the minimum resolvable contrast (MRC). The concept is the same as MRT, but the four-bar response is for contrast targets. Rosell gives the MRC in the vertical direction by [6]

$$MRC(\eta) = SNRT[\frac{\alpha}{\varepsilon t_{obs}}]^{1/2} \frac{\pi^2}{4} \frac{\eta FOV_V}{MTF(\eta)} [\frac{i^2_{total}}{(Gi_b/e_h e_v)}]^{1/2} \tag{12.28}$$

SNRT is the observer threshold SNR that is assumed to be around 2.5. α is the width to height aspect ratio of the displayed image and ε is the length-to-width ratio of the bars in the periodic bar pattern (i.e., 7). The observer integration time t_{obs} is that of the eye time constant and is set between 0.1 and 0.2 sec. Note that η is the vertical spatial frequency in cycles per milliradian, so the MRC given is that of the vertical direction. The horizontal MRC can be determined by changing the direction of each parameter including the MTF. The vertical MRC is a common specification in EO systems because of the limitations in discrimination in the vertical direction (especially in television systems). In fact, some MRCs are given where the vertical spatial frequency is in television line pairs per picture height (TVL/PH). The conversion from TVL/PH to cycles per milliradian is

$$\eta = \frac{N}{2FOV_v} \tag{12.29}$$

where FOV_v is given in milliradians and N is the number of video lines on the TV display. Note that there are two TV lines per cycle. If the individual noise terms are provided, the MRC becomes

$$MRC(\eta) = SNRT[\tfrac{\alpha}{\varepsilon t_{obs}}]^{1/2} \tfrac{\pi^2}{4} \tfrac{\eta FOV_V}{MTF(\eta)} \tfrac{1}{(Gi_b/e_he_v)}[\tfrac{(2-C)ei_b\Delta fG^2}{e_he_v} + (Mi_b)^2 + \tfrac{4\Delta f_f^2(n_{readout}e)^2}{(e_he_v)^2}]^{1/2}$$

$$(12.30)$$

The contrast and the MRC (the same contrast) are on both the left and right sides of the equation. The typical solution for MRC is obtained by assuming an initial value for the contrast and calculating MRC in an iterative fashion until the contrasts match. Usually, this process provides an MRC that converges quickly. Also, MRC is a function of background current (and background light level). So MRC, unlike MRT, is a family of curves that are plotted as a function of light level and spatial frequency as shown in Figure 12.6.

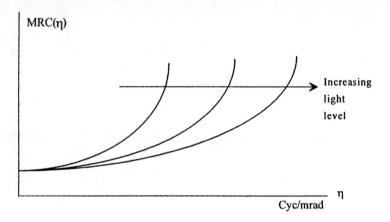

Figure 12.6 MRC family of curves.

As in the case with MRT, there are more accurate and sophisticated versions of MRC. (12.30) is an approximation for CCD systems that is easy to use.

The two-dimensional MRC is obtained in an identical manner to that of the two-dimensional MRT. However, a single MRC curve is given for a particular background light level. For a given light level, the horizontal and vertical MRCs are matched for each contrast. The geometric mean of the horizontal and vertical spatial frequencies for a given contrast gives the two-dimensional spatial frequency associated with the contrast. For graphical and mathematical detail in this procedure, see the two-dimensional MRT section in Chapter 11. The procedure for calculating the probabilities of detection, recognition, and identification is identical to that of the MRT case. Consider Figure 12.7.

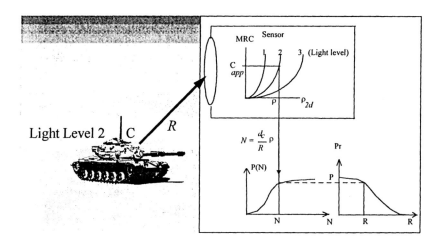

Figure 12.7 Electro-optical probability of discrimination.

The background light level sets the MRC curve as shown in Figure 12.7. MRC curves are determined for these corresponding light levels. The target-to-background contrast depends on the light source spectral distribution that illuminates the target. It also depends on the target and background reflectivities and the sensor responsivity. The contrast is calculated at the target position and is propagated to an apparent contrast at the input of the EO sensor. This apparent contrast is applied to the two-dimensional MRC curve to determine the maximum two-dimensional spatial frequency ρ that can be seen with the sensor. This frequency along with the range from the sensor to the target and the critical dimension of the target, d_c, is used to determine the critical number of cycles, N, across the target. The number of cycles is compared with the number of cycles required for 50% probability of detection, recognition, or identification. This comparison determines the probability associated with the appropriate discrimination level as a function of range.

The mathematics associated with the apparent contrast calculation are given in the previous section of this chapter. The only difference between this technique and that of infrared probability of discrimination is that the MRC curve is a function of background current (and, therefore, light level). The mathematics associated with finding the two-dimensional MRC curve, the critical target dimension, the number of cycles, and the probability of discrimination are identical to the infrared technique and are provided in Chapter 11.

Example

An EO camera has a narrow 1.2-deg (20.9-mrad) by 1.6-deg (27.9-mrad) FOV. The spectral bandpass is 0.65 to 0.90 μm with a spectral luminous sensitivity of .000560 A/lumen. The optical entrance pupil diameter is 11.3 cm and the focal length is 169 cm. The optics are not diffraction limited, but the horizontal MTF of the entire system can be described at 1.2, 3.6, 6.0, 8.4, 10.8, 13.2, 15.6, 18, 20.4, and 22.8 cyc/mrad as 0.866, 0.614, 0.403, 0.245, 0.133, 0.068, 0.032, 0.012, 0.004, and 0.001, respectively. The MTFs are identical in the vertical and horizontal directions. The aspect ratio of the system is 1.33 and the bar aspect, as usual, is 7. The observer integration time is set at 0.1 sec and the readout efficiency (includes both horizontal and vertical directions) is assumed to be 1. The pre-storage gain is 1. With 5000 lux illumination, the background current is measured to be 2×10^{-7} Amps and the system is operated in a light level low enough to be readout-limited with a readout noise level of 1.55×10^{-13} Amps. The target has a contrast of 0.5 and the atmospheric transmission can be assumed to be 0.91/km within the band of interest over the necessary calculation ranges. The MRC and probability of recognition for a 2.3 m by 2.3 m target are desired.

The solution is given by (12.37), with the last noise term replaced by the measured noise current. Note that with a readout noise-limited system, the entire bracketed term is replaced with the readout noise current. The MRC is then calculated and is shown below (Figure 12.8).

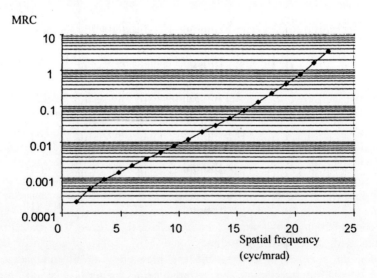

Figure 12.8 Rosell MRC example.

The MRCs are said to be identical in both the vertical and horizontal directions, so the two-dimensional MRC is as given above. The acquisition model described in Chapter 11 is used with this MRC curve and the information given; a 2.3 by 2.3 m target at a contrast of 0.5, and an atmospheric transmission of 0.91/km. The results are shown in Figure 12.9. The narrow FOV EO system, given sufficient illumination (5,000 lx corresponds to a bright day), yields a large recognition range. The 50% probability of recognition range is around 13 km.

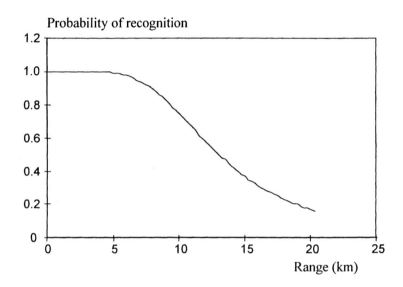

Figure 12.9 Rosell MRC acquisition results.

12.5 VOLLMERHAUSEN'S MRC MODEL

Vollmerhausen's model [8] is a signal detection theory model [12-19] similar to the Rosell model, but with two important enhancements. The first enhancement is that of *spectral signal calculations*. The electron flux is determined by a spectral integral that includes source, target, background, atmospherics, optics, and detector spectral characteristics. The second enhancement is the inclusion of Vollerhausen's contrast threshold performance model of the eye [20].

The spectral integrals can be written in terms of a perceived target radiance that is a radiometric quantity seen by the camera:

$$L_T = \int_0^\infty [\frac{E_{src}(\lambda)}{\pi}\rho_T(\lambda)\tau_{atm}(\lambda) + L_{path}(R, \lambda)]C(\lambda)d\lambda \quad [\text{W/cm}^2\text{-sr}] \quad (12.31)$$

where

R is the target to camera range in kilometers.

$E_{src}(\lambda)$ is the spectral irradiance of the source (e.g., the sun) in W/cm^2-μm.

$\rho_T(\lambda)$ is the target reflectivity (unitless).

$\tau_{atm}(\lambda)$ is the atmospheric transmission between the target and the camera (unitless).

$L_{path}(\lambda)$ is the atmospheric path radiance between the target and the camera in W/cm^2-sr-um.

$C(\lambda)$ is the relative spectral response of the camera (unitless).

The perceived background radiance is

$$L_T = \int_0^\infty [\frac{E_{src}(\lambda)}{\pi}\rho_B(\lambda)\tau_{atm}(\lambda) + L_{path}(R,\lambda)]C(\lambda)d\lambda \qquad (12.32)$$

where $\rho_B(\lambda)$ is the background reflectivity. The target and background in both cases have been assumed to be Lambertian surfaces (see the π in the first term denominator). Two important values can be calculated with the perceived target and background radiances. The target to background contrast is

$$C = |\frac{L_T-L_B}{L_T+L_B}| \quad \text{[unitless]} \qquad (12.33)$$

The average perceived radiance is the average of the target and background perceived radiances

$$L_A = \frac{(L_T+L_B)}{2} \quad \text{[W/cm}^2\text{-sr]} \qquad (12.34)$$

Both these values are used in the MRC calculation.

       The Vollmerhausen model, like the Rosell model, is based on three assumptions. First, the human visual system responds like a matched filter. The eye integrates the signal over the area corresponding to the object (such as a bar in a bar pattern) and also integrates the noise over this same area. Second, a visual SNR must be achieved for detection to occur. Third, the visual system establishes the required SNR for detection, where the SNR is a function of image light level and spatial frequency. The assumption of the matched filter is a simplification of the eye and the visual system; however, it provides accurate results to within some experimental error. The eye as a spatial filter is shown in Figure 12.10.

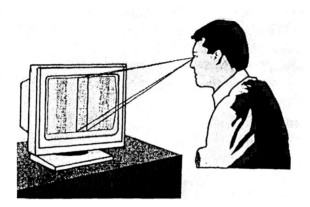

Figure 12.10 The eye as a matched filter.

If the pattern noise is corrected, shot noise dominates the performance of the EO sensor at high light levels. Readout noise is significant at lower light levels. With either limitation, the MRC is developed around the EO sensor electron flux per scene steradian. Consider the sensor of Figure 12.11 viewing a source as seen by a single detector in the CCD array. The area of the target seen by the detector is

$$A_T = \frac{ab}{f^2}R^2 \ \ [\text{cm}^2] \qquad (12.35)$$

where a and b are the detector width and height, f is the sensor focal length, and R is the range from the target to the sensor. Given a source irradiance on the target, $E_{src}(\lambda)$, the exitance of the target is

$$M_T(\lambda) = E_{src}(\lambda)\rho_T(\lambda) \ \ [\text{W/cm}^2\text{-}\mu\text{m}] \qquad (12.36)$$

where $\rho_T(\lambda)$ is the target reflectivity. If the target surface is Lambertian and the source has no emissive component, the radiance of the source is

$$L_T(\lambda) = \frac{E_{src}(\lambda)\rho_T(\lambda)}{\pi} \ \ [\text{W/cm}^2\text{-sr-}\mu\text{m}] \qquad (12.37)$$

The optical flux, or power, on the detector can be calculated with the solid angle of the sensor aperture as seen by the target:

$$\Omega_{sensor} = \frac{\pi D^2}{4R^2} \ \ [\text{sr}] \qquad (12.38)$$

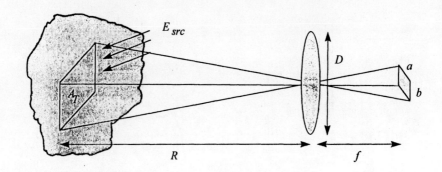

Figure 12.11 Source seen by a single CCD detector.

The power on the detector is radiance of the surface multiplied by the area of the surface seen by the detector and the solid angle of the sensor:

$$\Phi(\lambda) = L_T(\lambda)A_T\Omega_{sensor} = \frac{abD^2}{4f^2}E_{src}(\lambda)\rho_T(\lambda) \quad [\text{W}/\mu\text{m}] \tag{12.39}$$

The t-number ($T\#$) is similar to the f-number, where we include an account of the lens transmission, $\sqrt{\tau_o}\, f/D$, so that the flux on the detector is

$$\Phi(\lambda) = \frac{ab}{4T\#^2}E_{src}(\lambda)\rho_T(\lambda) \quad [\text{W}/\mu\text{m}] \tag{12.40}$$

The detector current can be calculated with power on the detector and the detector responsivity:

$$I = \int_0^\infty \frac{abE_{src}(\lambda)\rho_T(\lambda)R_{det}(\lambda)}{4T\#^2}d\lambda \quad [\text{A}] \tag{12.41}$$

where the detector responsivity is in units of A per W. Ultimately, the number of electrons per second per steradian is desired. The current in A can be converted to electrons per second by dividing by the charge on an electron e at 1.6×10^{-19} Coulombs per electron. At small angles, a steradian is approximately a square radian. If we divide (12.41) by the two-dimensional angle in square radians that caused the signal, ab/f^2, the number of electrons per second per solid (EPSS) angle is obtained:

$$EPSS = \int_0^\infty \frac{f^2E_{src}(\lambda)\rho_T(\lambda)R_{det}(\lambda)}{4T\#^2e}d\lambda \quad [\text{Electrons/sec-sr}] \tag{12.42}$$

A duty cycle, G_{duty}, can be included since the detector integration time does not correspond to an entire field time (i.e., image display rate). This duty cycle is the fraction of time that the detector actually integrates compared to a field time. An atmospheric transmission, $\tau_{atm}(\lambda)$, along with a path radiance, $L_{path}(\lambda)$, between the target and the sensor can also be included. Finally, the responsivity of the detector can be written as a constant responsivity in Amperes per Watt times a relative spectral dependency, $R_{det}(\lambda) = R_{det}C(\lambda)$. With all of these additions to (12.42), *EPSS* becomes

$$EPSS = \frac{f^2 G_{duty} R_{det}}{4T\!H^2 e} \int_0^\infty [E_{src}(\lambda)\rho_T(\lambda)\tau_{atm}(\lambda) + \pi L_{path}(\lambda)]C(\lambda)d\lambda$$
$$\text{[electrons/sec/sr]} \qquad (12.43)$$

This equation can be used to determine the number of electrons per second per steradian corresponding to the target or the background. The only difference would be the target or background reflectivity parameter.

MRC is a little different than MRT in that it is the ability of an observer to detect a single bar in a three-bar target. If the degradation in the image from the MTF is ignored, a perceived signal and noise estimate of a target bar can be obtained. We assume here that the visual system performs like a matched filter and perfectly integrates the signal and noise over the bar. The signal is considered the difference in the number of electrons due to the bar with respect to the signal level of the spaces between the bars. The signal is determined by

$$S = (EPSS_b - EPSS_s)LWt_e \text{ [electrons]} \qquad (12.44)$$

where $EPSS_b$ and $EPSS_s$ are the number of electrons per second per steradian corresponding to the bar and the space, respectively. L and W are the length and width of the bar in radians and t_e is the integration time of the eye in seconds. The integration time of the eye varies from around 200 ms at low light levels to 50 ms at high light levels.

The noise associated with most tactical EO systems operating in the daytime is not limited by readout or fixed-pattern noise, but by shot noise. The shot noise is related to the square root of the number of electrons and is multiplied by the square root of two because of the subtraction between the bar and the space:

$$N = \sqrt{2E_{av}LWt_e} \qquad \text{[electrons]} \qquad (12.45)$$

where the average scene flux

$$E_{av} = (EPSS_b + EPSS_s)/2 \text{ [electrons/sec-sr]} \qquad (12.46)$$

The signal to noise is then

$$S/N = (EPSS_b - EPSS_s)LWt_e/\sqrt{2E_{av}LWt_e} \text{ [unitless]} \qquad (12.47)$$

This SNR can be expressed in terms of the modulation of the target:

$$M = \left| \frac{EPSS_b - EPSS_s}{EPSS_b + EPSS_s} \right| \quad \text{[unitless]} \tag{12.48}$$

where the SNR of the bar target is now

$$SNR = M\sqrt{2E_{av}LWt_e} \quad \text{[unitless]} \tag{12.49}$$

This equation relates the SNR of the bar target to the modulation of the bar target. Given that a threshold SNR is required for the bar target to be discerned, (12.49) can be rewritten to give the MRC required to discern the target:

$$MRC = SNRT / \sqrt{2E_{av}LWt_e} \quad \text{[unitless]} \tag{12.50}$$

The assumptions for this expression are that the transfer functions of the optics, detector, and other sensor components did not degrade the amplitude of the signal. The SNR was derived for a perfect imaging system with only shot-noise limitations. We continue the derivation with the inclusion of the system transfer function (i.e., the blurring of the bar target by the optics, detector, etc.).

The blurring of the bar pattern by the system components can be characterized in space by the convolution of the system, eye, and matched filter impulse responses with the bar pattern:

$$s_{out}(x,y) = s_{4bar}(x,y) * *h_{sys}(x,y) * *h_{eye}(x,y) * *h_{4bar}(x,y) \tag{12.51}$$

In the bar length direction (here, we assume the vertical direction), the signal and matched filter are separable and are identical

$$s_{4bar}(y) = h_{4bar}(y) = \frac{1}{L}rect(\frac{y}{L}) \tag{12.52}$$

We assume that the blurred signal level at the center of the bar's length can be integrated over the length of the bar to give a matched filter integrated signal. The value of the signal at the center of the bar can be written in terms of (12.51) transformed to the frequency domain

$$s_{out}(0) = \int_{-\infty}^{\infty} [sinc(\pi L\eta)]^2 H_{sys}(\eta)H_{eye}(\eta)d\eta \tag{12.53}$$

In the limit, where H_{sys} and H_{eye} are both unity, the integral yields $1/L$, so an L must be used to scale the amplitude to 1. Also, the integrated signal modulation over the length of the bar is now obtained in the bar length direction (another scale of L):

$$S_L = L^2 \int_{-\infty}^{\infty} [sinc(\pi L\eta)]^2 H_{sys}(\eta) H_{eye}(\eta) d\eta \qquad (12.54)$$

In the periodic direction, the modulation is approximated as the amplitude of the first harmonic of the input square wave as shown in Figure 12.12. The amplitude of the first harmonic of a square wave is $4/\pi$ times the amplitude of the original square wave. The amplitude of the first harmonic through the system transfer function and the eye transfer function is

$$S_W(\xi) = \tfrac{4}{\pi} H_{sys}(\xi) H_{eye}(\xi) \int_0^W \sin(\pi x/W) dx \qquad (12.55)$$
$$= \tfrac{8}{\pi^2} W H_{sys}(\xi) H_{eye}(\xi)$$

where W is the width of the bar and the integral takes care of the matched filter integration. The total signal integrated over the bar (degraded by the system and the eye) is

$$S = 2t_e M E_{av} S_L S_W \qquad (12.56)$$

The noise power is the noise power spectral density multiplied by the square of the bandwidth. The noise is filtered by the electronics, display, the eye, and by the perceptual matched filter. Using $H_T(\xi)$ to describe the combined electronics and display MTF, the noise is

$$N_s^2 = t_e E_{av} B_L B_W \qquad (12.57)$$

where

$$B_W = W^2 \int_{-\infty}^{\infty} [H_T(\xi) H_e(\xi) H_W(\xi)] d\xi$$

$$B_L = L^2 \int_{-\infty}^{\infty} [H_T(\eta) H_e(\eta) H_L(\eta)] d\eta$$

Note that $H_W(\xi) = sinc(\xi L)$ and $H_L(\eta) = sinc(\eta W)$. The SNR of the sensor with system and eye transfer function effects is

$$S/N_s = 2MS_W S_L (E_{av} t_e)^{1/2} / \sqrt{B_W B_L} \qquad (12.58)$$

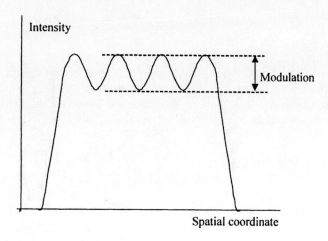

Figure 12.12 Bar target modulation.

At the threshold SNR (SNRT), the modulation is the MRC so that the MRC can be written as

$$MRC = SNRT \sqrt{B_W B_L} / [2S_W S_L (E_{av} t_e)^{1/2}] \qquad (12.59)$$

This model includes the sensor signal, the sensor noise, the system transfer, and the eye transfer. It does not, however, include eye noise. The eye noise is important when the sensor noise becomes small and approaches the sensitivity of the eye. Vollmerhausen states that (12.59) works reasonably well for cases where the observer has control of the display brightness and contrast, such as in the laboratory. Most sensors in the field, however, cannot be optimized, and the model can give significant errors. Kornfeld and Lawson provide that adding visual noise to the sensor noise in quadrature can improve the accuracy of the model. Given that N_t is the total noise and N_e is the visual noise:

$$S/N_t = [(\frac{N_s}{S})^2 + (\frac{N_e}{S})^2]^{-1/2} \qquad (12.60)$$

The adapting luminance of the display A_L determines the signal to the eye:

$$S = 2A_L M H_{sys}(\xi) \qquad (12.61)$$

The total SNR becomes

$$S/N_t = \{(\frac{N_s}{S})^2 + (\frac{CTF}{SNRT_t M_t H_{sys}(\xi)})^2\}^{-1/2} \qquad (12.62)$$

where

$$N_e = 2CTFA_L/SNRT \qquad (12.63)$$

CTF is the just-visible difference in luminance between the bars divided by twice the average luminance. At the threshold, S/N_t and $SNRT$ are the same quantity. Using (12.55) for S_W:

$$MRC = \frac{1}{H_{sys}(\xi)} \left\{ \frac{\pi^4 SNRT^2 B_W B_L \xi^2}{256 S_L^2 H_e^2(\xi) t_e E_{av}} + CTF^2(\xi) \right\}^{1/2} \qquad (12.64)$$

and note that $W = 1/(2\xi)$. A fundamental assumption here is that the eye noise is a fixed fraction, $SNRT$, of the just-visible difference in luminance between the bar and the space.

With the assumptions so far, it turns out that model predictions are not yet accurate. To fully model a real sensor and a real observer, the CTF is modified. The CTF is proportional to factors that increase with eye noise and detection threshold and is inversely proportional to factors which affect signal. The CTF gives a relative indication of the eye's ability to detect a pattern. If a measurement is performed to determine SNRT at one spatial frequency and at one light level, then the ratio CTF/CTF_o can be used to adjust the signal-to-noise threshold at other frequencies and light levels. The eye MTF is included in the CTF, so H_e is dropped from the MRC equation. Given that SNF is defined as $SNRT/CTF_o$

$$MRC = \frac{1}{H(\xi)} \left[\frac{\pi^4 SNF^2 CTF^2(\xi) B_W B_L \xi^2}{256 S_L^2 t_e E_{av}} + CTF^2(\xi) \right]^{1/2} \qquad (12.65)$$

Another idealized aspect of this model leads to substantial errors at lower spatial frequencies. No limits have been placed on the observer's ability to integrate a signal over very large bars. Psychophysical experiments show that the eye-brain is limited in its spatial integration to a few milliradians. Therefore, the spatial integration is limited to 4 mrads as is consistent with Vollmerhausen and Rosell and Wilson. This modification can be implemented with the definitions

$$W_l = W, \text{ for } W < 4 \text{ mrads}$$
$$= 4 \text{ mrads otherwise.}$$
$$L_l = L, \text{ for } L < 4 \text{ mrads}$$
$$= 4 \text{ mrads otherwise.} \qquad (12.66)$$

The noise bandwidth and peak signal from the length of the bar become

$$B_W = W_1^2 \int_{-\infty}^{\infty} [H_T(\xi) H_e(\xi) H_{W_1}(\xi)]^2 d\xi \qquad (12.67)$$

$$B_L = L_1^2 \int_{-\infty}^{\infty} [H_T(\xi) H_e(\xi) H_{L_1}(\xi)]^2 d\xi \tag{12.68}$$

$$S_L = L L_1 \int_{-\infty}^{\infty} H(\xi) H_e(\xi) H_L(\xi) H_{L_1}(\xi) d\xi \tag{12.69}$$

S_W does not change because the eye's ability to integrate a signal over the width of the bar is characterized by the CTF function. The new definitions of B_W, B_L, and S_L are then used in (12.65).

Vollmerhausen's last enhancement to the MRC model is that of monitor brightness control. An increase in display brightness corresponds to a decrease in display contrast. Because the monitor has an independent brightness control, the display brightness does not necessarily correspond to the scene brightness. Let

$$L_{\min} = \text{display luminance for zero-level video input}$$
$$L_{\max} = \text{display luminance for peak-level video input}$$
$$M_{disp} = (L_{\max} - L_{\min})/(L_{\max} + L_{\min}) \tag{12.70}$$

The MRC now becomes

$$MRC = \frac{1}{H(\xi)} \left[\frac{\pi^4 SNF^2 CTF^2(\xi) B_W B_L \xi^2}{256 S_L^2 t_e E_{av}} + CTF^2(\xi) \right]^{1/2} / M_{disp} \tag{12.71}$$

This is the MRC of a CCD camera when the display contrast is degraded by the display brightness control. Display contrast can also be degraded by light reflected off the display, or in the case of helmet displays with see-through combiners, by transmitted light.

The MRC model of (12.71) assumes that the system is limited by shot noise. That is, the light level of the scene is large enough to place the sensor in a shot-noise-limited region. In low-light-level situations, it is more accurate to include amplifier, or readout, noise in the MRC equation. Given that n_{pix} is the number of equivalent amplifier noise electrons per pixel per field. The noise power in electrons per steradian (source solid angle) per second is

$$E_{CCD} = n_{pix}^2 \sqrt{\frac{f^2 F_r}{A_{cell}}} \tag{12.72}$$

where A_{cell} is the detector area (in the same units as the focal length). The MRC equation becomes

$$MRC = \frac{1}{H(\xi)} \left[\frac{\pi^4 SNF^2 CTF^2(\xi) B_W B_L \xi^2 [E_{av} + E_{CCD}]}{256 S_L^2 t_e E_{av}^2} + CTF^2(\xi) \right]^{1/2} / M_{disp} \tag{12.73}$$

This is one of the more recently developed MRC models that is useful for a wide variety of conditions.

A useful addition to the MRC equation is the numerical approximation of the eye CTF. Provided by Barten, the CTF is

$$CTF(u) = \frac{1}{aue^{-bu}\sqrt{1+ce^{bu}}} \tag{12.74}$$

where

$$a = \frac{540(1+0.7/L)^{-0.2}}{1+12/[w(1+u/3)^2]}$$

$$b = 0.3(1 + 100/L)^{0.15}$$

$$c = 0.06$$

and u is the spatial frequency in cycles per degree, w is the square root of the picture area in degrees, and L is the display luminance in candela per square meter. One candela per square meter is equal to 0.314 millilamberts or 0.292 foot-Lamberts. Also, the spatial frequency in cycles per degree can be converted to cycles per milliradian by $\xi = [180/(1000\pi)]u$. The above CTF is given for two eyes looking at the same pattern. For a monocular display, the CTF is increased by a factor of $\sqrt{2}$. Figure 12.13 shows the CTF for three different display luminances.

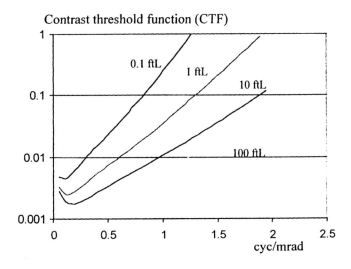

Figure 12.13 CTF for different display luminances.

It can be seen from the EPSS expressions that the responsivity of the detector is needed in MRC calculations. Many times the responsivity of an EO detector is measured with a 2,045 deg K source and the results of the responsivity measurement is given in saturation illuminance and the CCD detector well saturation. Using a test configuration where the detector is 1m from the source, the saturation power is calculated:

$$\Phi_{sat} = 1.67x10^{-6} A_{cell} L_{sat} \int_0^\infty M(\lambda, 2045)C(\lambda)d\lambda \quad [W] \qquad (12.75)$$

where

A_{cell} = the detector cell area in cm^2

L_{sat} = the saturation illuminance in lux (Lumens per m^2)

$M(\lambda, 2045)$ = the emittance (W/cm^2-μm) of the 2,045 K source

$1.67x10^{-6}$ = the conversion of candela to lux at a 1 meter distance units are square meters per lumen.

The candela is defined as the luminous intensity of a 1/60th of a 1-cm^2 source that is at 2,045 deg K in units of lumens per steradian. At a 1-m source distance (and because Lux is in lumens per square meter) the 1.67×10^{-6} factor converts the luminous intensity to a luminous irradiance.

Once the saturation power is determined, the responsivity of the detector can be calculated:

$$R_{det} = \frac{1.602x10^{-19} n_{sat} F_r}{\Phi_{sat}} \quad [A/W] \qquad (12.76)$$

where n_{sat} is the saturation well capacity in electrons, F_r is the field rate in sec^{-1}, and the constant gives Coulombs per electron.

Vollmerhausen Example

Table 12.1 gives the parameters for an EO sensor. Determine the sensor's horizontal MRC. The system horizontal MTF (for application to the signal) at 1.78, 3.56, 5.35, 7.13, 8.91, 10.69, 12.48, 14.26, 16.04, 17.82, and 19.61 cyc/mrad is 0.85, 0.68, 0.50, 0.35, 0.23, 0.14, 0.07 0.03, 0.01, 0.00, and 0.00. The vertical MTF at these frequencies is 0.87, 0.72, 0.56, 0.42, 0.31, 0.21, 0.11, 0.06, 0.02, 0.01, 0.00, and 0.00. The combined CCD and display filter MTF (for application to the noise) at the same frequencies is 0.91, 0.77, 0.62, 0.48, 0.36, 0.25, 0.15, 0.07, 0.03, 0.01, and 0.00. The horizontal MRC is provided in Figure 12.14.

Table 12.1
Vollmerhausen system example

Sensor parameters	
Entrance aperture diameter	3.18 cm
Focal length	21.0 cm
Array size	768 by 494
Frame rate	60 Hz
Fields per frame	1:1
Horizontal detector size	7.0 μm
Vertical detector size	8.2 μm
Horizontal pitch	8.4 μm
Vertical pitch	9.8 μm
Optics transmission	0.95
System magnification	17.2
Readout noise	89 electronics
Saturation lux	0.65 Lx
Well saturation	50,000 electrons
Average scene radiance	0.01 W/cm^2-sr
Number of eyes used	1
Max display luminance	15 fL
Min display luminance	0 fL
SNRT ratio	1.7
Spectral wavelengths	[0.40 0.45 0.50 0.55 0.60 0.70 0.80 0.90 1.0]
Spectral response	[0.45 0.93 1.00 0.97 0.83 0.45 0.23 0.10 0.0]

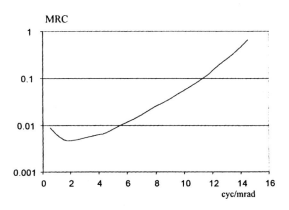

Figure 12.14 Vollmerhausen horizontal MRC example (provided by R. Vollmerhausen).

12.6 GENERAL IMAGE QUALITY EQUATION

As reconnaissance systems evolved in the 1970s, physical measures such as scale and resolution no longer adequately defined the performance of imaging systems [21]. A perceptually based measure of interpretability was developed called the National Imagery Interpretability Rating Scale (NIIRS). The initial NIIRS was developed for use with visible spectrum imagery. The first version of NIIRS was published as a Standard NATO Agreement (STANAG) but was called the Imagery Interpretability Rating Scale (IIRS). The IIRS is no longer considered valid and has been replaced by an updated version of NIIRS [22]. A separate NIIRS has been developed for use with midwave infrared systems.

GIQE was developed to provide NIIRS predictions for a given system design and operating parameters. Version 4.0 [23] was released in 1996. The GIQE is currently being used to model Unmanned Aerial Vehicle (UAV) sensor performance as well as upcoming commercial satellite systems. Performance goals for the Predator and Global Hawk UAVs have been specified in terms of the NIIRS. It is expected that this model will become the standard in the acquisition process for the evaluation of ISR sensors.   Also, as ISR sensors become more capable and can support tactical missions, it is important to understand the relationship between this ISR model and the tactical MRT acquisition model.

National Imagery Interpretation Rating System

Before the consideration of the GIQE, one must understand the NIIRS scale. The NIIRS scale is an intelligence community measure that is used by imagery analysts (IA) to perform quantitative judgments on the interpretability of a particular image. The process of "rating" an image corresponds to the assignment of a number that describes the image interpretability. The NIIRs rating has been developed to ensure that imagery collection and exploitation meets the informational needs of the end user. The NIIRS is a scale from 0 to 9 that can be used to compare the products of different imaging systems. The scale has become an important tool for defining image requirements, selecting and tasking imaging systems, providing quality control feedback to operational systems, and specifying performance of new imaging systems.

The NIIRS is defined by a set of exploitation tasks or criteria equally spaced across a psychophysically defined quality or interpretability scale [24, 25]. The NIIRS rating of an image defines the exploitation tasks that can be performed on that image. Given a NIIRS rating, all lower valued NIIRS tasks can also be performed on the image. A NIIRS rating accounts for all of the factors affecting interpretability including resolution and sensitivity. Table 12.2 shows a subset of visible NIIRS criteria, the complete sets are published in [10]. Note that the NIIRS rating provides inherent target sizing within the definitions. For example, NIIRS 4 allows identification of large fighter aircraft and NIIRS 6 allows model discrimination among small and medium helicopters. An example of an image rated at NIIRS 4 is provided in Figure 12.15.

Table 12.2
Sample NIIRS descriptions

Rating level 0 Imagery of no interpretative value.	**Rating level 5** Identify individual rail cars by type (gondola, flat, box). Identify air surveillance radar on particular ships.
Rating level 1 Detect a medium-sized port facility. Distinguish between taxiways and runways at a large airfield.	**Rating level 6** Distinguish between models of small/medium helicopters. Identify the spare tire on a medium-sized truck. Identify automobiles as sedans or station wagons.
Rating level 2 Detect large hangars at airfields. Detect large static radars. Detector military training areas. Detect large buildings.	**Rating level 7** Identify fitments and fairings on fighter-sized aircraft. Identify ports, ladders, vents on electronics vans. Detect the mount for antitank guided missles.
Rating level 3 Identify wing configuration of large aircraft (straight, swept, delta). Detect a helipad by configurations and markings. Identify a large ship in port by type (cruiser, auxilliary, merchant). Detect trains or strings of rolling stock on standard railroad tracks.	**Rating level 8** Identify the rivet lines on bomber aircraft. Identify a hand-held SAM. Detect winch cables on deck mounted cranes. Identify windshield wipers on a vehicle.
Rating level 4 Identify all large fighters by type (F-15, Foxbat, Fencer, F-14). Detect presence of large individual radar antennas. Identify tracked vehicles by general type (artillery, river crossing eq, etc). Detect an open missile silo door. Determine the shape of the bow on a medium-sized submarine.	**Rating level 9** Identify vehicle registration numbers on trucks. Detect individual spikes in railroad ties. Identify braid in 1 to 3 inch diameter rope. Differentiate cross-slot from single-slot heads on aircraft skin panel fasteners.

GIQE Model

The GIQE predicts NIIRS as a function of image scale, sharpness or resolution, and signal-to-noise. The model was developed on a large database of images and IA responses and predicts a NIIRS rating with a standard error of 0.3. The GIQE allows system designers and operators to perform tradeoffs for the optimization of image quality. The GIQE was originally released in 1994 and has been updated recently.

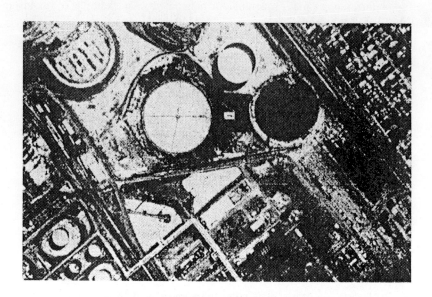

Figure 12.15 An NIIRS-4 rated image (Courtesy of J. Leachtenauer).

The electro-optical GIQE model comprises a constant and four terms:

$$NIIRS = 10.251 - a\log_{10}(GSD_{GM}) + b\log_{10}(RER_{GM}) - 0.656H_{GM} - 0.344(G/SNR) \quad (12.77)$$

where RER_{GM} is the relative edge response (the GM subscript corresponds to the geometric mean of the horizontal and vertical components), GSD_{GM} is the ground sample distance in inches, H_{GM} is the overshoot from edge sharpening, G is the noise gain from edge sharpening, and SNR is the signal-to-noise ratio. The variables a and b are defined as follows:

$$a = 3.32 \text{ and } b = 1.559 \text{ for } RER_{GM} \geq 0.9 \quad \text{and}$$
$$a = 3.16 \text{ and } b = 2.817 \text{ for } RER_{GM} < 0.9.$$

The relative edge response and overshoot terms require the system edge response. This edge response is found using the system MTF

$$ER_x(x) = 0.5 + \frac{1}{\pi}\int_0^\infty \frac{MTF_x(\xi)}{\xi}\sin(2\pi x\xi)d\xi \quad (12.78)$$

x is the response position (in pixels) from the center of a horizontal pixel edge and ξ is the spatial frequency in cycles per sample spacing. This edge response has to be normalized such that when x is a large negative value, ER is 0; and when x is a large positive value, ER is 1 as shown in Figure 12.16. The $ER_y(y)$ calculation is identical, but in the vertical direction. The edge response can be measured in the laboratory with a knife-edge target. The geometric mean of the relative edge response is determined from the product of the differences in edge response at $x =$ +0.5 and -0.5 pixels from the edge in each direction:

$$RER_{GM} = \sqrt{[(ER_x(0.5) - ER_x(-0.5)][(ER_y(0.5) - ER_y(-0.5)]} \qquad (12.79)$$

The ground-sampled distance is the projection of the detector pixel pitch onto the ground, but perpendicular to the sensor's line-of-sight. GSD_x is found by

$$GSD_x = [\frac{pixelpitch}{focallength}]\frac{Range}{\cos(\theta_{look})} \qquad [in] \qquad (12.80)$$

where the pixel pitch and focal length are in the same units and the range from the sensor to the target is in inches. The look angle, θ_{look}, is 0 deg for sensors pointing directly downward at the top of targets and nearly 90 deg for targets on the horizon. The geometric mean must be taken of the horizontal and vertical ground sample distances. With EO systems, this term can account for the majority of the NIIRS rating.

The edge height overshoot term is due to *modulation transfer function compensation (MTFC)*, or edge sharpening. H_x is the value of the horizontal maximum edge response in the region of 1.0 to 3.0 pixels from the edge (using (12.78)) unless the edge is monotonically increasing. For the monotonically increasing H_x, the edge response at 1.25 pixels from the edge is taken. Again, the geometric mean of the horizontal and vertical responses is used in the equation.

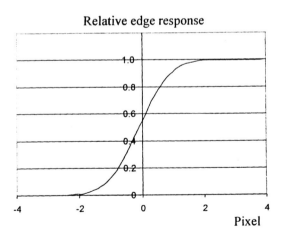

Figure 12.16 Relative edge response.

The noise gain G is determined by the gain of the MTFC filter kernel elements

$$G = \sqrt{\sum_{i=1}^{M} \sum_{j=1}^{N} (Kernel_{ij})^2} \qquad (12.81)$$

where the MTFC kernel elements are in an M by N matrix.

The SNR is the ratio of the dc differential scene radiance to the equivalent rms noise radiance. The SNR is the electronic output SNR and does not include MTFC compensation. In EO sensors, the signal is calculated using the reflective properties of the target and background, the atmospheric and illumination conditions, and the sensor characteristics. The noise term includes all the noise contributors.

This GIQE has been frequently applied to photographic and EO visible systems. It has also been recently applied to midwave infrared systems and is currently the infrared design tool for a number of high-altitude UAVs. For the infrared version, the only difference is that the constant in (12.77) becomes 9.751.

Example

As an example, the GIQE was applied to a narrow FOV EO system. The system FOV was 1.0 by 1.2 deg with a spectral bandpass of 0.65 to 0.90 μm. The f-number of the sensor was 6.1 and the optical transmittance was 0.91. The focal length was 167 cm and the entrance pupil diameter was 11.3 cm. A 480 by 640 CCD detector array was used with 15-μm by 15-μm elements. The center-to-center spacing was 21.8 μrad for a 67% fill factor. The optics were not diffraction limited and an estimate for the optical MTF was used. The display was a 10-fL CRT with a 15.24-cm display height and a 30-cm viewing distance. The eye integration time was set to 0.1 sec and the eye signal-to-noise threshold was set to 2.5. The GSD term provided a significant decrease in the NIIRS estimate with range. The RER term gave a normalized slope of 0.542 to yield an overall decrease of 0.2 NIIRS. The H term decreased the NIIRS by around 0.5. The NIIRS as a function of range is given in Figure 12.17.

NIIRS

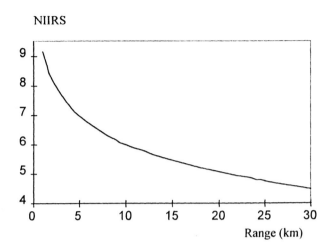

Figure 12.17 GIQE Results.

A number of differences exist between the GIQE and probability of discrimination techniques. First, the GIQE currently defines the GSD in the ground plane and is limited to elevation angles (angle between ground plane and sensor line-of-sight) of 20 deg or greater. There is evidence to suggest that GSD should be defined in the plane orthogonal to the line-of-sight at lower angles but insufficient data are currently available to model the transition. The probability of discrimination approach uses the target's critical dimension, which accounts for the transition from plan to side view.

Second, the GIQE currently predicts NIIRS for hardcopy (film) imagery. Performance on a good quality softcopy (CRT) display provides an increase of around 0.2 NIIRS better than predicted. A poorly designed or maintained CRT, however, can result in interpretability of one NIIRS or even lower than predicted. The probability of discrimination is typically performed on softcopy display. It is important to note, however, that the prediction is valid only for the display used for prediction.

Some general trends can be stated for both the Pr and the GIQE (NIIRS) approaches to sensor performance. The ability to recognize an object increases with increasing target size for a given acquisition system and set of operating conditions. For the NIIRS/GIQE characteristics, the target size relationship is implicit in the criteria definitions, but is not directly evident from the GIQE predictions. Therefore, the relationship between Pr and NIIRs changes dramatically with target size.

For the sensor in the previous example, the Pr was computed for a standard NATO target and the top view of an M1A tank. The NATO target was

2.3m by 2.3m with a contrast of 0.5. The M1A tank was 3.6m by 7.9m at a contrast of 0.5. The atmospheric degradation was set at 0.85 per kilometer over the ranges that were used in the calculation. The recognition criterion was set at three cycles across the target for a 50% probability of recognition. Recall that the Pr changes with target size, but the NIIRS estimate does not. Therefore, the relationship between Pr and NIIRS shifts with target size. The comparison is shown in Figure 12.18.

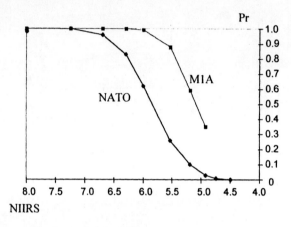

Figure 12.18 Pr as a function of NIIRS.

Note that the 50% probability of recognition occurs at around NIIRS 6 for the NATO target and just over a NIIRS 5 for the M1A target. Also, note the target acquisition definitions of recognition were developed for the discrimination of smaller tanks, such as a T-62, from trucks and not discrimination of large bridge-crossing equipment from larger and even smaller tracked vehicles. Next, Johnson's criteria were developed for low aspect angles, where the NIIRS were developed with large aspect angles. It is possible that the larger aspect angles require a different amount of information for discrimination tasks. There is evidence from preliminary experiments at the National Imagery Management Activity (NIMA) that three cycles across the target dimension gives a higher-than-50% probability of recognition. This would account for some of the recognition capacity at lower NIIRS levels. Finally, Johnson's original criteria were given as discrimination definitions for detection, orientation, recognition, and identification. The imagery analyst is trained to detect, distinguish, differentiate, and identify. The levels of discrimination are not identical, so there are some discrepancies when comparing task-oriented sensor performance.

EXERCISES

12.1. CCD cameras are progressing to large arrays with uniform fixed-pattern modulations of 0.000005 with 4,000 by 3,000 pixels. Readout efficiencies are on the order of 0.99. Using a background current of 1 μA, a target to background contrast of 50%, and a readout noise of 50 electrons, determine the total rms noise on the system output. Assume a pre-storage gain of 1.

12.2. Using the EO system described in the MRC example, suppose the effective focal length of the system were shortened while holding all other parameters constant. How are the sensitivity and resolution affected? What would happen to the probability of recognition? To the NIIRS versus range?

12.3. Determine the NIIRS level required to recognize a farm tractor.

12.4. Calculate the horizontal MRC for the following EO sensor. Assume the sensor is readout noise-limited. The sensor has a vertical FOV of 250 mrad and an aspect ratio of 1.33. Assume the eye integration time is 0.1 sec and the threshold SNR is 2.5. The sensor is extremely sensitive with a pre-storage gain of 30. There are 600 horizontal detector elements spaced 0.557 mrad apart. Assume a scan efficiency of 1. The optics f-number is 0.5 and the optical transmission can be assumed to be 100%. The responsivity covers a bandwidth of 0.4 to 0.9 μm with a responsivity of 0.25E-3 A/lumen. The readout noise is 0.6E-8 A. The sensor is used in low light levels of 0.3 lx where the background current is 0.4E-6 A. The system MTF values at spatial frequencies of 0.12, 0.24, 0.36, 0.48, 0.60, 0.72, 0.84, 0.96, 1.08, and 1.2 cyc/mrad are 0.892, 0.719, 0.537, 0.376, 0.249, 0.155, 0.091, 0.050, 0.026, and 0.013.

12.5. For the system described in Exercise 12.4, determine the probability of recognition as a function of range. The target is a 2.3m by 2.3m object with a contrast of 1. Assume the transmission to be 0.8 per kilometer.

12.6. For the EO system described in Exercise 12.4 and the target described in Exercise 12.5, use the GIQE to determine the sensor NIIRS as a function of range.

REFERENCES

[1] *Night Vision and Electronic Sensors Directorate Television Model,* U.S. Army CECOM Report: Ft. Belvoir, VA , 1994.

[2] Imagery Interpretation Rating Scale, *Air Standard Agreement,* AID STD 101/11A, Jan. 1980.

[3] Frame, W., "Minimum Resolvable and Minimum Detectable Contrast Prediction for Monochrome Solid-State Imagers," *SMPTE Journal* p. 454, May 1987.

[4] Frame, W., "Minimum Resolvable and Minimum Detectable Contrast Prediction for Vidicon Cameras," *SMPTE Journal,* p. 21, Jan. 1985.

[5] Van Meeteren, "Characterization of Task Performance With Viewing Instruments," *JOSA,* Vol. 36, No. 11, Nov. 1946.

[6] Rosell, F., "Review of the Current Periodic Sensor Models," *Proceedings of IRIS Imaging,* 1981.

[7] Rosell, F., "Prediction the Performance of Infrared Staring Arrays," *SPIE Infrared Technology XVIII,* Vol. 1,762, 1992.

[8] Vollmerhausen, R., *Chapter 12: Modeling the Performance of Imaging Sensors,* in *Electro-Optical Imaging Systems and Modeling,* edited by L. Biberman, Ontar Corp., North Andover, MA, [in publication, 1999], 1998.

[9] *General Image Quality Equation User's Guide Version 3.0,* HAE UAV Teir II+ Project Office, Arlington, VA, 1994.

[10] *Night Vision and Electronic Sensors Directorate Television Model,* U.S. Army CECOM Report: Ft. Belvoir, VA, 1994.

[11] Holst, G., *CCD Arrays, Cameras, and Displays,* Winter Park, FL: JCD Publishing, 1996.

[12] Coltman, J. W., "Scintillation Limitations to Resolving Power in Imaging Devices," *J. Opt. Soc. Am.* 44(3), pp. 234 - 237, 1954.

[13] Kornfeld, G. H., and W. R. Lawson, "Visual Perception Models," *J. Opt. Soc. Am.* 61:811, 1971.

[14] Lawson, W. R., "Electrooptical System Evaluation," In *Photoelectronic Imaging Devices,* Vol. 1, p. 375. L. M. Biberman and S. Nudelman, eds., New York, Plemun: 1971.

[15] Ratches, J. A., et al., "Night Vision Laboratory Static Performance Model for Thermal Viewing Systems," Research and Development Technical Report ECOM-7043, U.S. Army Electronics Command, Fort Monmouth, NJ, 1975.

[16] Richards, E. A., "Fundamental Limitations in the Low Light-Level Performance of Direct-View Image-Intensifier Systems," Infrared Physics, Pergamon, U.K., 1967.

[17] Rose, A., "The Sensitivity Performance of the Human Eye on an Absolute Scale," *J. Opt. Soc. Am.* 38(2):196 - 208, 1948.

[18] Rosell, F. A., "Electro-Optical System Evaluation," in *Photoelectronic Imaging Devices*, Vol. 1, p. 307., L. M. Biberman and S. Nudelman, eds., New York, Plenum: 1971.

[19] Rosell, F. A., and R. H. Wilson, "Recent Psychophysical Experiments and the Display Signal-to-Noise Ratio Concept," in *Perception of Displayed Information*, p. 167, L. M. Biberman, ed., New York, Plenum: 1973.

[20] Vollmerhausen, R., "Incorporating Display Limitations into Night Vision Performance Models," *1995 IRIS Passive Sensors*, V2:11 - 31, 1995.

[21] Leachtenauer, J., W. Malila, J. Irvine, L. Colburn, and N. Salvaggio, "General Image Quality Equation (GIQE)," *Applied Optics*, Vol. 36, No. 32, p. 8,322.

[22] Leachtenauer, J. C., "National Imagery Interpretability Rating Scales: Overview and Product Description," *ASPRS/ASCM Annual Convention and Exhibition,* Technical Papers, Vol. 1, "Remote Sensing and Photogrammetry," *American Society for Photogrammetry and Remote Sensing and American Congress on Surveying and Mapping*, Baltimore, MD, pp. 262 - 272, Apr. 22 - 25, 1996.

[23] National Imagery and Mapping Agency, *General Image Quality Equation-Users Guide,* Ver. 4.0, Data and Systems Analysis Division, Springfield, VA, 1996.

[24] Irvine, J., and J. Leachtenauer, "A Methodology for Developing Image Interpretability Ratings Scales," *ASPRS/ASCM Annual Convention and Exhibition,* Technical Papers, Vol. 1, "Remote Sensing and Photogrammetry," *American Society for Photogrammetry and Remote Sensing and American Congress on Surveying and Mapping*, Baltimore, MD, pp. 273 - 281, Apr. 22 - 25, 1996.

[25] Mohr, E., D. Hothem, J. Irvine, and C. Erdman, "The Multispectral Imagery Interpretation Rating Scale (MS IIRS)," *ASPRS/ASCM Annual Convention and Exhibition,* Technical Papers, Vol. 1, Remote Sensing and Photogrammetry, *American Society for Photogrammetry and Remote Sensing and American Congress on Surveying and Mapping*, Baltimore, MD, pp. 300 - 310, April 22 - 25, 1996.

Chapter 13

Sensor Design Considerations

The last two chapters have described the specifics of modeling infrared and electro-optical sensor systems. In this chapter, several system-level aspects are presented that must be considered and defined in the early phases of any sensor design. These system-level requirements include waveband selection, resolution, field-of-view, coverage area, basic optics, and search capabilities. Each of these system-level requirements affects the design and selection of each component (described in Chapters 5 through 10) in the sensor system. Also, an outstanding example of infrared and electro-optical systems is the missile seeker. Missile seekers are designed according to their task at hand. This chapter describes various seekers for given tasks and analysis methods.

13.1 WAVEBAND SELECTION

A good starting point in the design of an optical imaging sensor is to determine a reasonable operating band or bands. The selection of the spectral band influences many of the sensor's key components, including optics, detector array, cooling system (if required), electronics, and signal processing. The primary optical bands for broadband sensors are shown in Table 13.1.

Table 13.1
Primary optical bands

	Ultraviolet	0.1 to 0.4 μm
	Visible	0.4 to 0.7 μm
EO systems	Near infrared (NIR)	0.7 to 1.1 μm
	Shortwave infrared (SWIR)	1.1 to 3.0 μm
I²R systems	Midwave infrared (MWIR)	3.0 to 5.0 μm
	Longwave infrared (LWIR)	8.0 to 14 μm
	Far infrared	14 to 100 μm

The discussion here does not include the ultraviolet or the far infrared bands. The primary difference between EO and I²R detection phenomena is that the EO sensors respond to reflected light (primarily solar), where I²R sensors respond to light that is self-emitted (by the target, background, and atmosphere).

Multispectral and hyperspectral sensors are increasing in usage for target detection and discrimination. These types of sensors have many (hundred or even thousands) very narrow spectral bands within one or more of the regions listed above. They have proven to have significant utility for commercial applications such as the detection and classification of various kinds of vegetation and have military applications such as the detection of camaflouged targets.

The selection of the spectral band is driven by the type of mission scenario, target characteristics, operating location, look angle, and atmospheric climate (transmission window). A summary comparison of some of the key sensor considerations is shown in Figure 13.1. One clarification is that the figure is not intended to be all-inclusive but provide typical parameters. For example, the number in parenthesis for the detectors are typical operating temperatures in Kelvin.

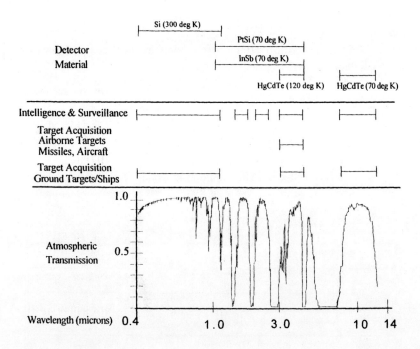

Figure 13.1 System-level sensor considerations.

Two primary considerations in spectral band selection are the solar spectrum curve and the blackbody curve for terrestrial objects. The solar irradiance at sea level is shown in Figure 13.2. The sun's temperature is around 5,600 deg C (5,873 deg K) with a peak wavelength of around 0.55 μm, which corresponds to the peak response of the human eye. The irradiance in the visible band indicated by the dashed lines accounts for approximately 38% of the sun's radiant energy that reaches Earth. Also of interest is that approximately 98% of the sun's solar energy is below 3 μm [1]. This large percentage of energy is one of the primary reasons why the EO bands are of such interest for sensor designers. The limitation of EO sensors is that they work during the day when reflected light is available. Otherwise, a large pre-storage gain is required to amplify moonlight or starlight. If natural light is not available, either illumination must be provided or an I²R system must be used.

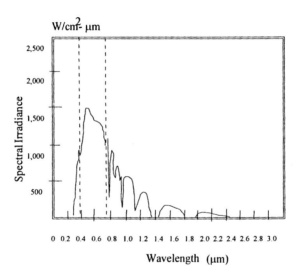

Figure 13.2 Solar spectrum.

It has long been an issue in the tactical community as to whether the midwave or the longwave band [2] is a better sensor for given applications. The short answer is that "it depends." The long answer is provided by going through a case study as outlined in Chapters 5 through 11 and determining which of two candidate sensors gives better performance for a given target, background, atmosphere, optics, detector, etc. The probability of recognition as a function of range is a good measure for sensor comparison given that the FOVs are comparable. While this exercise can be long and tedious, it is worth the effort if a sensor is to really be considered for a tactical application. The following are some general guidelines for rough comparisons.

Consideration of All Bands

1. If the sensor-to-target line-of-sight is blocked by heavy cloud cover, forget EO and I^{2}R sensors. Consider using synthetic aperture radar (SAR) or some other imaging modality.

2. If it is daylight and the line-of-sight is not obscured by fog or smoke, use EO sensors. They are less expensive than I^{2}R sensors and generally have higher performance.

3. If it is night and there is good moonlight or starlight and the line-of-sight is not obscured by fog or smoke, then use an EO system with an image intensifier containing sufficient pre-storage gain.

4. If it is night with little to no natural or active illumination or if a system has to be guaranteed to work day and night (majority of conditions; this is the case with many tactical systems), then consider an infrared sensor either as a primary sensor or as an augmentation to an EO sensor.

Consideration of Midwave and Longwave

5. **Target consideration.** For most terrestrial objects with a 300 deg K background and a few-degree target-to-background temperature differential, the equivalent radiance differential can be 20 times more in the longwave than in the midwave. Recall that 300 deg K sources peak at around 10 μm. Conversely, for a missile plume at an effective temperature of 800 deg C, or 1,073 deg K, the peak emission is in the midwave. With a cold-sky background, the differential radiance is around four to five times more in the midwave than in the longwave.

6. **Atmospheric consideration.** While atmospherics are extremely complicated and MODTRAN should be used for accurate predictions, longwave light propagates through cold, dry air much better than midwave light. The reason here is that little absolute humidity exists so that the moisture extinction of the longwave light is decreased. For paths of around 10 km, longwave light can have a factor of three times the transmission of midwave. In hot, humid, or maritime scenarios where there is a good deal of moisture in the air, the difference between midwave and longwave transmission is usually not significant, although some people maintain that midwave performs a little better in some maritime conditions. Also, the differences in midwave and longwave transmission decrease with increases in altitude.

7. **Detectivity consideration.** Another significant difference in the performance of midwave versus longwave sensors is that of *detectivity*. While it is always difficult to keep up with the changing detector world, higher detectivities can always be found in the midwave. The theoretical limit of detectivity gives roughly a factor of 10 to the midwave over the longwave. This factor is not seen in midwave detectors such as PtSi, however, which has detectivities on the order of HgCdTe detectors in the longwave (sometimes even less). For InSb detectors, the midwave advantage usually stands, and the midwave factor over longwave can be between 3 to 10.

8. **Integration time consideration.** While this may not be a consideration in a few years, there is usually a large difference in midwave and longwave integration times. This is because most midwave sensors are staring arrays and the more advanced longwave sensors include second-generation detectors. Staring arrays have longer integration times, where scanners have much smaller integration times. With 400 to 600 horizontal samples (with both sensors) and a four-detector time-delay-integration, the staring array can give a factor of 10 to 13 times the performance as that of the second-generation scanner. This estimate should be reduced to five to seven times the performance because the integration time of staring arrays is limited by the electron well capacity (i.e., the well fills up in less than a frame time). Also, the performance is less if the staring-array pattern noise is considered. If the sensor is first-generation with no time-delay-integration, the staring array factor would be again 10 to 13 times the performance of the scanning system.

9. **Other consideration.** There are many other considerations, such as optics transmission, that should be included in a detailed trade study. Only the differences considered to be major contributors are covered.

13.2 RESOLUTION, FIELD-OF-VIEW, AND COVERAGE

Following the spectral band selection, the next important step is the sensitivity and resolution requirement for detection and recognition. An example of a tactical requirement is "the system shall provide recognition of a T-62 tank at a range of 4 km with a probability of at least 90%."

The resolution of a sensor is designed around the most stringent requirement of recognition (identification if necessary). Recall that the probability of recognition Pr is a function of target size and radiant contrast. The operational specification for a particular target can be converted to an MRT or MRC specification using a reversal of the discrimination versus the range procedure given in Chapter 11. Usually the more stringent recognition (or identification) task is performed in the narrow field-of-view (NFOV) as shown in Figure 13.3. The sensor shown is for an airborne sensor, but the same concepts apply to ground sensors. Because focal planes and scanning systems are limited in the number of detectors and corresponding total samples across the object, the NFOV distributes these samples across a smaller area within the scene. This higher resolution imaging configuration allows the selection of optics diameter, focal length, optics transmission, detector size, sample spacing, and other system parameters to satisfy a more stringent recognition requirement.

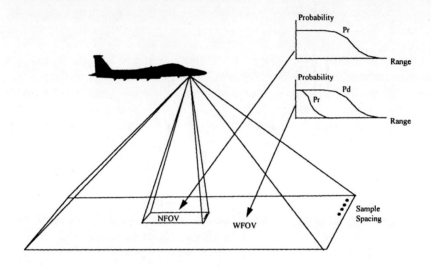

Figure 13.3 Sensor FOV and performance.

The designer is careful not to overdesign in the sensor's recognition performance because the result is a smaller NFOV. The goal is simply to give sufficient resolution and sensitivity performance to satisfy the Pr requirement while still providing the largest NFOV possible. The reason is that small FOVs are difficult to point accurately and are more sensitive to platform stability factors. An even more important reason is that only small areas can be monitored with a smaller NFOV.

When searching over a large area for an object, it is better to have a wide field-of-view (WFOV). Most sensors are designed with multiple FOVs so that the object can be detected (with a high probability, Pd) in the WFOV and the sensor can be switched to the NFOV for the recognition or identification task. For sensors that do not have dual or zoom (continuous) FOVs, the sensor must be designed to achieve the performance of the most stringent requirement in a single FOV. However, for the dual-FOV sensor, the FOV switch is usually accomplished with an effective decrease in focal length (this increases the sensor's magnification by the ratio of the two focal lengths). For most sensors and scenarios, the Pd and Pr curves (recall, they are both a function of range) match with respect to range for the WFOV and NFOV, respectively. This is shown in the curves of Figure 13.3. This makes sense in that a large area can be monitored by the sensor's WFOV until an object is detected. Then, the sensor is switched to the NFOV, where the sensor can then provide recognition.

Usually, the sensor's WFOV is three to four times the size of the NFOV. In the WFOV, the sample spacing is much farther apart, so recognition cannot be accomplished. The Pr curve has dropped in range significantly. Note that Johnson's criteria are 0.75 cycles across the target for detection and three cycles across the target for recognition. Recognition requires a higher resolution by a factor of 4. The reason that the WFOV to NFOV magnification is not exactly 4, but between a factor of 3 and 4 is that sensitivity issues and atmospheric transmission issues must be considered.

Now we have a sensor that can detect objects over a large area in the WFOV and can be switched for object recognition in the NFOV. Some good design rules are:

1. The more stringent sensor operational requirements are met in the NFOV.

2. An MRT or MRC specification can be determined using the reversal of the probability of discrimination procedure given in Chapter 11.

3. The MRT or MRC performance is derived with a small error margin, but do not overdesign, as the result will be a smaller NFOV.

4. Small FOVs are difficult to point accurately and are more susceptible to vibration, jitter, and drift artifacts.

5. A dual-FOV sensor provides flexibility in area coverage and discrimination performance.

6. The ratio of WFOV to NFOV (magnification) should be between 3 and 4.

While the FOVs are shown to be rectangular, those in air-to-ground applications usually have a "keystone" shape as shown in Figure 13.4. An angular FOV that is rectangular grazes the ground in this keystone shape. Therefore, the area coverage on the ground is larger than a typical square FOV.

The area is computed with an integral of arc lengths, but rough approximations of the area length and width going through the keystone center is sometimes sufficient for dynamic area coverage exercises. The keystone length in the vertical direction (in the flight path direction) is

$$l_v = \frac{\sin(VFOV)}{\cos(\theta)}R \qquad (13.1)$$

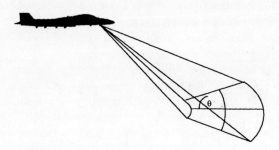

Figure 13.4 Key-shaped area coverage.

where VFOV is the sensor's vertical FOV and R is the range, or the distance between the aircraft and the center of the key. The cross-flight path direction is taken as the sensor's horizontal FOV.

13.3 STARING VERSUS SCANNING PERFORMANCE

In recent years, there has been significant progress in infrared detector manufacturing techniques, resulting in the production of large detector arrays. This progress has led to trade studies in the evaluation of staring versus scanning sensor performance. The trade studies are primarily for the infrared region because large format arrays have been available in the EO wavebands for some time. In Chapter 8, staring and scanning detector arrays were discussed along with their associated parameters. Table 13.2 summarizes their basic differences.

Table 13.2
Scanning and staring sensor comparisons

Scanning sensors	*Staring sensors*
Wide field of view	Improved sensitivity due to longer integration time
Signal conditioning necessary to process TDI	FOV limited to array size
Optics must accomodate scanner	Simpler optical design
Scanner increases size and reduces reliability	No moving parts, more reliable
Requires line-to-line equalization	Requires individual detector non-uniformity correction
High resolution in scan direction	

As with any imager, there are two fundamental considerations in the evaluation of staring versus scanning systems: sensitivity and resolution. The staring system provides improved sensitivity because of its longer integration times. Because staring detectors do not have to be shared with multiple points in the image space, they can stay at one position and soak up photons for as much as a frame time. This can be seen mathematically by evaluating the NETD equation from Chapter 11:

$$NETD = \frac{2\sqrt{\Delta f}}{\sqrt{\alpha\beta\eta_{cx}\eta_q}\, D_o\tau_o D_{BLIP}^{**}(\lambda_p)\frac{\Delta M}{\Delta T}} \tag{13.2}$$

For a staring array, $F_r = 1/\tau_d$, where τ_d is the detector dwell time:

$$NETD = \frac{2\sqrt{1/2\tau_d}}{\sqrt{\alpha\beta\eta_{cx}\eta_q}\, D_o\tau_o D_{BLIP}^{**}(\lambda_p)\frac{\Delta M}{\Delta T}} \tag{13.3}$$

so, a maximum dwell time for the staring array is 1/30 sec. The increased sensitivity is taken as the square root of the ratio of the dwell times. For a scanning system with 600 samples across the horizontal scan (in one frame time) as a staring system with a 1/30th-sec frame time, the improvement is $\sqrt{(1/30)/(1/30 * 600)}$ or around a factor of 25. If the scanner has TDI (say, four detectors in series), then the improvement is $\sqrt{600/4}$, or around 12.5. In practice, the improvement is less because the detector well fills with electrons (saturates) in less than a frame time and pattern noise (sometimes called *fixed-pattern noise*) limits the sensitivity. Closely associated with sensitivity is a sensor's capacity to reject background clutter. In general, staring systems outperform scanning systems for detecting dim targets.

The second fundamental consideration for the evaluation of starers and scanners is that of resolution. Chapter 8 showed that the sampling frequency of a sensor should be twice that of the sensor cutoff frequency. While this is possible with scanners by sampling at smaller angular intervals than the detector angular subtense, it is not possible with staring systems. This forces staring systems to be undersampled. For a scanning system and a staring system with the same detector angular subtense, the scanning system has a capacity for higher resolution. However, a relatively new technique known as *microscanning* can help circumvent this problem. Microscanning is a technique whereby the line-of-sight is stepped or dithered to increase the effective sampling frequency.

13.4 OPTICS CONSIDERATIONS

Top-level optical designs are worth considering during the preliminary concept formulation of I²R and EO systems. A common system-level parameter that describes the optics of a sensor system is the f-number (or F/#), which is defined as

$$F/\# = \frac{f}{D_{pupil}} \qquad (13.4)$$

where f is the effective optics focal length and D_{pupil} is the pupil diameter. The F/# describes the light-collecting ability of a sensor and is often referred to as the *speed* of the lens. In terms of light collection, a smaller F/# is faster. As an initial consideration, a fast optical system is desirable where around F/1 is a feasible limit. Faster is not always tangible because a fast optical system is typically heavier and more expensive. Also, low-F/# systems can be accompanied by significant diffraction and aberrations.

Consider the simple design example of an F/2 system shown in Figure 13.5. The case shown corresponds to the case where a fast F/# is desired, but the FOV and detector angular subtense (detector width divided by the focal length) of the system must be held constant.

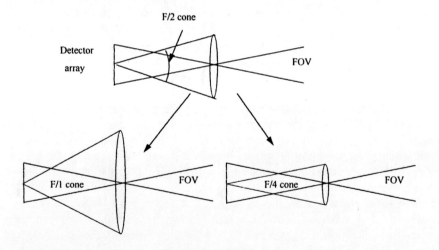

Figure 13.5 Optical speed comparisons.

If the optics are changed to an F/1 system, then the system requires much larger optical elements, but the system collects more photons (i.e., improved sensitivity). Also, the diffraction MTF improves from the larger aperture. If a slower, F/4 system is considered, the system light collection capability is reduced, causing a degradation in MTF. In summary, fast optics are typically desirable unless prohibited by size, weight, cost, or sophistication.

13.5 SEARCH (DYNAMIC DISCRIMINATION)

So far, we have discussed only the static performance of I²R and EO sensors. Static performance corresponds to a stationary sensor pointing direction (i.e., line-of-sight) and stationary objects within the sensor's FOV. In more cases than not, the operation of most sensors is in a dynamic mode where the sensor is "panned" while an observer searches for an object of interest (a target). This search process limits the time in which an observer has to discriminate objects, and as a result, the probability of discrimination is degraded. For static performance models, the observer is assumed to be given as much time as needed to perform the discrimination task. In this section, we quantify this degradation for the dynamic case.

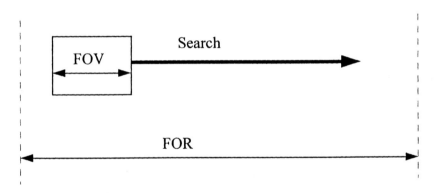

Figure 13.6 Searching with an FOV over an FOR.

Consider Figure 13.6 where an FOV is panned across a field-of-regard (FOR). The FOV corresponds to the area that the sensor can image each frame time. The FOR is an area of interest that the observer intends to search. For a small FOV and a large FOR, it takes the observer significant time to perform the search.

To quantify discrimination performance, we first consider a search process where an observer searches a static FOV for a target within time *t*. The probability of detection as a function of time takes on the simple form of

$$P(t) = P_\infty[1 - e^{-t/t_{FOV}}] \tag{13.5}$$

where P_∞ is the static probability of detection (given an infinite amount of time) and t_{FOV} is the mean target acquisition time. Field test results have given two different expressions for t_{FOV}, depending on the static detection probability:

$$\frac{1}{t_{FOV}} = \frac{P_\infty}{3.4} \qquad \text{for} \qquad P_\infty \leq 0.9 \qquad\qquad (13.6)$$

$$\frac{1}{t_{FOV}} = \frac{1}{6.8}\frac{N}{(N_{50})_D} \qquad \text{for} \qquad P_\infty > 0.9$$

Where N is the critical number of cycles that can be resolved across the target and $(N_{50})_D$ is the number of cycles required for a 50% probability of detection.

For an observer to use the FOV to search the FOR in some time t, the number of FOVs required to cover the FOR must be determined:

$$n = \frac{FOR}{FOV} \qquad\qquad (13.7)$$

Now the dynamic probability of detection for an FOV to search the FOR in time t is

$$P(t) = P_\infty[1 - e^{-t/nt_{FOV}}] \qquad\qquad (13.8)$$

Example

A 2-deg by 2-deg FOV is used to search an area of 10 deg by 20 deg. The sensor has an 80% probability of static detection for a given target for the given atmospheric conditions. Determine the probability of detection if the FOR is searched every 70 sec. Solution: The FOR/FOV ratio is (10x20)/(2x2), or 50. We use the $P_\infty \leq 0.9$ approximation for t_{FOV} to yield a 22% dynamic probability of detection. Obviously, this dynamic probability of detection is not high enough to satisfy many requirements.

13.6 EXAMPLE OF IMAGING INFRARED SYSTEMS

I^2R sensors can be categorized into two broad groups: military and commercial systems. Military systems are, in general, accompanied with stringent requirements such as operation in a wide range of temperature, shock, vibration, and other environments. They are typically longer range sensors with higher sensitivity and resolution. Because they are usually higher performance systems, they require good stabilization. The military I^2R sensors are commonly known as forward-looking infrared receivers (FLIRs) [3].

Commercial systems are designed in the same manner as military with the exception of the harsh environmental requirements. Medical applications include skin-damage analysis and healing progress. In law enforcement, applications include night driving, surveillance, and documentation of evidence for case preparation. Commercial systems are also found in astronomical applications such as high-sensitivity, calibrated cameras with strict calibration requirements. Possibly the largest commercial application is in temperature diagnostics. Utility companies use I^2R sensors for the monitoring of power lines, fault analysis, and component failure.

Examples of military systems include hand-held night sights, target acquisition systems, and fire control systems. The U.S. Army's AN/PAS is a hand-held thermal night viewer with a 6- by 12- deg FOV and a recognition range of around 1,000 m. The AN/TAS-4C is a TOW missile acquisition sensor that has two FOVs: 1.13- by 2.26-deg and 3.4- by 6.8-deg. Its purpose is the engagement of armored vehicles and it has a recognition range of around 3,000 m. Two airborne systems are LANTIRN (Low Altitude Navigation and Targeting Infrared System for Night) and TADS/PNVS (Target Acquisition Designation Sight/Pilot Night Vision System).

The LANTIRN is a U.S. Air Force system with two pods mounted on the F-16 as shown in Figure 13.7. The LANTIRN system includes a navigation pod and a targeting pod. The navigation pod is for night flying, where its image is overlaid on the pilot's heads-up display (HUD) as shown in Figure 13.8. The targeting pod is for detection, recognition, acquisition, and fire control of ground targets. Once a target is acquired by the system, the imagery can be handed off to a Maverick missile for correlation tracking, or a laser is fired at the target in a pulsed manner to guide a Hellfire missile to the target.

Figure 13.7 LANTIRN pods (courtesy of LMC).

Figure 13.8 LANTIRN heads-up display (courtesy of LMC).

The TADS/PNVS is very similar in concept but was designed for the Apache helicopter. Figure 13.9 shows the TADS/PNVS on the nose of the helicopter. It provides pilot vision in adverse weather, where the PNVS is steered by the pilot's head. The pilot views the image through a helmet-mounted display. The TADS/PNVS system includes visible, infrared, and laser range-finding systems. Also, a laser designator is boresighted (aligned with) to the acquisition FLIR so that the laser can designate a target for Hellfire missile (laser-guided) delivery.

There are both ground-based and airborne commercial I^2R systems. The Amber 4265 system is a 256 by 256 InSb staring camera with 38 μm pitch detectors. It is a midwave sensor with a 1- to 5.5-μm passband. The Inframetrics 760 sensor is a HgCdTe serial-scan system with a microcooler. The standard FOV is 15 by 20 deg, but various lenses are available. The passband is 8- to 12- μm and the output imagery has 8 bits of resolution. Finally, the FLIR Systems, Inc. (FSI) FSI-2000 is a HgCdTe 2 by 4 (TDI) cryogenically cooled system that is mounted in a sky-ball for use on helicopters and other aircraft. Police departments and news organizations are primary users with an increase in military interest from a number of countries. The system's pixel pitch ranges from 250 μrads to 1.4 mrads and the sensor turret can point from -120 to 120 deg in azimuth and 30 to -180 deg in elevation.

Figure 13.9 Apache TADS/PNVS (courtesy of LMC).

13.7 MISSILE SEEKERS

Missile seekers are an excellent example of I^2R and EO systems because the constraints of these systems are usually extreme. They must be small, lightweight, and rugedized for acceleration. They are designed to provide the required guidance information while being implemented with the least complexity and cost. There are four types of missile seekers: ground-to-air, ground-to-ground, air-to-ground, and air-to-air (Figure 13.10). The seekers in these systems are usually quite different, depending on the application. A few examples of seeker systems are presented along with a discussion of the challenges associated with each one.

Ground-to-Air

The ground-to-air example is that of the Stinger (FIM-92) missile. It is a portable air defense missile that is shoulder-launched. It was developed in the 1960s as an infrared homing missile with a speed of around Mach 2 and a range of around 5 km. The waveband is 4.1 to 4.4 μm where the spectral response is matched to the exhaust plume of an aircraft rather than to the hot metal.

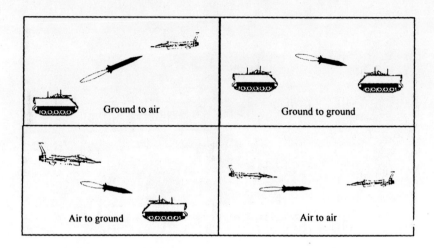

Figure 13.10 Types of missile seekers.

The seeker is that of a "rosette" scan where the optical system and the detector scan are shown in Figure 13.11. A rotating secondary mirror and a rotating wedge causes the detector to scan the seeker FOV in the rosette pattern shown. The scan shown is only to present the concept, as the actual rosette scan covers the entire FOV (i.e., no missing regions).

Note that the seeker is not an imaging seeker, but responds to a small target signal as the detector traverses the target. The Stinger was upgraded to have two detectors that cover the rosette scan at the same time: an infrared detector and an ultraviolet detector. The presence of an infrared signal coupled to a lack of ultraviolet light (from the solar scatter blockage by the aircraft) offers rejection of countermeasures such as flares.

The sensitivity performance of such a rosette scan seeker is given by the noise equivalent irradiance (NEI) at the entrance pupil of the seeker:

$$NEI = \frac{\sqrt{A_d(\pi \Delta f/2)}}{A_o \tau_o D*(1-e^{-2\pi \tau_d \Delta f})} \qquad [\text{W/cm}^2] \qquad (13.9)$$

where A_o is the entrance pupil area, τ_o is the optical transmission, $D*$ is the detectivity, and A_d is the area of the detector. The amplifier, if given by a one-stage filter, gives $\Delta f = 1/2\pi RC$. The resolution performance of the system is determined by the detector IFOV (this is the detector diameter divided by the focal length). However, signal processing techniques can increase the resolution of the target position estimate to less than the IFOV.

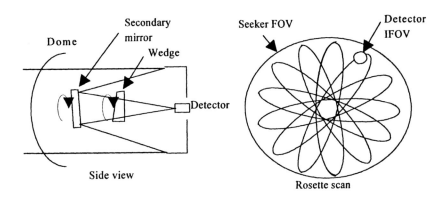

Figure 13.11 Rosette scan seeker.

Advantages of this seeker are that it is inexpensive, simple in construction, and can be packaged small and lightweight. It has worked well in many scenarios. Although it is a relatively old technology, it will be used for many more years. This type of seeker works well for small, hot, point-source targets. It does not work well with ground targets, however. The clutter levels and low target contrast of ground scenarios require more sophisticated seekers.

Ground-to-Ground

An example of the ground-to-ground missile seeker is that of the tactical Javelin missile system. The system (shown in Figure 13.12 along with a trajectory photograph) leverages a staring focal plane array. The seeker comprises an optical system and a 64 by 64 detector Mercury Cadmium Telluride (HgCdTe, sometimes called MCT) focal plane array. This array cannot provide high resolution over a large FOV. It achieves good sensitivity because the system includes a staring array with good detector dwell times. Even at the high frame rates required for missile flights, the dwell times provide good sensitivity.

The analysis of this seeker (Figure 13.13) in terms of resolution and sensitivity is performed in the same manner as that of the I²R systems described in Chapter 11. The appropriate parameters here are MTF and Noise NETD. MRTD is not applicable to this type seeker because humans do not perform the target discrimination task. There are new seeker performance quantities under development, such as the Trackability Metric (TM). The missile processor performs the target discrimination with a high-performance tracker. Benefits of the staring-array seeker are good sensitivity and frame rate, clutter rejection, and suppression of countermeasures. Flexibility for image processing growth is also a benefit.

Figure 13.12 Javelin missile system and trajectory.

This technology was not available until recently because of the advances in detector manufacturing and high-speed processing. The high-rate production of infrared arrays is expected to drive down the cost of staring arrays for future seeker applications.

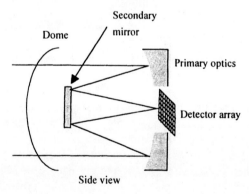

Figure 13.13 Staring-array seeker.

Air-to-Ground

Maverick (AGM-65) is one of the more successful air-to-ground missile systems. The four types of Maverick guidance systems include radar, laser-guided, electro-optical, and infrared seekers. The Maverick was developed in the 1960s for use against tanks and hardened targets. Later versions were developed to attack ships and bunkers. The EO seeker entered service in 1972. It had a television camera installed with optics that allowed magnification of the target area. The AGM-65C has an I²R sensor as the seeker (Figure 13.14) with a scanner specially designed to obtain a frame of imagery from a 16-element HgCdTe array. The imager operates in the longwave infrared and the sensitivity is around twice that of the EO version.

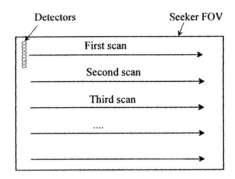

Figure 13.14 Maverick seeker FOV.

The analysis of this type of seeker is performed in the scanning FLIR manner without the display and human perception components. Ground targeting requires this type of sophisticated imaging seeker because the clutter and sensitivity issues are critical. This scanning system was, however, developed in the 1960s where staring systems were not available in the longwave.

Air-to-Air

The last example is that of a Sidewinder (AIM-9), which is a reticle seeker [4-6]. It is still widely used with the third generation in development. It is currently used by the U.S. Navy, U.S. Air Force, and U.S. Marines along with the military forces of a large number of other countries.

Reticle seekers can be divided into two classes: *spinning reticle seekers* and *nutating reticle seekers* as shown in Figure 13.15. The spinning reticle seekers are the most common. For both systems, the entrance optics provide an image of the small target onto an image plane where the reticle is placed. The reticle is intended to provide a temporal modulation that corresponds to the target position. This modulation is provided in the spinning reticle case by the chopping of the small target light by a complex reticle pattern that encodes target position. In the nutating reticle case, the reticle is stationary, but the small target traverses the reticle through the natural nutation motion of the missile. The nutation provides shifting of the target image on the reticle and a chopping action of the light. In both cases, the chopped light is collected by condensing optics and is converted to a voltage by a detector.

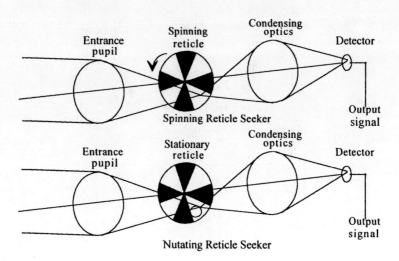

Figure 13.15 Spinning reticle and nutating reticle seekers.

The reticles shown in Figure 13.15 are only shown for informative purposes and are not the actual reticles that would be required for the modulation of target positions. The patterns are very different for the nutating case and the spinning reticle case. Here, we focus on the spinning reticle case to illustrate reticle concepts.

Consider the frequency-modulated spinning reticle shown in Figure 13.16. Assume that the small target flux is focused at point A on the reticle. As the reticle spins, the target light is chopped or modulated, so that the frequency of the chopped light corresponds to the target radial (distance from the reticle center) position. All the light is collected by a single detector and is converted to a voltage. The voltage is analyzed by a processor to determine the radial target position. There are four different modulation frequencies on the reticle to encode four different radial regions. Point A is modulated with four cycles per reticle rotation. Figure 13.16 also shows a frequency versus radius function that describes the reticle. Note that this reticle can only modulate the target for four position bands, so the resolution in radial location is poor. A linear frequency versus radius reticle is shown in Figure 13.17, along with its frequency versus radius plot. It may appear odd at first, but any circular arc drawn around the center of the reticle traverses a perfect square wave on the reticle. A point source that is imaged onto the reticle would provide such a temporally modulated signal on the detector. The target frequency increases linearly with radius. The maximal reticle chopping frequency is near the periphery, where the modulation frequency is 18 cycles per reticle rotation.

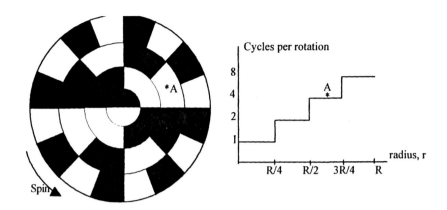

Figure 13.16 Simple frequency-modulated reticle.

To obtain angular target location, a phasing sector is frequently used. The reticle shown in Figure 13.18 shows such a reticle with a phasing sector. The top is transparent and the bottom transmits around half the target flux. Suppose a synchronization signal (a reference voltage) is generated each time the reticle traverses through the initial position shown. The chopping phase of the reticle with respect to the reference voltage gives the angular position of the target. The target position A, is located at ϕ_A in angular units from the reference position. As the reticle traverses in angle, the chopping edge converts the detector voltage from high to low. The corresponding chopping action is shown in Figure 13.18. A combination reticle of the phasing sector and the frequency modulation has been used to obtain both angular and radial target positions. The Lovell reticle, shown in Figure 13.18, is such a combination reticle. The phasing sector gives the angular target position and the frequency modulation gives the radial target position.

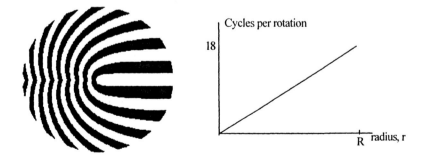

Figure 13.17 Linear frequency-modulated reticle.

Many other techniques have been used, such as frequency modulation in both the angular and radial directions. Amplitude modulation has also been successful in target position encoding. Finally, a "phase" or "spoke" function is imposed on some reticles to reduce background signals such as cloud clutter and horizon signals. Biberman [6] is an excellent reference in the design and analysis of reticle seekers.

Seeker Engagements

Missile seeker engagement performance is typically described as an irradiance at the entrance aperture of the seeker. The target and background flux levels must be compared and propagated through the atmosphere to give an effective target-to-background irradiance differential at the seeker input aperture. Take, for example, the air-to-air case, where the intensity of a missile plume or aircraft signature is known. The intensity $I(\lambda)$ is given in units of watts per steradian per micrometer. With an atmospheric transmission of $\tau_{atm}(\lambda)$ and a seeker-to-target range of R, the target irradiance at the entrance aperture of the seeker is

$$E_{tgt}(\lambda) = \int_{\lambda_1}^{\lambda_2} \frac{I(\lambda)\tau_{atm}(\lambda)}{R^2} d\lambda \ . \qquad \text{W/cm}^2 \qquad (13.10)$$

The actual units are typically picowatts per square centimeter. The tracking irradiance of a missile seeker must be met for tracking and lock to occur. Tracking irradiance is usually specified in seeker performance specifications. If a tracking irradiance specification is not given, a SNR of around 5 to 10 is usually sufficient for a successful engagement.

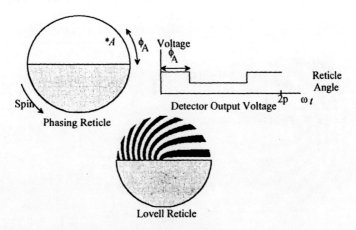

Figure 13.18 Phasing sector and Lovell reticles.

REFERENCES

[1] Waldman, G., and Wootton, J., *Electro-Optical Imaging System Performance,* Boston, MA: Artech House, 1993.

[2] Findlay, G., and Cutten, D., "Comparison of 3-5 and 8-12 μm Infrared Systems," *Applied Optics,* Vol. 28., No. 23, Dec. 1989.

[3] Miller, J., *Principles of Infrared Technology: A Practical Guide to the State of the Art,* New York: Van Nostrand Reinhold, 1994.

[4] Driggers, R., C. Halford, G. Boreman, D. Lattman, and K. Williams, "Parameters of Spinning FM Reticles," *Applied Optics,* Vol. 30, Mar. 1991.

[5] Lovell, D. J., "Electro-Optical Position Indicator System, " U.S. Patent No. 2,997,699, Aug. 1961.

[6] Biberman, L., *Reticles in Electro-Optical Devices,* London: Pergamon Press, 1966.

Symbols List

Symbol	Quantity	Units
a	horizontal detector dimension	cm
a	absorption coefficient	km^{-1}
A_o	area of optical entrance pupil	cm^2
A_v	voltage gain	V/V
A_{src}	area seen by detector	cm^2
b	vertical detector dimension	cm
c	speed of light, 3.0×10^8	m/sec
f_e	frequency, electrical	Hz
f	focal length	m or cm
Δf	bandwidth	Hz
h	Planck's constant, 6.626×10^{-14}	Joule-sec
c	speed of light	m/sec
C	capacitance	farad
C	contrast	unitless
C(l)	relative spectral response	A (or V)/Watt
C_n^2	index structure parameter	m$^{-2/3}$
C_T^2	temperature structure parameter	K^2/m$^{2/3}$
D	lens diameter	m or cm
$D_n(r)$	index structure function	unitless
$D_T(r)$	temperature structure function	K^2
e	electron charge, 1.6×10^{-19}	Coulombs
e_h	horizontal readout efficiency	unitless
e_v	vertical readout efficiency	unitless
E	irradiance	W/cm^2
$E(\lambda)$	spectral irradiance	W/cm^2-μm
E_p	photon irradiance	photons/sec-cm^2

E_g	energy gap	electron-volts
F	noise factor	unitless
F_R	frame rate	frames per second
F/#	f-number	unitless
FOV_h	horizontal field of view	degrees, radians, milliradians
FOV_v	vertical field of view	degrees, radians, milliradians
h_c	critical target dimension	meters
G	gain	unitless
G_{duty}	duty cycle	second/second
$H(\xi, \eta)$	coherent transfer function	unitless
$H(\xi, \eta)$	incoherent transfer function	unitless
I	current	A
I	intensity	W/sr
I_s	detector saturation current	A
J	current density	A^2/Hz
K	heat transfer coefficient	W/K
k	Boltzman's constant 1.38×10^{-23}	J/K
$K(\lambda)$	luminous efficacy	lumens/W
$I(\lambda)$	intensity (wavelength dependent)	W/sr-μm
l_d	detector length	m
L	radiance	W/cm^2-sr
$L(\lambda)$	radiance	W/cm^2-sr-μm
M	emittance or exitance	W/cm^2
M	standard deviation of fixed-pattern noise	unitless
M_T	transverse magnification	unitless
$M(\lambda)$	emittance (wavelength-dependent)	W/cm^2-μm
$M(h)$	aerosol density	cm^{-3}
$MTF_a(\xi)$	aerosol MTF	unitless
$MTF_{aberr}(\xi)$	aberration MTF	unitless
$MTF_{crt}(\xi)$	cathode ray tube MTF	unitless
$MTF_{diff}(\xi)$	diffraction MTF	unitless
$MTF_{le}(\xi)$	turbulence MTF (long exposure)	unitless
$MTF_{optics}(\xi)$	optics MTF	unitless
$MTF_{se}(\xi)$	turbulence MTF (short exposure)	unitless
n	index of refraction	unitless
NF	noise figure	dB
N	molecular number density	cm^{-3}
N_q	number of electrons/detector integration	electrons
P_T	pyroelectric coefficient	Coulombs/cm^2-K
P_∞	static probability of detection	unitless
q	charge	Coulombs

Q	energy	Joules
R	range	cm, m, or km
R	resistance	ohms
$R(\lambda)$	detector responsivity	V(or A)/Watt
$S_p(l)$	detector responsivity	A/W
t	time	sec
t_f	frame integration time	sec
tq	charge carrier mean lifetime	sec
t_d	detector dwell time	sec
t_{int}	detector integration time	sec
SNRT	threshold signal-to-noise ratio	unitless
T	temperature	Kelvin or Celsius
T#	T number	unitless
V	voltage	V
V	vergence	diopters (m^{-1})
$V(\lambda)$	photopic efficiency	unitless
Z	impedance	ohms
α	absorptance	unitless
α	horizontal detector angular subtense	mrads
b	display brightness	footLambert (fL)
β	vertical detector angular subtense	mrads
β	surface power	diopters (m^{-1})
Df_l	information bandwidth	Hz
γ	scattering coefficient	km^{-1}
γ	display constant	unitless
$\gamma(0)$	aerosol coefficient at sea level	km^{-1}
ε	emissivity	unitless
η	vertical spatial frequency	cyc/mrad or cyc/m
η_q	quantum efficiency	electrons/photon
η_{ct}	charge transfer efficiency	unitless
λ	wavelength	μm
μ	carrier mobility	m^2/V-sec
ν	frequency of light	Hz
ξ	horizontal spatial frequency	cyc/mrad or cyc/m
ρ	reflectivity	unitless
ρ	radial spatial frequency	cyc/mrad or cyc/m
ρ_{2d}	two dimensional spatial frequency	cyc/mrad or cyc/m
σ	extinction coefficient	km^{-1}
σ	spot-size parameter	millimeters or milliradians
σ	Stephan-Boltzmann's constant	W/(cm^2-K^4)
σ_{atm}	atmospheric scattering coefficient	Km^{-1}
σ_s	photo-induced conductivity	mhos/cm

σ_{tvh}	three-dimensional spatio-temporal noise	Kelvin
$\tau(\lambda)$	transmission	unitless
τ	band-averaged transmission	unitless
t_d	detector dwell time	sec
Φ	flux	W
Ω	solid angle	steradians (sr)
θ_R	Rayleigh criterion	radians
θ_S	Sparrow criterion	radians
θ_A	Airy blur	radians

About the Authors

Ronald G. Driggers graduated from the University of Memphis with the Ph.D. degree in electrical engineering in 1990. He performed his dissertation at the University of Central Florida's Center for Research in Electro-Optics and Lasers. He has specialized in infrared and electro-optical systems with an emphasis on performance modeling, sampled imaging systems, and radiometry. He has 12 years of electro-optics experience and has worked for or consulted to Lockheed Martin, Science Applications International Corporation, EOIR Measurements, Amtec Corporation, Joint Precision Strike Demonstration Project Office, and Redstone Technical Test Center. He is currently a senior engineer at the U.S. Army's Night Vision and Electronic Sensors Directorate. Dr. Driggers is the U.S. representative to the NATO panel on advanced thermal imager characterization and is an Associate Editor of *Optical Engineering*. Dr. Driggers is an Engineering Duty Officer in the U.S. Naval Reserves and is assigned to the Naval Research Laboratory.

Paul G. Cox is currently the director of the image and signal processing group at Trident Systems Inc., in Fairfax Virginia. Mr. Cox has an extensive and varied background in imaging sensors and advanced image and signal processing. His specializations include infrared systems performance modeling and testing, automatic target recognition algorithm development, and image and video compression. Prior to joining Trident Systems, he held positions with the U.S. Army's Night Vision and Electronic Sensors Directorate, LTV Missiles, and Teledyne Brown Engineering. Mr. Cox received his BSEE degree from the University of Alabama in Huntsville and his MSEE from Catholic University of America in Washington, D.C.

Timothy Edwards received a BSME from Duke University in 1976. The next four years were spent in basic manufacturing engineering working for Singer Corporation and Control Data Corporation in Nebraska. He then moved to Orlando, Florida and worked for Martin Marietta Corporation. During this time, he worked on both production and deliverable test equipment design for two major EO fire control system programs: TADS/PNVS for the Apache helicopter and LANTIRN for the F-15/F-16 fighter. In 1991, he became a full-time graduate student in the Electrical Engineering department at the University of Memphis where he received an MSEE and Ph.D. in 1993 and 1996, respectively. He currently works in sensor systems analysis for Science Applications International Corporation (SAIC) at Night Vision Labs, Fort Belvoir, Virginia.

Index

Aberrations, 171, 177
Absorption, 87, 127, 191
Absorption coefficient, 131
Achromats, 182
Acousto-optical scanning technique, 217
ACQUIRE, 107
Active pixel sensors (APS), 224
Aerosol attenuation coefficient, 138
Afocal, 182
AGC, 42
Aided target recognizer (AiTR), 253
Airy disc, 47, 173
Aliasing, 220, 222, 263
Altitude, 129
Analytical parameters, 7
Angular spatial frequency, 235
Apparent delta T, 105
Astigmatism, 179
Atmosphere, 128
Atmospheric consideration, 127, 376
Atmospheric models, 145
Atmospheric transmission, 3, 4, 127, 131, 204
ATR, 253, 273
        operating curve, 275
        performance evaluation curve, 276
Avalanche photodiode, 196
Bandgap, 191
Beer's law, 106, 132
Blackbody
        D^*, 204
        flux to detector, 287
        radiation, 87, 96, 98
BLIP, 207
Blur circle, 171
Bode plot, 238
Bolometer, 191, 198, 229, 234

Boltzmann's constant, 195, 240
BRDF, nomenclature, 116
Broadband flux, 208
Candela, 95
Carbon dioxide, transmission of, 134
Cascaded network, 244
CCD, 200, 248
Charge transfer efficiency (CTE), 224
Chromatic aberrations, 177
Ciliary muscles, 267
Circularly symmetric functions, 24
Classification, 274
Closed-loop gain, 231
Clutter, 122
Coherence, 65
Coherent OTF, 175
Cold shield, 289
Collimated light, 157, 161, 183
Color, 117
Coma, 179
Complex functions, 15
Cones, 266
Contrast, 113
Converging focal length, 158
Convolution, 25, 31, 222
Cornea, 266
Correlation, 25, 31
CREEP, 116
CRT, 255
Cryogenic cooling, 191
Crystalline lens, 266
CTF, eye, 271
Current, 206
Current mode detector, 231
Cutoff frequency, 176
Cylinder functions, 22

The Artech House Optoelectronics Library

Brian Culshaw and Alan Rogers, *Series Editors*

Optical Fiber Communication Systems, Leonid Kazovsky,
   Sergio Benedetto, Alan Willner

*Optical Fiber Sensors, Volume Four: Applications, Analysis, and
   Future Trends,* John Dakin and Brian Culshaw, editors

Optical Measurement Techniques and Applications, Pramod Rastogi

Optical Network Theory, Yitzhak Weissman

*Optoelectronic Techniques for Microwave and Millimeter-Wave
   Engineering,* William M. Robertson

Reliability and Degradation of LEDs and Semiconductor Lasers,
   Mitsuo Fukuda

Reliability and Degradation of III-V Optical Devices, Osamu Ueda

Semiconductor Raman Laser, Ken Suto and Jun-ichi Nishizawa

Smart Structures and Materials, Brian Culshaw

Tunable Laser Diodes, Markus-Christian Amann and Jens Buus

Wavelength Division Multiple Access Optical Networks,
   Andrea Borella, Giovanni Cancellieri, and Franco Chiaraluce

For further information on these and other Artech House titles, including previously considered out-of-print books now available through our
In-Print-Forever™ (IPF™) program, contact:

Artech House	Artech House
685 Canton Street	46 Gillingham Street
Norwood, MA 02062	London SW1V 1AH England
781-769-9750	+44 (0) 171-973-8077
Fax: 781-769-6334	Fax: +44 (0) 171-630-0166
Telex: 951-659	Telex: 951-659
e-mail: artech@artech-house.com	e-mail: artech-uk@artech-house.com

Find us on the World Wide Web at: www.artech-house.com

Printed in the United States
26647LVS00001B/232-258